$ 8.35

D1482935

MILWAUKEE SCHOOL
OF ENGINEERING
LIBRARY

CIRCUIT ANALYSIS
by Laboratory Methods

PRENTICE-HALL ELECTRICAL ENGINEERING SERIES

W. L. EVERITT, Ph.D., *Editor*

ANNER *Elements of Television Systems*
BENEDICT *Introduction to Industrial Electronics*
DAVIS AND WEED *Industrial Electronic Engineering*
FICH *Transient Analysis in Electrical Engineering*
GOLDMAN *Information Theory*
GOLDMAN *Transformation Calculus and Electrical Transients*
HERSHBERGER *Principles of Communication Systems*
JORDAN *Electromagnetic Waves and Radiating Systems*
LO, ENDRES, WALDHAUER, ZAWELS, CHENG, *Transistor Electronics*
MARTIN *Electronic Circuits*
MARTIN *Ultrahigh Frequency Engineering*
MOSKOWITZ AND RACKER *Pulse Techniques*
PUMPHREY *Electrical Engineering*, 2d ed.
PUMPHREY *Fundamentals of Electrical Engineering*
RIDEOUT *Active Networks*
RYDER *Electronic Engineering Principles*, 2d ed.
RYDER *Electronic Fundamentals and Applications*
RYDER, *Networks, Lines and Fields*, 2d ed.
SHEDD *Fundamentals of Electromagnetic Waves*
SKRODER AND HELM *Circuit Analysis by Laboratory Methods*, 2d ed.
STOUT *Basic Electrical Measurements*
THOMSON *Laplace Transformation*
VAIL *Circuits in Electrical Engineering*
VAN DER ZIEL *Noise*
VON TERSCH AND SWAGO *Recurrent Electrical Transients*
WARD *Introduction to Electrical Engineering*, 2d ed.

CIRCUIT ANALYSIS
by Laboratory Methods

by

CARL E. SKRODER

Associate Professor of Electrical Engineering
University of Illinois

and

M. STANLEY HELM

Professor of Electrical Engineering
University of Illinois

SECOND EDITION

Englewood Cliffs
PRENTICE-HALL, INC.
1955

TK
147
.S57
1955

Copyright, 1946, 1955, by
PRENTICE-HALL, INC.
Englewood Cliffs, N.J.

All rights reserved. No part of this book
may be reproduced in any form, by mimeo-
graph or any other means, without per-
mission in writing from the publishers.

Library of Congress
Catalog Card No.: 55-11156

PRINTED IN THE UNITED STATES OF AMERICA

13393

PREFACE TO THE SECOND EDITION

THE authors are grateful to the many teachers who have indicated that the basic philosophy of the first edition of *Circuit Analysis by Laboratory Methods*, that is, THE PROBLEM METHOD OF EXPERIMENTATION, made this book not just another laboratory manual but a real contribution in the teaching of electric circuits. The enthusiastic acceptance of the first edition of this book and constructive criticisms from its users encouraged the authors to produce this second edition.

Many of the teachers using the first edition suggested adding material to widen the scope of the text. In view of this, the revision consists mainly of extending the coverage by adding material on electromagnetic and cathode-ray oscillographs; non-sinusoidal periodic waves including the determination of Fourier coefficients, effective values, and power; filters including *m*-derived types, terminating half sections, and insertion loss; magnetically coupled circuits including driving-point impedance, equivalent circuits, and impedance transformation; network theorems including the superposition theorem, reciprocity theorem, maximum power transfer theorem, T and π equivalent four-terminal networks, Thevenin's theorem, and Norton's theorem.

A more complete picture of what the authors have attempted to do in this volume can be obtained by reading the Preface to the First Edition and the section "To The Student" on page xvii.

The authors appreciate the suggestions that have been made by many who have used the first edition and also the courtesy of the manufacturing firms which have supplied photographs and drawings. The authors wish to express sincere thanks to Dean W. L. Everitt of the College of Engineering, University of Illinois, for his constructive criticism of the manuscript, and again to Professor Emeritus E. F. Heater of the University of Illinois Engineering Experiment Station for new drawings.

CARL E. SKRODER
M. STANLEY HELM

PREFACE TO THE FIRST EDITION

THIS book has been written with the thought that it will be used as a guide and as a text in conjunction with a laboratory course in electrical circuits. Accordingly it is assumed that the student is taking a theory course in d-c and a-c circuits concurrently with the laboratory course or has already completed such a course. Although the book is intended primarily for electrical engineering students, it contains a sufficient variety of experiments that it can be used by non-electrical engineering students.

From considerable experience gained in administering and teaching theory and laboratory courses in electrical circuits, the authors have a strong conviction that the circuits laboratory course should afford the student an opportunity to put to work his knowledge of electric circuit theory, should clarify and prove by experiment circuit phenomena about which he may be in doubt, should bring to light facts of which he may not have been aware, and should awaken him to the realization of the existence of practical limitations.

The foregoing objectives can be attained by presenting the so-called *experiment* in the form of a *problem* rather than as an experiment, if the word *experiment* is interpreted in the usual sense. When the experiment is presented as a problem, the student is confronted with three phases: (1) The analysis of the problem to determine the experimental data that are needed, (2) the determination of the circuits that must be used and the measurements that must be made in order to obtain the needed data, and (3) the analysis and synthesis of the observed and calculated data in order to arrive at a rational interpretation and explanation of the circuit performance. Thus the laboratory experiment with the preliminary planning and final study of the results is a problem of design, experiment, analysis, and synthesis.

This book is the result of the authors' efforts to make available a single volume containing a wide selection of laboratory circuit experiments, presented as much in the nature of problems as is feasible, and including a very comprehensive coverage of the related circuit theory and laws, the theory and limitations of instruments used in circuit measurements, and the methods of making measurements in circuits so that the student will have a ready source of information to which he can refer when preparing plans for the laboratory work and when analyzing the data and results.

The large number of experimental problems contained in the book permits the instructor to make selections according to his own preference and the adaptability of the available apparatus. The directions stated in each of the problems have, as far as it seemed advisable, been made as general as possible in order that the apparatus available in most college laboratories can be used successfully. However, an attempt has been made to be sufficiently specific so that very few, if any, supplemental directions will be needed.

Whenever feasible, the laboratory problems are so stated that the responsibility for the determination of the circuits to be used, procedure to be followed, data to be taken, and use to be made of the data rests largely upon the student, thus contributing to the development of his ability to analyze and synthesize and to the development of initiative, ingenuity, self-reliance, and resourcefulness.

Included in the contents of this book are discussions of matters which from their own experience the authors have found to be time consuming when they are presented to the student by lecture. Chapter 1 is a good example. The entire chapter is devoted to general instructions which cover such matters as planning for a test; conduct for personal safety; protection of circuits; use, handling, protection, and reading of instruments; precautions pertaining to the use of machines and auxiliary equipment; and recording data. Chapter 2, which covers the subject of report writing, is another example. It is not intended that the rules stated in this chapter shall be construed as being hard and fast or that they conform to any set of universally accepted standards. The authors recognize the fact that most instructors have their own personal notions regarding the contents of and construction of a written report; however, they have had considerable success in obtaining well-written reports from students who have followed the suggestions given in this chapter. The chapter has been included merely as an offering to those who may be inclined to use it. Therefore the word Report as used in connection with each problem must be interpreted in accordance with the meaning given it by the individual instructor. As used in the book, it is intended to designate the work required subsequent to the laboratory work, such as calculations, drawing of curves, and other written work; and is not intended to imply that the form in which this work is to be put up must necessarily comply with the directions and suggestions given in the second chapter.

Why chapters on the d-c shunt motor and the a-c generator have been included may call for some explanation, since the theory of the operation of these machines can hardly be included under the subject of circuits. An a-c generator driven by a d-c shunt motor is used in many college laboratories as a source of a-c voltage of variable magnitude and frequency. Since the course in circuits precedes courses in machines in many colleges, a need for chapters covering the elementary theory of these machines seemed essential.

The authors offer no apologies for the large amount of space devoted to the discussion of Kirchhoff's laws. Without a full understanding of these laws and their applications, no student of electrical engineering can ever hope to cope successfully with circuit problems. In order to make clear the true meaning of the laws, the authors have resorted to use of instantaneous values in the discussion. The reasons why vector quantities can be used in the application of the laws are explained also, and considerable space is devoted to the significance and use of single-and double-subscript notation.

Because of the growing interest in the field of electrical communication, considerable space has been given to the subject of resonance. An entire chapter is devoted to a discussion of reactive volt-amperes, a subject of growing importance and one to which most laboratory books give little if any space.

Where illustrations have been made from photographs and drawings supplied by manufacturing firms, acknowledgment has been indicated in the figure. The drawings in this book are the work of Professor E. F. Heater of the University of Illinois Engineering Experiment Station.

CARL E. SKRODER

M. STANLEY HELM

CONTENTS

CONTENTS

CONTENTS

TO THE STUDENT

TOO often a student discounts the value of a laboratory course and looks upon laboratory work somewhat with distaste. However, when a student approaches laboratory work with the right point of view, both the laboratory course and the associated theory course will be more valuable and interesting. In order to obtain the right perspective for a course, the engineering student must have an appreciation of the objectives toward which the course is directed and a realization that the attainment of these objectives will contribute a great deal toward the making of a good engineer. To the electrical engineering student, the following are important objectives of a laboratory course in circuits:

1. To develop the power of engineering analysis and synthesis.
2. To develop initiative, ingenuity, self-reliance, and resourcefulness.
3. To develop the ability to visualize a physical circuit from a schematic diagram.
4. To give experience in making circuit connections and in using instruments and control devices.
5. To verify theory by experiment.
6. To develop the facility of organized self-expression in writing.
7. To develop the ability to analyze and interpret experimental data.
8. To develop an appreciation of the limitations of data obtained by measurement.

The solution of an engineering problem consists of an analysis of the various related factors and the synthesis of these factors to obtain a practical and economical solution. Hence it is important that the student develop the ability to analyze and synthesize. Considerable progress toward the accomplishment of this objective and also the second—the development of initiative, ingenuity, self-reliance, and resourcefulness—can be made by the use of *experiments* that are actually in the form of *problems*. With the problem type of experiment the responsibility for the determination of the circuits to be used, the test procedure to be followed, the data to be taken, and the use to be made of the data are left mostly to the student. To assume this responsibility, the student must thoroughly digest the discussion of the related circuit theory given with a particular laboratory problem. A good supposition for the student to make is that he is an engineer in industry and the laboratory problem is a job given him by the chief engineer.

The accomplishment of the third, fourth, and fifth objectives—namely, to develop the ability to visualize a physical circuit from a schematic diagram, to give experience in making circuit connections and in using instruments and control devices, and to verify theory by experiment—results from active participation by the student in the laboratory work. As a matter of fact active participation is really necessary for the fulfillment of all the objectives. It yields its greatest return when the student has a thorough understanding of the theory involved in the laboratory problem.

The sixth objective, to develop the facility of organized self-expression in writing, can be accomplished by writing a report on each laboratory problem. Since engineering tests are usually summarized in the form of reports, the importance of the ability to organize material and present it clearly and concisely in written form cannot be overemphasized.

The seventh and eighth objectives, to develop the ability to analyze and interpret data and to develop an appreciation of the limitations of data obtained by measurement, can be accomplished by the inclusion in the report of a complete discussion of the accuracy of the results and an analysis and interpretation of the facts the results represent. Test data are of little value unless the engineer has the ability to analyze the data and then draw correct conclusions.

The quality of the work done by the student on a laboratory problem is judged by the way the problem was approached and carried through, by the results obtained, by the analysis and interpretation of the results, and by the written report. The fact should not be overlooked that the data submitted are an indication not only of the student's ability but also of his integrity and reliability. When the student has an appreciation as to why and how his laboratory work will be judged, much progress has been made toward the accomplishment of all of the course objectives.

CHAPTER 1
GENERAL LABORATORY INSTRUCTIONS

IN A laboratory test it is important that good and adequate data be obtained and that the data be properly recorded. Furthermore, it is essential that all tests be performed with the greatest possible safety to the student and to the laboratory equipment. To help the student achieve these ends, general instructions on planning the test, safety precautions, circuit protection, instruments, machines and equipment, and recording data are given in this chapter.

1. Planning the Test. It should be apparent that a thorough knowledge of the circuit under test and a definite plan of procedure are necessary for the performance of a successful test. Accordingly, the preliminary steps to any test should be to draw circuit diagrams and outline the sequence in which the various steps of the test should occur. The circuit diagrams should be in detail to the extent that they show all switches, circuit breakers, instruments, rheostats, load resistors, and such other apparatus as may be necessary for the test. The magnitude and the type—a-c or d-c—of the voltages to be applied to the test circuits should be indicated. The student should submit the circuit diagrams and the outline of the test procedure to the supervising instructor for advice and approval before proceeding with the test.

An important part in planning a test in which data are to be taken for plotting a curve is the consideration of the number of points needed and their spacing. The number of points that will be needed depends upon the purpose of the curve. In any case enough points will be needed to insure that the resulting curve is truly representative. The spacing of the points will depend upon the expected shape of the curve to be obtained. When it is expected that the curve will have a fairly uniform curvature, it is preferable that the points be uniformly spaced. When pronounced changes of curvature are expected, the points should be closer together in the vicinity of these changes. In cases in which it is not possible to foretell the approximate shape of a curve, plans should be made to study or plot the data as the test progresses.

2. Safety Precautions. 1. Learn the details of one method of resuscitation from electrical shock, preferably the newly developed "arm-lift back pressure" method. In case of an accident to a fellow student you will then be able to start the work of resuscitation immediately. Directions for administering artificial respiration can be found in any first-aid manual such as that of the *Red Cross* or the *Boy Scouts of America.*

2. Become familiar with the location of the nearest first-aid cabinet.

3. Regard all circuits and component parts as "hot"* unless proved otherwise.

4. Regard all circuits as "hot" to ground unless proved otherwise.

5. Do not look at electric arcs, since they are very injurious to the eyes.

6. Do not wear long, loose ties and other loose clothing in the laboratory, since they may become entangled in the machines.

7. Form the habit of using one hand at a time.

8. Keep the body, or any part of it, out of the circuit at all times.

9. Be as neat as possible in wiring circuits. Neatness is a great aid to safety.

10. Always insert a disconnect switch between a source of power and the test circuit or any part of the test circuit. Be certain that the disconnect switch is open before making connections to the power source.

11. Do not connect the source of power to the test-circuit disconnect switch until all other test-circuit connections have been made. Never take down a test circuit without first having removed the connections to the source of power.

12. In making connections from a source of power to the disconnect switch of the test circuit, first connect one end of one connecting wire to one terminal of the disconnect switch and then connect the free end to one terminal of the power source. Proceed in the same order when connecting the second wire. Reverse the procedure when disconnecting the test circuit. This procedure eliminates the danger from handling "hot" leads.

13. In making connections to the terminals of a power source, make every effort to insure a positive connection the first time. If there is trouble in the circuit, the circuit breakers will operate and a dangerous arc will be averted. If a poor connection is made, arcing will probably occur, with the possibility that the operator may be seriously burned or his eyes injured by the ultraviolet radiation. Furthermore, such arcs may generate sufficient heat to fuse portions of the metal terminals and may weld the connection.

---

* A circuit is said to be "hot" when potential differences exist between points in the circuit or between any of such points and points external to the circuit.

14. When operating switches, close them without hesitation in order to avoid dangerous arcs. Be sure to close them completely, and be certain they are opened wide when open.

15 Do not make alterations within a test circuit while the circuit is "hot." Always open the disconnect switch first.

16. Always connect instrument potential leads to the instrument first. The free ends may then be connected to the source of voltage.

17. Whenever making any change at an instrument, such as a voltmeter or a wattmeter, which requires disconnecting one or both of a pair of potential leads, remove the leads at the circuit end before making the change at the instrument.

18. Whenever making any change that requires disconnecting one or both of the leads to an ammeter or the current coil of a wattmeter, close the protective short-circuiting (shunting) switch, which is used with these instruments, before the change is made at the instrument.

19. In order to safeguard the operator, use instrument transformers to isolate all instruments from a-c circuits operating at 440 volts or above, and ground the core and secondary winding (side to which the instrument is connected) of the transformer.

20. Never open the secondary circuit of a current transformer without first opening the primary circuit. Failure to adhere to this rule may result in the appearance at the secondary terminals of an extremely high voltage which is dangerous to the operator and which, in addition, may damage the transformer. *Always keep the secondary of the current transformer short-circuited, except when taking the instrument reading.*

ALWAYS BE CAREFUL. IT IS EASIER TO PREVENT AN ACCIDENT THAN TO RECTIFY ONE.

3. Circuit Protection. 1. Every circuit should be protected by placing fuses or circuit breakers in all of the lines which supply power.* The fuse holders are usually mounted on the base of the disconnect switch. When this switch is inserted in the circuit, it should be so connected that the fused side connects to the circuit under test. Thus, when the disconnect switch is open, the fused side of the switch is "dead," and the fuses can be replaced without hazard to the operator.

2. The rating of the fuses or the setting of the circuit breaker used in a circuit should, in general, be only slightly higher than the maximum

---

* Exception to this rule is made in the case of the neutral line, which is not protected when power is supplied from a three-wire d-c source or from a three-wire single-phase a-c source.

current expected.   Exception to this rule is made in the case of motor circuits.   The maximum ratings or settings of the protective devices for use in motor circuits are shown in Table 3-2, page 19.

3. A magnetic circuit breaker with instantaneous trip should always be connected in one of the line wires supplying a d-c motor. The setting of this breaker should not exceed 250 per cent of full-load motor current.

4. Instruments. 1. Instruments for making electrical measurements are by necessity delicate and should be treated accordingly.

2. Ammeters, since they are used to measure the current, or rate of flow of electricity, are inserted in series with a circuit or an element of a circuit.   They are never bridged across the circuit or any part of it.

3. In general, an ammeter should have a single-pole single-throw switch, or its equivalent, connected between its terminals, so that it can be short-circuited when not in use.   When this switch is closed and makes good contact, it provides a very low resistance path around the ammeter, allowing the greater portion of the current to flow through the switch, thus protecting the ammeter.   In order to be effective, the switch must have a very low resistance when closed.   Accordingly, the switch should be carefully inspected to be certain that it has good terminal connections and a tight hinge and that the blade, when closed, makes good contact with the clip.   The switch should be opened only when a reading or a series of readings of the ammeter in a given test is being taken.

4. Voltmeters, since they are used to measure a difference of potential, are always connected to the points between which it is desired to determine the voltage.

5. When readings are not being taken, a voltmeter should not be connected to a circuit.   Connection should be made only when an observation or a series of observations in a given test is being made. When a voltmeter is not in use and is not provided with a push-button switch, one of the voltmeter leads should be disconnected at the circuit end—not at the instrument end.

6. A wattmeter current coil is always inserted in series with a circuit or portion of it in the same manner as an ammeter.   The current coil must therefore be protected by a short-circuiting switch, and the same precautions should be exercised in the selection and operation of this switch as outlined in the paragraph dealing with ammeters.

7. A wattmeter potential circuit is always connected across a difference of potential in the same manner as a voltmeter and hence

should not be connected to the circuit when readings are not being taken.

8. An ammeter should always be used in conjunction with a wattmeter current coil, and a voltmeter should be used with a watt-meter potential circuit as assurance that the ratings of these elements will not be exceeded.

9. When reading an instrument indication, the observer should be in a position such that his line of vision is perpendicular to the instrument scale at the pointer position. This position is accurately determined in the case of an instrument equipped with an antiparallax mirror when the pointer and the image of the pointer in the mirror coincide.

10. The accuracy of an observation is limited by the accuracy of the instrument and the degree to which the observer is able to estimate a fractional part of the smallest division of the instrument scale.

Instrument manufacturers state the accuracy of an instrument as a certain percentage of full-scale deflection. For example, an instrument having an accuracy of $\frac{1}{2}$ of 1 per cent is correct to within $\pm.005$ of the full-scale value at all points on the scale. Since it is possible for this instrument to be in error by $\pm.005$ of the full-scale value at any point on the scale, observations should not be made in the lower portion of the scale if the possible per cent error is to be kept within reasonable limits.

In the case of an instrument with a uniform scale, it is possible that every observation will also be in error by a magnitude equal to the fractional part of the smallest scale division which the observer can estimate. Thus, if the observer is able to estimate to $\pm\frac{1}{10}$ of the smallest division, each observation, regardless of whether the pointer deflection is great or small, will have a possible error of $\frac{1}{10}$ of a division. However, since the magnitude of the error is the same, the per cent error is much greater when the pointer deflection is small than when it is large.

In order to keep the instrument and observational errors from being excessive, readings from instruments with uniform scales should not be taken when the pointer deflection is less than 25 per cent of full scale and preferably not this low. Since the scales of d-c instruments and of wattmeters are usually uniform, this rule should generally be applied when these instruments are used.

The scales of most instruments used for making measurements of a-c voltages and currents are not uniform, but are very much cramped at the lower end. Thus, the per cent error resulting from the error of observation is magnified in the cramped portion of the scale. The observer must judge for himself just how far down the scale it is advisable to take readings. In some instances it may be wise not to take readings from an instrument when the pointer deflection is less than 50 per cent, while in other cases readings may be taken down to 25 per cent without introducing appreciable error. A fairly safe general rule for minimizing the possible per cent error resulting from both the instrument and observational errors in the case of instruments having scales cramped at the lower end is to avoid taking readings of less than 40 per cent of full scale.

The scales of some a-c instruments are also cramped at the upper end, and hence the precautions stated in the preceding paragraph should be kept in mind when the upper portion of the scale of such an instrument is used.

11. In adhering to the foregoing suggested rules for minimizing the possible error, it may be necessary in many instances to use several instruments of the same kind but with different ranges. When in the progress of a test it becomes advisable to change to an instrument of another range, the latter should be inserted in the circuit before the instrument already in the circuit is removed, and the indications of the two should be checked against each other. By following this practice the observer will become aware of errors introduced as a result of a faulty instrument, since obviously the indications should not differ appreciably. In case an instrument is found to be faulty, it should be replaced, or it may be used and then later calibrated.

12. In the case of a-c measurements, the necessity for using more than one range of a given kind of instrument can be avoided by using instrument transformers to extend the range of the instrument.

5. Machines and Equipment. 1. Laboratory equipment must not be overloaded at any time except by specific direction of the instructor.

2. All rotating machines should be inspected while running to see that the bearings are being properly lubricated. A record of this inspection should appear on the laboratory data sheet.

3. Field rheostats should not be used in any circuit except the shunt field circuit of a motor or generator. They should never be used as a load or to control the current in the series field winding of a machine.

4. All portable field rheostats and potentiometers should be tested for continuity before they are connected in motor or generator field circuits.

5. Generators should always be started with minimum field current.

6. When a circuit containing the field winding of a generator is to be opened, the current in the winding should be reduced to a minimum and the circuit broken slowly but unhesitatingly in order to

reduce as much as possible the self-induced voltage in the field winding. A field winding circuit should never be opened when a voltmeter is connected across the circuit terminals, since the self-induced voltage in the winding may be high enough to damage the voltmeter.

7. D-c motors should be started with maximum field current.

8. Ordinary motor starters are designed for intermittent duty and should not be operated in the starting positions longer than is necessary to bring the motor into operation.

9. The shunt field winding circuit of a d-c motor should never be opened while the motor is in operation, since opening the field circuit may cause the motor to run at a sufficiently high speed to damage the armature.

6. Recording Data. It is important that all pertinent information regarding a test be recorded and that the recording be done in a neat and orderly manner. This is necessary because the test data in most cases will have to be used by persons other than the recorder. Furthermore, the data sheet may have to be referred to at a later time when many of the facts pertaining to the test are not fresh in the minds of the observers. Therefore it is imperative that the record include information other than just the observed data; in addition to the latter, it should contain the following items:

1. Title of test.
2. Date.
3. Names of participants in test.
4. Circuit diagram of test circuit showing all switches, circuit breakers, instruments, rheostats, and such other pieces of equipment as were necessary. The magnitudes and kinds of voltages—a-c or d-c—applied to the circuit should be indicated.
5. Name-plate data, or equivalent, of the apparatus tested.
6. Instrument identification numbers.

The first five items are self-explanatory. They are, however, very necessary parts of a complete data sheet.

Instrument identification numbers are also an important part of the data sheet, since they make it possible to refer to these instruments later if it becomes necessary to check scales or instrument calibration.

The data should be arranged systematically as they are taken. Each column of data should be headed by a symbol indicating what the numbers in the column represent. It is good practice to list directly under the symbol the following: Identification number of the instrument used, range used, and multiplying factor that applies to the scale indications in the column. Multiplying factors arise from the use of multirange instruments and instrument transformers.   When an instrument, instrument range, or ratio of an instrument transformer is changed during the progress of a test, the new instrument number, range, or multiplying factor should be recorded in the column at the point of change.

In making a record of readings taken from an indicating instrument, the actual scale indications are the ones that should be recorded.   If it is necessary to apply a multiplying factor in order to obtain the true value, this should be done at a later time.

Whenever the data for several tests of the same general character are recorded on a single data sheet, the set of data for each test should be headed by a descriptive title.

CHAPTER 2

THE REPORT

1. General Comments. Usually engineering tests are summarized in the form of reports. In many cases, these reports are submitted to superiors who have not been actively engaged in the test; hence the reports must be clear and concise enough to leave no doubt concerning the method of test and the interpretation of the results. It is therefore of the utmost importance that an engineering student learn to write good reports.

In general, a report is written in the past tense and in the third person. It should be impersonal throughout, personal pronouns being avoided. The report should be written under the assumption that none of the readers will be familiar with the work covered. Thus the report must be complete in itself. The student too frequently is careless in this respect and writes a report that cannot be followed without a previous knowledge of the test under consideration. A good report is thorough, orderly, neat, and grammatically correct.

2. General Specifications. In order to observe the accepted rules of good writing form, the following specifications for the general makeup of the report are suggested:

1. Use $8\frac{1}{2} \times 11$ in. white paper. Ruled paper may be used.
2. Write with ink or use a typewriter.
3. Write on one side of the paper only.
4. Draw all illustrations, circuit diagrams, and curves neatly and carefully.
5. Letter or type all information on drawings, circuit diagrams, and curve sheets.

3. Report Outline. The material covered and its arrangement in a report varies somewhat with the type of work being reported. For the usual tests made in an electrical engineering laboratory, the following report outline is suggested for content and order of presentation:

    I. Title Page
   II. Introduction
  III. Method of Investigation
       A. Procedure
       B. Circuit Diagrams

IV. Results
    A. Data
        1. Name-Plate Data
        2. Observed and Calculated Data
    B. Sample Calculations
    C. Curves
V. Analysis of Results
VI. Questions
VII. Original Data Sheet

4. Discussion of Report Outline. A discussion of each section of the report outline follows:

I. Title Page

On the title page should be given the course number, problem number and title, date performed, name of student reporting, names of co-workers, and squad identification number. When form report covers with spaces for these items are used, the cover properly filled in may serve the purpose of a title page.

II. Introduction

The introduction should be a concise statement setting forth the aim and scope of the investigation.

III. Method of Investigation
    A. Procedure

In this section a general description of the procedure should be given. This description should be comprehensive but brief. The enumeration and detailed description of multitudinous mechanical operations or sequence of such operations, such as closing switches, reading instruments, turning rheostat knobs, and so forth, should in general be avoided. However, when a specific method of mechanical operation or sequence of such operations is necessary in order to assure the validity or accuracy of the test data, it is important that the essential details be included in the description.

    B. Circuit Diagrams

Circuit diagrams should be fitted into the description of the procedure where they best help to clarify it. The circuit diagrams should show all switches, circuit breakers, instruments, rheostats, load resistors, and all other apparatus that was necessary for the test. The magnitude of the voltages and the type—a-c or d-c—which were applied to the test circuits should be indicated. Each diagram should have a figure number for reference purposes.

IV. Results
  A. Data
    1. Name-Plate Data
      The first item under results should be the name-plate data, or equivalent, of the apparatus tested.
    2. Observed and Calculated Data
      All observed and calculated data should be tabulated when possible. However, observed data should be corrected before they are tabulated. All related data, whether observed or calculated, should be included in a single table. Headings and subheadings (titles) identifying individual items of data or sets of data should be used whether or not the data are tabulated. Instrument identification numbers and ranges need not be copied from the original laboratory data sheet.
  B. Sample Calculations
    This section should consist of a sample of a complete calculation of each type involved in the determination of calculated data and the solution of problems. These sample calculations should first be shown in symbol form, each symbol being properly defined.
    When a succession of calculations are required to reach a final result, the same set of observed data should be used in carrying through the successive sample calculations.
  C. Curves
    All curve sheets should conform to the following specifications:

    1. Use "twenty to the inch" coordinate paper—in general, $8\frac{1}{2} \times 11$ in.
    2. Plot in the first quadrant.
    3. In general, make the axes intersect within the sectioned part of the paper. Leave the curve-sheet margins blank.
    4. Plot the independent variable as abscissa and the dependent variable as ordinate.
    5. In general, start the scale of the dependent variable, but not necessarily the scale of the independent variable, at zero.
    6. Choose scales that are easy to use and that do not allow

points to be plotted to a greater accuracy than justified by that of the data.

7. Indicate the points plotted from data by visible dots or very small circles.

8. Draw a smooth average curve through the plotted points, except in cases in which discontinuities are known to exist.

9. Place a title containing all pertinent information on each curve sheet. The title should be lettered or typed.

10. Draw only related curves on the same sheet.

11. Insert curve sheets in the report so that they can be read from the bottom or right side.

V. Analysis of Results

The analysis of results is the most important section of the entire report. As the name implies, it should be a complete discussion of the results obtained.

Part of this discussion should deal with the accuracy or reliability of the results. It is suggested that this section consist, when applicable, of a careful treatment of the effect upon the results of the following: (1) Errors resulting from the necessity of neglecting certain factors because of physical limitations in the performance of the test, (2) errors in manipulation, (3) errors in observation, and (4) errors in instruments.

A very important part of the discussion should be a comparison of the results obtained with those which would reasonably have been expected from a consideration of the theory involved in the problem. Whenever the theory is apparently contradicted, the probable reasons should be discussed.

When results are given in graphical form as curves, the shape of each curve should be carefully explained. Such an explanation should state the causes for the particular shape the curve may have. It is not sufficient simply to state that a particular curve has a positive slope; the reason for such a slope should be given. If the slope is not constant—that is, if the curve is not a straight line—its nonlinearity should also be explained.

Any original conclusions drawn as a consequence of the laboratory procedure and a study of the results obtained should be given in this section.

Such constructive criticism of any phase of the problem as may seem pertinent may also be included here.

VI. Questions

In this section should be given the answers to any questions that may be included as part of the problem.

VII. Original Data Sheet

The original laboratory data sheet should be the last page of the report.

CHAPTER 3

CIRCUIT PROTECTION

1. Fuses

1. Function of a Fuse. A fuse is a device designed to open an electric circuit whenever the current exceeds the safe value for that circuit. Failure to open a circuit under such a condition may result in serious damage to the circuit connecting wires, control equipment, instruments, and machine windings that may be part of the circuit. The destructive action is due mainly to the heat developed by the abnormal current in the various parts of the circuit, each of which has some resistance. The heating effect of current in a resistance is discussed in a following chapter, where it is shown that the heat developed is proportional to the square of the current, to the resistance, and to the time the current flows. Even in cases in which the current is not large enough to develop sufficient heat to melt any of the conducting parts of the circuit, enough heat may be generated to damage insulation. It is necessary, therefore, to have in an electric circuit a protective device to open the circuit under an abnormal current condition. In order to serve its protective function, a fuse is connected in series with the circuit and is purposely made the weakest link in it. For this reason the fuse has been referred to as electricity's safety valve.

PLUG TYPE FUSE

0-30 Amperes
0-125 Volts

CARTRIDGE TYPE FUSES

0-60 Amperes
125-250 Volts

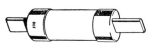

70-600 Amperes
125-250 Volts

Courtesy of Bussmann Mfg. Co.

Fig. 3-1. Fuse types for various voltage and current ratings.

2. Fuse Types. In its elementary form a fuse is a strip of metal such as zinc, lead, or lead-tin alloy that melts at a much lower temperature and has a higher resistance than a piece of copper of the same physical dimensions.

Common types of fuses are shown in Fig. 3-1. Fuses for 250- and 600-volt circuits are made in cylindrical forms called *cartridges*. The contact terminals of this type of fuse in the 0- to 60-amp sizes are the caps at the ends of the cartridge, while in the 70- to 600-amp sizes blades are used as contact terminals. Fuses for circuits of not over 125 volts are of the familiar plug type, which screw into an *Edison* base receptacle. These fuses are made only in 0- to 30-amp capacities. One of the contacts in this type of fuse is the threaded shell, and the other is the small disc at the end of the plug.

Various types of fusible elements used in cartridge fuses are shown in Fig. 3-2. Fuses which must be discarded after blowing are known as *one-time fuses*. Except in the very small sizes, the fusible elements of one-time cartridge and plug-type fuses are made of zinc. Zinc is used because it has a reasonably low melting point and is a fairly good conductor. The latter property permits a small volume of metal, a marked advantage, since the vapors and pressure developed on a short-circuit blow are in proportion to the volume of metal in the fusible element. In fuses of very low ampere rating, lead is used instead of zinc because, if made of zinc, the fusible element might be so small as to lack the necessary mechanical strength.

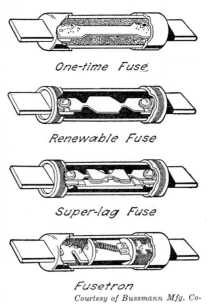

One-time Fuse

Renewable Fuse

Super-lag Fuse

Fusetron

Courtesy of Bussmann Mfg. Co.

Fig. 3-2. Types of cartridge fuses.

The shells of *one-time* cartridge fuses are usually made of fiber tubes and are filled with an insulating, fire-resisting powder. Fiber is well suited for this application, since it withstands high internal pressures and yet does not carbonize from the high temperature of the arc that occurs when a fuse blows. One-time plug fuses are made with a porcelain, glass, or bakelite body. Since this type of fuse is used only in circuits of 125 volts or less and is rated at not more than 30 amperes, the porcelain, glass, or bakelite is strong enough to prevent rupture should a short circuit occur.

A *renewable* fuse is one which can be restored to its original usefulness simply by replacing the fusible element or link after it has blown. This type of fuse is made in all sizes (0- to 600-amp) in the cartridge type. A fire-resisting filler is not required in the renewable fuse, since the fiber tube is made much stronger than in the one-time fuse and because venting is provided in the larger sizes.

The *super-lag* fuse is a renewable fuse of the cartridge type with the fusible link so designed that it takes a longer time to blow on a given current than does an ordinary link. In any fuse the terminals tend to conduct the heat resulting from an overload away from the ends of the fusible link. The center portion of the ordinary link therefore melts first. In super-lag fuses pieces of metal called "lag-plates" are attached to the link. When an overload occurs, these "lag-plates" absorb considerable heat and increase the time required to heat the link to the melting point. The super-lag fuse was designed for motor-circuit protection. Here a time-lag characteristic is required in order to prevent fuses from blowing in the short interval during which a motor is being started, since in this interval the current may be several times the rated motor current.

One of the more recent developments in motor-circuit protection is the *Fusetron*, a cartridge-type fuse with a time lag much greater even than that of the super-lag fuse. The Fusetron consists of a fusible link and a thermal cutout connected in series. The fusible link is designed to blow at a higher current than in ordinary fuses of the same rating. It is made of copper, which permits the use of a smaller amount of metal than if it were made of zinc, and it protects only against short circuits. On overloads the fusible link remains inactive, and the circuit is opened by the thermal cutout. The movable part of the cutout consists of a small copper block which is attached by a spring to a heating element. The copper block is secured to the fusible link by means of a low-melting-point solder. The fusible link is located at one end of the Fusetron and the heating element at the other. When an overload occurs, the heat generated in the heating element and the fusible link raises the temperature of the solder to the melting point, and the spring pulls the copper block out of place, thereby opening the circuit. Obviously, whether the Fusetron opens the circuit as a result of the fusible link blowing or the thermal cutout opening, it can no longer be used but must be replaced. The thermal cutout has a very long time lag, so that the Fusetron will not open on motor-starting currents or harmless overloads of short duration. The rating of the Fusetron is based upon the current at which the thermal cutout operates. Because of these characteristics the Fusetrons used in a motor circuit may, under ordinary conditions, have a rating equal to the full-load current of the motor, thus affording actual overload protection to the motor. This advantage cannot be secured with any other type of fuse. The Fusetron is also made in the plug type for use on 125-volt circuits.

A circuit may be fused merely by inserting a piece of fuse wire if suitable terminals are available for securing the wire.   Fuse wire is not used in industry because of the fire hazard in unattended locations. It is used, however, in many electrical engineering laboratories for protecting low-voltage test circuits because of its very low cost.   Fuse wire is usually made of an alloy consisting mostly of lead because the melting point of lead is much lower than that of zinc and because the lead alloy does not have a tendency to glow for an extended period as do some other metals when blowing on slight overloads.

3. Characteristics of Round Lead-Alloy Fuse Wire.   In Table 3-1 are shown the characteristics of round lead-alloy fuse wire.   It should be noted that the values given under the headings "Size" and "Carrying Capacity" do not agree.   The values listed under the latter

TABLE 3-1

RATING-DIMENSION TABLE FOR ROUND LEAD-ALLOY FUSE WIRE

Size (amp)	Diameter (in.)	Carrying Capacity* (amp)	Size (amp)	Diameter (in.)	Carrying Capacity* (amp)
1	.016	2.2	30	.103	38
2	.025	4.3	40	.122	49
3	.031	6	50	.137	59
5	.039	8	60	.158	75
10	.055	14	70	.170	85
15	.068	20	80	.189	101
20	.082	27	90	.212	125
25	.094	33	100	.226	141

* Based on a distance of 2 in. between fuse terminals and on operation in the open.

heading are for a 2-in. spacing between fuse terminals and operation in the open.   Experience has shown that in general usage these two conditions seldom exist.   Either the fuse terminals are more than 2 in. apart or the fuse wire is used in an enclosure, or both these conditions may be found.   These possibilities along with terminal conditions reduce the carrying capacity; and, since the average user does not take these factors into consideration but expects a 10-amp fuse wire to carry a 10-amp load, it is common practice to compensate for this by underrating the fuse as indicated in the table.   Thus the values listed under "Size" represent the rating under average conditions found in use.   However, if the conditions applying to the data in the column "Carrying Capacity" are met, the fuse wire will indefinitely carry the currents shown under this heading.

4. Premature Blowing. The blowing of a fuse is not always due to a current of greater value than that for which the fuse is rated, but may be caused by the heat developed by a much smaller current flowing through the high resistance of a poor contact at the fuse, near the fuse, or in the fuse. The heat developed at a poor contact may cause the shell of a cartridge-type fuse to become charred and, in fuse holders of the clip type, may destroy the spring tension of the clip. It is essential, therefore, that care be taken to insure good contact at the fuse and at all the contacts near the fuse. In renewable fuses, the contacts at the connections between the fusible link and the fuse terminals should not be overlooked. Failure to observe these precautions will usually result in premature blowing and in shortening the life of the fuse shell and clips.

Premature blowing of fuses also results from the installation of fuses in locations where a high ambient temperature exists, for, if the temperature of the surrounding air is very high, a fuse cannot carry its rated current. If it is impossible to avoid such locations and there are no means for circulating air around the fuse, the only alternative is to use a fuse of higher rating.

5. Selecting a Fuse. The rating of the fuses used in a test circuit should, in general, be only slightly higher than the maximum current expected. Motor circuits are, however, an exception to this rule. In order to keep the fuses in a motor circuit from blowing on the motor starting current, the rating of the fuses must be considerably above the rated current of the motor, except when super-lag fuses or Fusetrons are used. Because of the time-lag characteristic of super-lag fuses and Fusetrons, a much lower rating may be used when these types are utilized. The maximum sizes of fuses that are recommended for use in circuits supplying current to various types of motors are shown in Table 3-2.

6. Standard Requirements for Fuses. The standards for fuses require that they be of certain dimensions within specified tolerances and that they satisfy the following conditions:

1. The fuse must withstand a large short-circuit current without exploding.

2. The temperature of the fuse must not rise above a reasonably low value when the circuit is operating under normal conditions.

3. All fuses must carry a 10 per cent overload indefinitely when tested in the open.

4. Fuses must blow at a 35 per cent overload when tested in the open. In the 0- to 60-amp sizes they must blow within one hour and in the larger sizes within two hours.

TABLE 3-2

MAXIMUM RATING OR SETTING OF MOTOR-CIRCUIT PROTECTIVE DEVICES

| Motor Type | Per Cent of Rated Motor Current | | | | |
| | Fuse Rating | | | Circuit-Breaker Setting | |
	One-Time Fuse, Renewable Fuse, or Fuse Wire	Super-Lag Fuse	Fusetron	Time-Delay Circuit Breaker	Instantaneous-Trip Circuit Breaker
Squirrel-cage or synchronous motor—full voltage, resistor, or reactor start.................	300	250	150	250	. . .
Squirrel-cage or synchronous motor rated less than 30 amp—auto-transformer start........	250	210	145	200	. . .
Squirrel-cage or synchronous motor rated over 30 amp—auto-transformer start.................	200	167	140	200	. . .
Wound-rotor induction motor................	150	140	133	150	. . .
Direct-current motor rated less than 50 hp........	150	140	133	150	250

2. Magnetic Circuit Breakers

7. Principle of Operation and Types. Another device commonly used for protecting circuits is the magnetic circuit breaker. A simple form of magnetic circuit breaker consists of a solenoid placed in series with the circuit to be protected, an iron plunger within the solenoid, a set of contacts that are normally closed, a toggle mechanism that holds the contacts in the normal position, and a trigger to trip the mechanism. When an excessive current flows through the solenoid, the plunger is forced upward, striking the trigger; the latter trips the holding mechanism and opens the breaker contacts.

Many different types of magnetic circuit breakers are used; the type selected depends upon the application. For low voltages the breaker contacts operate in air, whereas for high voltages the contacts are submerged in oil to prevent arcing when they open. The actuating solenoid, or trip coil, of breakers used in d-c and low-voltage a-c circuits is inserted in series with the circuit to be protected. In breakers for use in high-voltage a-c systems the trip coil is usually energized from a 125-volt d-c source. The circuit of the trip coil is connected to the d-c source through the contacts of a protective relay. The latter is used in conjunction with a current transformer, excessive current in which causes the relay to operate, closing the contacts. Some breakers do not trip instantaneously on overloads but trip after a short time delay, the tripping time usually being inversely proportional to the overload current. Some breakers must be reset manually, some may be either tripped or reset from a remote point, and others reset automatically. The latter type does not reclose immediately after being tripped but remains inoperative for a given time interval before reclosing. Regardless of the type, the fundamental operating principle of all magnetic circuit breakers is the same.

8. Magnetic Breakers versus Fuses. In comparison with the magnetic circuit breaker the fuse has a much lower first cost and occupies less space. The fuse, however, unless it is of the renewable type, is worthless after being blown. Even with renewable fuses there is considerable inconvenience and time consumed in changing links. Furthermore, there is always the possibility that spare fuses and links may not be readily available. In contrast, the magnetic circuit breaker has a higher first cost and requires more space; but, on the other hand, it operates an indefinitely great number of times without damage to itself, and it is easily reset. An important advantage of the breaker is that, unless it has a time delay, its action is faster than that of a fuse, and hence it opens a circuit under abnormal conditions much more quickly.

9. Low-Voltage Manually Operated Breaker. In Fig. 3-3 is shown the operating mechanism of one type of low-voltage, a-c or d-c, manually operated magnetic circuit breaker such as is used in many electrical engineering laboratories. When this breaker is in its closed position, nearly all of the current is carried by the main contacts, which consist of copper laminations pressing on copper blocks. As shown in the figure, the carbon contacts and secondary contacts are in parallel with the main contacts but ordinarily carry only a small portion of the total current. The electrical path through the breaker is from the upper terminal through the contacts and then through the solenoid to the lower terminal, the solenoid being connected to the lower main contact block by means of conductor C.

In the toggle mechanism the points at which there is rotation about a fixed center are indicated in the figure by F. The pivoting points that are free to move are designated by M. When the breaker is closed, the free pivot M_1 is slightly to the left of its dead-center position, thereby holding the contacts tightly closed. When a current of sufficient magnitude flows in the solenoid, the plunger is drawn upward into the solenoid and strikes the trigger. This action and the pull of spring S_1 cause the free pivot M_1 to move to the right past its dead-center position. The spring action of the compressed contacts along with the pull of springs S_1 and S_2 then rapidly open the breaker.

This breaker can also be tripped manually by pressing a button (not shown) which actuates the trigger.

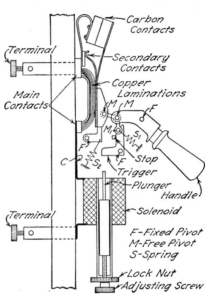

When the breaker trips, the main contacts open first, thus directing the current carried by the breaker through the secondary and carbon contacts. The secondary contacts then open, and the final break is made at the carbon contacts, carbon being used to prevent the contacts from fusing. The function of the secondary contacts is to prevent the main contacts from arcing under severe short circuits. The breaker is reset by simply moving the handle back to its normal position, causing the carbon contacts to close first, the secondary contacts next, and the main contacts last.

Fig. 3-3. Low-voltage manually operated magnetic circuit breaker.

In order to adjust the breaker to operate at a given current, the locknut shown in the figure is loosened and the adjusting screw is turned in the proper direction until the desired current is shown by the indicator and scale of the breaker (not shown in the figure). To set the breaker so that it will trip on a current smaller than that for which it had previously been set, the adjusting screw is turned in such a direction as to lift the plunger farther up into the solenoid, thus making a smaller current necessary to cause the plunger to strike the trigger. To increase the value of current required to trip the breaker, the adjusting screw is turned so that the plunger is lowered. After the adjusting screw has been properly set, the locknut should be tightened so that vibration cannot change the setting.

3. Thermal and Thermal-Magnetic Circuit Breakers

10. Operating Principle of Thermal Breakers. The thermal circuit breaker is an important protective device for low-voltage circuits (less than 600 volts). The essential parts of one type are shown in Fig. 3-4(a). Starting from the lower terminal of the breaker, the path of the current is through the bimetallic strip and flexible connecting lead to the contact bar and then through the contact bar and contacts to the upper terminal (not shown).

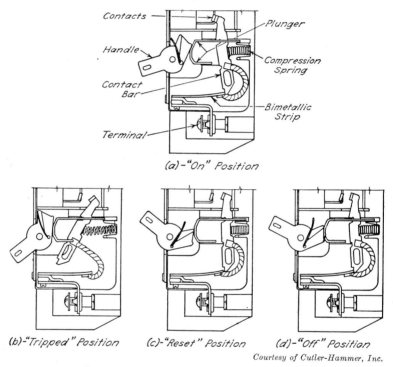

Courtesy of Cutler-Hammer, Inc.

Fig. 3-4. Mechanism of a thermal circuit breaker.

On overloads—that is, when the current continuously exceeds the value for which the breaker is rated—the bimetallic strip becomes heated sufficiently to cause it to bend. The resulting displacement of the tripping end of the bimetallic strip releases the contact bar. The compression spring then actuates the contact bar and plunger so as to open the breaker contacts. Fig. 3-4(b) shows the breaker mechanism in the "tripped" position.

The breaker mechanism is restored to the "on" position by moving the handle to the "reset" position shown in (c) of the figure and then moving it through the "off" position shown in (d) to the "on" position of (a). The cause of the overload should, of course, be removed before an attempt is made to move the handle to the "on" position. However, if the overload should still exist when the handle is moved from the "tripped" position to the "on" position, the contacts will again open. Such a breaker is said to be "trip free."

The "off" position is provided so that the handle can also be used to open a circuit manually. Thus, this type of circuit breaker can also serve as a disconnect switch. The internal parts of an actual circuit breaker of the type discussed above are shown in Fig. 3-5.

11. Tripping Characteristics of Thermal Breakers. As indicated in Fig. 3-6, a bimetallic tripping element

Courtesy of Cutler-Hammer, Inc.

Fig. 3-5. Assembly of the internal parts of a thermal circuit breaker.

has an inherent time lag which is inversely proportional to the overload current. This inverse-time tripping characteristic is desirable because it prevents unnecessary tripping of the breaker within the normal range of current surges due to motor starting, welder operation, or the characteristic operation of other equipment supplied through the breaker. The recommended maximum ratings of thermal breakers for use in motor circuits are shown under the heading of time-delay breakers in Table 3-2.

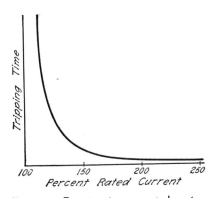

Fig. 3-6. Tripping time-current characteristic of a thermal circuit breaker.

In order to conform with the requirements of the Underwriters' Laboratories, a thermal breaker must trip at 125 per cent and 200 per cent overloads within certain specified times, which depend on the breaker rating. On a short circuit, the tripping time of a thermal breaker varies from a fraction of a second to a second or more, depending on the breaker rating.

Since the operation of a thermal breaker depends upon the temperature rise of its bimetallic strip, the tripping characteristic of the breaker is influenced by the temperature of the surrounding air—that is, by the ambient temperature. Over normal ranges of ambient

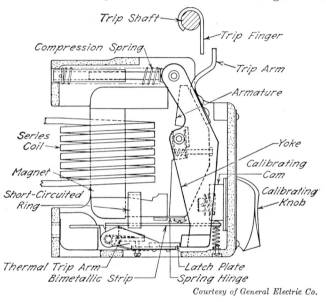

Courtesy of General Electric Co.

Fig. 3-7. Mechanism of an a-c thermal-magnetic tripping device.

temperature, however, the rating is affected very little, and in most instances the ambient temperature need not be considered.

12. Thermal-Magnetic Breakers. Thermal breakers are often equipped with an auxiliary magnetic trip, which provides instantaneous tripping on excessive overloads or short circuits. The parts of the tripping device of one type of a-c thermal-magnetic breaker are shown in Fig. 3-7. The armature is attached to the lower part of the magnet by a spring hinge and is restrained by the yoke pivoted at the center of the armature. The yoke is restrained at the bottom by the latch plate and at the top by two compression springs. The bimetallic strip is fastened to the thermal trip arm at one end and held at the other end between the calibrating cam and a spring.

Alternating current in the series coil induces current in the short-circuited ring, mounted around the bottom member of the magnet, generating heat, which is conducted to the bimetallic strip. When sufficient heat has been developed, the bimetallic strip bends with the convex surface downward and causes the thermal trip arm to disengage the latch plate from the yoke. This allows the armature and trip arm to move and operate the trip finger on the trip shaft, causing the main breaker contacts to open.

At currents exceeding approximately 10 to 12 times the breaker rating, the magnetizing action of the series coil overcomes the restraint of the two compression springs and draws the armature against the pole face of the magnet, so that the breaker trips immediately without waiting for the release of the latch plate by the heating of the bimetallic strip as described above.

Fig. 3-8 is a photograph of the thermal-magnetic tripping device shown in Fig. 3-7. The tripping time for a given current

Courtesy of General Electric Co.

Fig. 3-8. External view of an a-c thermal-magnetic tripping device.

can be varied within limits by means of the calibrating knob. The setting of the knob determines the distance through which the bimetallic strip must bend before releasing the latch plate. Approximate tripping characteristics for three settings of the calibrating knob are shown in Fig. 3-9.

Laboratory Problem No. 3-1

FUSES AND MAGNETIC CIRCUIT BREAKERS

Laboratory

1. (a) Examine a manually operated magnetic circuit breaker and make a neat sketch of the operating mechanism.

(b) Adjust the mechanism that determines the value of the tripping current to the position which should cause the breaker to open on a current that is 25 per cent of the rated value for the breaker.   Connect the circuit breaker, a suitable d-c ammeter, and a load rheostat in series.   (See the section "Use of the Ammeter" in Chapter 5 and the

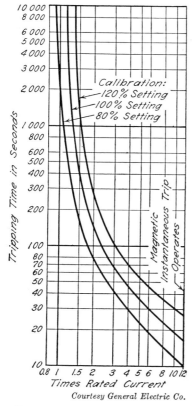

section "Load Rheostats" in Chapter 4).   Using a d-c source to supply the current, slowly increase the current in the circuit and record the value of current which causes the breaker to operate.

(c) Across the terminals of the circuit breaker connect a single-pole single-throw switch which when closed will provide a low-resistance shunt around the circuit of the breaker.   With this shunting switch closed, adjust the circuit current to a small value.   Read and record the ammeter indication.   Rapidly open and then immediately close the breaker shunting switch, causing the load current to flow suddenly through the breaker circuit.   Make successive repeat tests, each time with a slightly greater current than in the test which preceded, until a current value is reached which causes the breaker to operate when the shunting switch is suddenly opened.

(d) Repeat the tests of (b) and (c), but for breaker settings of 50 per cent, 75 per cent, and 100 per cent of rated breaker current.

Fig. 3-9. Approximate tripping time-current characteristics for three settings of the calibrating knob of an a-c thermal-magnetic tripping device.

Courtesy General Electric Co.

2. (a) Obtain two lengths of fuse wire in each of four different current ratings.   Suitably mount one length of the fuse wire with the smallest current rating.   Using a test procedure similar to that of (b) of part **1**, determine the current required to melt the fuse wire when the current is increased slowly.

(b) Mount the other length of the fuse wire having the same current rating as that used in (a).   Using a test procedure similar to that of (c) of part **1,** determine the current required to melt the fuse wire when the current is suddenly introduced.

(c) Repeat tests (a) and (b), using the remaining sizes of fuse wire.

Report

A. From data obtained in (b), (c), and (d) of **1,** plot the following curves, using the same set of coordinate axes:

(1) Current required to trip the circuit breaker vs the breaker setting when the current is slowly increased.
(2) Current required to trip the circuit breaker vs the breaker setting when the current is suddenly introduced.

B. On a second sheet and from data obtained in (a), (b), and (c) of **2,** plot the following curves, using the same set of coordinate axes:

(1) Current required to melt the fuse wire vs the fuse-wire rating when the current is slowly increased.
(2) Current required to melt the fuse wire vs the fuse-wire rating when the current is suddenly introduced.

C. Discuss the results obtained in (b), (c), and (d) of **1,** as indicated by the curves plotted in **A.**

D. Discuss the results obtained in (a), (b), and (c) of **2,** as indicated by the curves plotted in **B.**

CHAPTER 4
RHEOSTATS

1. Elementary Form. The term *rheostat* is applied to a resistance that can be varied at will by mechanical means. The actual physical construction of such a device takes many different forms, but in general it consists of a fixed resistance element and a movable contactor which can be moved over the element or over contacts connected to

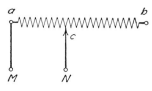

Fig. 4-1. Schematic representation of a rheostat.

points along the element. Connections are brought out to two terminals, one from one end of the fixed resistance element and one from the movable contactor. A schematic sketch of such a device is shown in Fig. 4-1. The fixed resistance is shown as *ab* and the movable contactor as *c*. The two terminals are indicated by *M* and *N*.

2. Slide-Wire Rheostats. As stated above, rheostats may take a number of various forms in their mechanical structure. One is the slide-wire type, in which the resistance wire is wound around some kind of a core made of insulating material. In rheostats suitable to handle currents of several amperes this core is generally tubular in shape

Courtesy James G. Biddle Co.

Fig. 4-2. Tubular-type slide-wire rheostat.

and the contactor is made to slide lengthwise with the tube and over the wire. This type is shown in Fig. 4-2. A variation of this form is used in radio and communication circuits. In this type the resistance wire is usually wound on a flat strip of insulating material, and the strip is then bent into a circular shape. The contactor is pivoted at the center of this circle and moves in an arc so as to slide over the wire, as shown in Fig. 4-3.

3. Field Rheostats. For heavier duty, such as for use with electrical machines, a sturdier rheostat is made. A rheostat of this type usually consists of resistance wire imbedded in some heat-resisting, insulating material such as porcelain. The insulating material and resistance wire are supported in a cast-iron frame, circular in shape, and so designed as to make possible good heat radiation. Instead of having the movable contactor make direct contact with the resistance wire, taps are brought out at intervals along the wire. Each tap is

Courtesy Ohmite Manufacturing Co.

Fig. 4-3. Circular-type slide-wire rheostat.

terminated with a flat metal button. These buttons are arranged in a circle so that the movable contactor, fitted with a shoe on its end, can be moved over them, making contact with them. This type is illustrated in Fig. 4-4. .. Rheostats of this type usually are the kind used in the field circuits of generators and motors. For this reason they are commonly referred to as *field rheostats*.

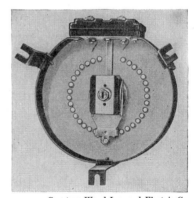

Courtesy Ward Leonard Electric Co.

Fig. 4-4. Front and rear views of a field rheostat.

Where unusually large currents must be handled, the resistance elements consist of large iron grids.

4. Rheostat Rating. Every rheostat of the type shown schematically in Fig. 4-1 has a resistance rating. This rating is the number of ohms in the fixed resistance element. Each rheostat also has a current rating—that is, a maximum current which it can safely carry continuously. For this reason, a rheostat should not be connected directly to a source of power, but should be used in conjunction with some other piece of apparatus having sufficient resistance so that the current in the rheostat will at no time exceed the rated value. Fig. 4-5 shows how a rheostat is used. In this circuit, the rheostat governs the brilliance of the lamp by controlling the circuit current.

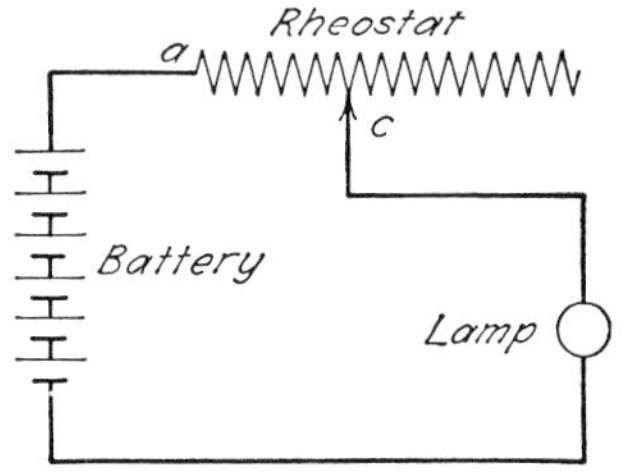

In general, field rheostats have a resistance rating and two current ratings. For example, the rheostat name plate might read

RESISTANCE 160 OHMS

AMPERES   2—1

Fig. 4-5. Use of a rheostat to control the current in a lamp.

This rating signifies that the total resistance is 160 ohms and that the rheostat will safely carry 1 ampere through all of its resistance and 2 amperes in the first step. If a rheostat having such a rating were to be used in a 110-volt circuit, it would be necessary that it be connected in series with some other piece of apparatus having a fixed resistance of not less than 55 ohms. This would have to be done in order that the current in the rheostat would at no time be greater than 2 amperes regardless of the position of the movable contactor of the rheostat.

The selection of the proper rheostat to be used in a circuit is determined by the resistance of the apparatus in series with which the rheostat is to be used and the variation of current desired.

5. Potentiometer Rheostats. A variation of the type of rheostat discussed above is that known as the *potentiometer rheostat* or *potentiometer.* The potentiometer differs from the rheostat in that in the

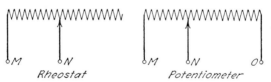

Fig. 4-6. Schematic diagrams showing the difference between a rheostat and a potentiometer.

former both ends of the resistance element are brought out to terminals. A schematic diagram of each type is shown in Fig. 4-6.

In Fig. 4-5 it can be seen that the magnitude of the current is controlled by either increasing or decreasing that portion of the rheostat resistance which is in the circuit. Hence a rheostat may be thought of as being a variable resistance. The potentiometer, on the other hand, is usually thought of as a voltage divider, controlling the current in a circuit by varying the voltage applied to the circuit.

Potentiometers are most commonly connected as shown in Fig. 4-7. If switch S is left open, and the resistance MO of the potentiometer is uniform per unit length, then, when the movable contactor is midway between M and O, the voltage between M and N will be exactly one-half the line voltage; and similarly, if the contactor is placed so that MN is one-fourth the distance from M to O, the voltage between M and N will be exactly one-fourth the line voltage. If the switch S is now closed, the current in the load can be varied by varying the voltage MN applied to the load. This, as would be concluded from the above discussion, may be accomplished by moving the contactor in either

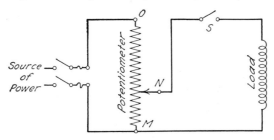

Fig. 4-7.   Use of a potentiometer as a voltage divider to regulate the voltage applied to a load.

direction. Moving the contactor down decreases the current, while moving it up increases the current. However, because of the fact that the current to the load passes only through the section ON of the potentiometer, the voltage per unit length of ON is no longer the same as that of NM, but greater. Therefore, the potentiometer does not divide the voltage in direct proportion to the displacement of the movable contactor when connected to a load, as might have been concluded from the earlier part of the discussion. However, the fact remains that it does divide the voltage and hence may be thought of as a voltage divider. The advantage of the potentiometer lies in the fact that, when used in a circuit as shown in the figure, the current to the load can be varied through a greater range than would be possible if a rheostat were used.

The resistance rating of a potentiometer is the number of ohms in the fixed resistance element. Usually a potentiometer has a resistance element of uniform cross-sectional area and, consequently, has a single current rating. At no time should the current in any portion of the potentiometer resistance element be allowed to exceed the rated value for the potentiometer. When a rheostat is used as a current control, the current in the portion of the rheostat in use is everywhere the same as in the apparatus whose current is being controlled; thus, in Fig. 4-5 the current in portion ac of the rheostat is the same as that in the lamp. This is not true when a potentiometer is used. In portion ON of the potentiometer in Fig. 4-7, the current is greater than that in the load which the potentiometer serves. This fact is made clear by noting that the current in section ON is the sum of the current in the load and that in the portion NM of the potentiometer. Hence, when selecting a potentiometer both of these currents must be considered, and when the potentiometer is in use it must not be assumed that the current in the potentiometer is less than rated value just because the load current is less.

6. Load Rheostats. Up to this point, the rheostats mentioned have been the types suitable only for use in circuits in which the current is limited to a few amperes at the most.

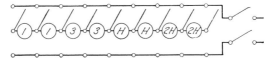

Fig. 4-8. Schematic diagram of a load rheostat consisting of lamps and heater elements.

In making tests of electric circuits and machinery, occasions arise when some kind of a variable resistance is necessary which will handle current greater than can be handled by rheostats of the types already described—for example, when a load test is to be made on a generator. In such a case, the rheostat must be capable of safely carrying the rated output current of the machine. For machines found in the average college laboratory this load may be as great as a hundred amperes.

One of the most flexible types of load rheostats for use in low-voltage circuits, such as 115- or 230-volt circuits, consists of ordinary lamps or heater elements which may be connected in parallel, series, or series-parallel by means of a suitable switching device. Fig. 4-8 shows one system that can be used. In this figure the number in the circle indicates a group of that number of lamps that are permanently connected in parallel. A circle with H within it indicates a heater element such as is used in the reflector type of electric heater often found in homes. It will be noted that, if the switches, which are single-pole double-throw, are closed alternately up and down, all the lamps and heater elements will be placed in parallel, whereas, if every other switch is left open and those which are to be closed are alternately closed up and down, the lamp groups and heater elements will be connected in series-parallel. If the lamps and heater elements have 115-volt ratings, they can all be connected in parallel when used in a 115-volt circuit. For a 230-volt circuit, however, they would need to be connected in series-parallel. In the latter case, care must be exercised in making these series-parallel connections in order to avoid the application of more than rated voltage on the lamps and heater elements.

The resistance of this type of load rheostat obviously is varied by increasing or decreasing the number of lamps or heater elements connected. The more connected in accordance with the above system of switching, the lower will be the resistance, since branches are paralleled in either case. Schematically this is indicated in Fig. 4-9. Groups connected for use in a 115-volt circuit are shown in (a) of the figure.

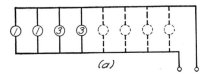 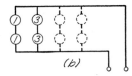

Fig. 4-9. Schematic diagrams showing the elements of the load rheostat in Fig. 4-8 connected for use with voltages not exceeding (a) the rated voltage of the elements and (b) twice the rated voltage of the elements.

In (b) of the figure the arrangement is for use in circuits of double this voltage. It is evident that in either case the resistance is reduced by adding more groups, as indicated by the dotted lines.

Although the types of connections indicated in Fig. 4-9 are the most commonly used, others are possible. For example, by closing the first and last switches to opposite sides with all other switches open, the lamp and heater groups are all connected in series, and the maximum possible resistance of the rheostat is obtained. Many resistance values between the possible maximum and minimum values can be obtained by properly using the switches to connect the lamp and heater groups in series, parallel, or various series-parallel combinations. In any case, care must be taken to avoid exceeding the rated voltage of the lamps and heaters.

Other high-current rheostats of this type are made in which cast-iron grids or strips of resistance wire are used in place of lamps and heaters.

Another form of load rheostat that is used to some extent, but that has several disadvantages, is the water rheostat. Such a rheostat usually consists of two electrodes in a water-tight container containing water or a brine solution. When the container is metallic, it serves as one of the electrodes; otherwise one electrode is usually a metal plate fastened to the inside of the container. The second electrode is mechanically arranged so that it can be raised or lowered in the liquid, thus increasing or decreasing the resistance. The chief disadvantage of this type of rheostat is its change in resistance under operation. Some of the factors which contribute to this change are evaporation of the water, change in temperature of the liquid, gassing at the electrodes, and corrosion of the electrodes.

Laboratory Problem No. 4-1
RHEOSTATS

Laboratory

Note: It should be remembered that rheostats have current ratings in addition to their resistance ratings.

1. Connect either a slide-wire rheostat or a field rheostat in series with a 115-volt incandescent lamp. Use a rheostat having approximately the same resistance as that of the lamp. In the circuit insert suitable instruments for measuring the lamp current and voltage when the circuit is connected to a 115-volt d-c source of power and the movable contactor of the rheostat is moved from the "all-in" position to the "all-out" position. (See the sections "Use of the Ammeter" and "Use of the Voltmeter" in Chapter 5.) Make measurements of lamp current and voltage for the "all-in" and "all-out" positions of the movable contactor and also for three or four intermediate positions.

2. Connect a potentiometer rheostat so that it can be used as a voltage divider to control the voltage impressed on a 115-volt incandescent lamp. Use a 115-volt d-c source of power. In the circuit insert suitable instruments for measuring the lamp current and voltage as the movable contactor is moved from the position that gives zero voltage at the lamp terminals to the position that gives full-line voltage. Make measurements of lamp current and voltage for the zero-voltage and full-line-voltage positions and also for three or four intermediate positions.

3. (a) Examine a load rheostat and determine what means are used to vary its resistance.

Determine whether the rheostat resistance is continuously variable as in a water rheostat or whether the variation is in steps of finite resistance values as in the type which is exemplified by the lamp-heater rheostat.

Determine whether the rheostat may be safely used with both 115 volts and 230 volts.

(b) Draw a circuit diagram of the load rheostat. Show the resistance element or elements and such essential auxiliary parts as switches, connecting links, and other control devices.

(c) If the load rheostat is one whose resistance is varied in steps of finite values, set up a circuit with the necessary instruments for measuring the current and voltage of the load rheostat. The instruments should be suitable for measuring these quantities when the rheostat is connected to a d-c source whose voltage is approximately equal to the rated voltage of the resistance elements and the switches or connecting links are operated in such a manner as to connect consecutively the resistance elements in parallel. Measure and record the current and voltage of the rheostat after each addition of a resistance element.

(d) If the load rheostat resistance is continuously variable, make a linear scale which can be attached to the device and used in connection with the control handle so that the position of the control handle can be expressed in terms of the scale graduations.

Set up a circuit with suitable instruments for measuring the current and voltage of the rheostat when it is connected to a 115-volt d-c source. Obtain data from which a curve can be drawn of the resistance of the rheostat vs the position of the control handle expressed in terms of the graduated scale.

Report

A. Explain the essential differences between the rheostat and the potentiometer as current-control devices.

B. If the load rheostat used in **3** is made of resistance elements of finite values as in the lamp-heater type:

(1) Calculate the resistance of each section of the rheostat from the data obtained in **3**(c).

(2) Assuming that the resistance elements are rated at 115 volts, explain how to use the rheostat as indicated below without exceeding the voltage rating of the elements:

(a) To control current with voltages not exceeding 115 volts.

(b) To control current with voltages between 115 and 230 volts.

(c) To obtain the maximum resistance when used with 115 volts and also when used with 230 volts.

(d) To obtain the minimum resistance when used with 115 volts and also when used with 230 volts.

C. If the load rheostat used in **3** is of the type whose resistance is continuously variable:

(1) Plot a curve of the resistance of the rheostat vs the position of the control handle expressed in terms of the graduated scale.

(2) Discuss the shape of the curve of (1).

D. A potentiometer has a resistance of 120 ohms uniformly distributed between its fixed terminals, which are connected to a 120-volt d-c source. The potentiometer is used to control the voltage impressed on a series circuit consisting of a field rheostat and the shunt field winding of a d-c generator. The field rheostat has a resistance of 40 ohms, and its movable contactor is set in the "all-in" position. The resistance of the field winding is 80 ohms.

(1) What is the current in the field winding when the movable contactor of the potentiometer is midway between its fixed terminals?

(2) From resistance and current values, calculate the voltage drop across each half of the potentiometer. Add the calculated voltage drops. The sum should be equal to the source voltage, 120 volts.

CHAPTER 5
AMMETERS AND VOLTMETERS

THE determination and control of the performance of electric circuits and machinery is dependent to a large extent upon the use of instruments. Two of the instruments most frequently used in testing are the ammeter and the voltmeter.

1. Use of the Ammeter. The ammeter is an instrument used for measuring current. Current is a movement of electric charge. It is measured on the basis of the amount of charge that passes a given point in a circuit per unit of time. Thus, to measure the current in a circuit, the circuit must be opened and an ammeter inserted. Fig. 5-1 shows an ammeter in position to measure the current furnished by a battery to a group of lamps. The ammeter is shown shunted by a single-pole single-throw switch. This switch is closed at all times except when a reading of the instrument indication is being taken. The purpose of the switch is to protect the instrument from possible damage

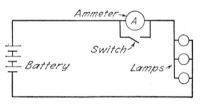

Fig. 5-1. Ammeter with protective shunting switch connected in a circuit to measure current.

should an abnormal current be produced by an accidental overload or short circuit.

In order that a circuit will not be appreciably affected by the insertion of an ammeter, the ammeter resistance is kept as low as practicable. The higher the range of an ammeter, the lower is its resistance. For example, a good-quality d-c ammeter designed to measure currents up to 1 ampere has a resistance of about .05 ohm, while a 50-amp instrument has a resistance of about .001 ohm. These figures, however, are not to be taken as exact values for ammeters of these ranges since they may be larger or smaller depending on the manufacturer and the quality.

When an ammeter is being used, great care must be exercised to insert it in series with a circuit as shown in the figure. An ammeter should not be connected between two points of a circuit; that is, it should not be bridged across any part of a circuit, for between two such points there might be sufficient voltage to cause a much greater current in the instrument than that for which it was designed.

2. Use of the Voltmeter. The voltmeter is an instrument used to measure voltage. Since voltage is the measure of the difference of electric potential between two points of a circuit or the terminals of a generator, the voltmeter is connected between the points whose difference of potential is to be determined. Fig. 5-2 shows several voltmeters connected to measure the voltages between several sets of points in the circuit. This figure also shows several ammeters inserted to measure the currents at various points in the circuit.

For reasons given in a later section of this chapter, the resistance of a voltmeter is much higher than that of an ammeter. The higher the

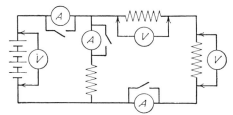

Fig. 5-2.   Ammeters and voltmeters connected for measuring various currents and voltages.

range of a voltmeter, the greater is its resistance. A good-quality d-c voltmeter intended for general use has a resistance of about 100 ohms for each volt of its range. Thus, such a voltmeter having a range of 150 volts has a resistance of 15,000 ohms, and one having a range of 300 volts has a resistance of 30,000 ohms. The tendency at present is to manufacture high-resistance voltmeters, and it is not unusual for a d-c voltmeter to have a resistance of 5000 ohms for each volt of its range. Voltmeters having resistances as high as 200,000 ohms for each volt of their ranges are being manufactured for special purposes. Because of its high resistance, a voltmeter is almost never inserted in series with a circuit or any element of a circuit. Exception to this rule is made in a few special tests.

3. Classification of Instrument Mechanisms. A great variety of mechanisms have been designed and built for measuring electric current. Except in a few cases, the torque that motivates the moving element of a mechanism is developed as a result of current in some element of the device, the displacement of the moving element being used as a measure of the current. In the majority of mechanisms the torque is directly produced by the force exerted when vanes of ferrous metal are placed in a magnetic field or when a current-carrying conductor is in such a field.

Since current is proportional to voltage, a given mechanism can readily be adapted for use in measuring voltages. In view of this fact, although constant reference is made to current in the following discussion of the various mechanisms, it should be understood that the same mechanisms are used in voltmeters.

In this chapter, only the types of mechanisms most commonly used in college laboratories and in industry are treated. These types may be classified as follows:

I. Moving-Coil Types
    A. D'Arsonval, or Permanent-Magnet
    B. Electrodynamometer
II. Iron-Vane Types
    A. Thomson, or Inclined-Coil
    B. Weston, or Concentric-Vane
    C. Radial-Vane

4. D'Arsonval Mechanism. The *D'Arsonval*, or permanent-magnet, type of mechanism is shown in Fig. 5-3. The permanent horseshoe magnet is fitted with soft-iron pole pieces N and S. Between the

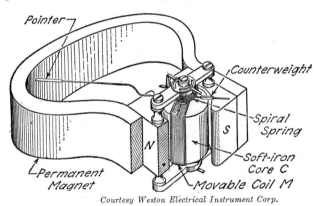

Courtesy Weston Electrical Instrument Corp.

Fig. 5-3. D'Arsonval mechanism (part of N pole not shown).

pole pieces is a soft-iron cylinder C, which is added in order to shorten the air gap between the poles of the magnet. The addition of this cylinder increases the density of the magnetic flux in the air gaps, thus increasing the sensitivity of the instrument. The pole pieces are so shaped that the radial distance between the surface of each pole piece and the surface of the iron cylinder is constant. The current to be measured is introduced into coil M, which is wound of very fine insulated wire on an aluminum frame. This coil is supported at the top and bottom by hardened steel pivots which rest in jewel bearings usually made of white sapphire. The sides of this coil move in the air gaps between the pole pieces and the soft-iron cylinder. The coil is carefully centered so that the radial distance between each coil side and adjacent pole piece is maintained constant throughout the range of motion. Current is introduced into the coil through two spiral springs, one attached to the coil shaft at the bottom end of the coil and the other attached to the shaft at the top end of the coil. These springs are insulated from the shaft and not only act as conductors to the coil but also supply the restraining torque for the coil. These springs are wound in opposite directions, so that, when the coil moves, one spring coils and the other uncoils. The springs are designed to offer a restraining torque that is directly proportional to the angular displacement of the coil and hence to the deflection of the pointer, which is attached to the coil shaft. Wear on the bearings is reduced to a minimum by balancing the moving element by counterweights attached to the pointer. The proper balancing of the moving element also reduces the error that might result if the mechanism is used in a position which is not level.

Since the radial length of the air gap between each pole piece and the soft-iron cylinder is maintained constant at every point, the strength of the magnetic field is uniform throughout the air gaps and the magnetic lines of force are normal to the surfaces of the pole pieces and the iron cylinder.

When current is introduced into the coil, a force is produced between the coil sides and the magnetic field which is proportional to the current in the coil and to the strength of the magnetic field in the air gaps. The torque resulting from this force causes the coil to move until the restraining torque of the spiral springs just balances that produced by the current in the coil. Since the air-gap flux density is constant, the torque produced by the current in the coil is directly proportional to the coil current. Further, since the restraining torque of the spiral springs is directly proportional to the angular displacement of the coil from its initial zero position, the pointer deflection is directly proportional to the current in the coil. Accordingly, the scale used with this type of mechanism is uniform; that is, the divisions are equal in size.

The direction of the force exerted on a current-carrying conductor situated in a magnetic field is determined by the direction of the lines of force of the field and the direction of the current in the conductor. In the D'Arsonval mechanism the direction of the pointer deflection will accordingly be determined by the direction of the current in the coil, since the direction of the magnetic field is fixed and determined by the permanent magnet. Consequently, this type of mechanism is suitable only for making d-c measurements.*

The damping element in a D'Arsonval mechanism is the aluminum frame on which the coil is wound. Any motion of the frame in the magnetic field of the air gaps results in an induced voltage in the sides of the frame and a flow of current around the frame. The torque produced by this current and the magnetic field is in such a direction as to oppose the motion of the coil, and its effect is either to prevent or to damp any oscillation of the moving coil.

5. Electrodynamometer Mechanism. The *electrodynamometer* type of mechanism is shown in Fig. 5-4(a). It consists of a pivoted movable

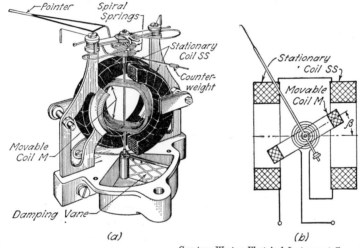

Courtesy Weston Electrical Instrument Corp.

Fig. 5-4. (a) Electrodynamometer mechanism. (b) Schematic diagram of an electro-dynamometer mechanism.

coil M and a stationary coil SS of two sections, as shown schematically in (b) of the figure. When current is introduced into the stationary coil, a magnetic field results. In the space within which the movable coil is intended to move, most of the lines of force of the field are uniformly distributed and parallel to the axis of the stationary coil. If the current in the stationary coil is maintained constant, this magnetic field will also remain constant. Such a coil with its constant current might be used to replace the permanent magnet of the D'Arsonval

---

* When a D'Arsonval mechanism is used in conjunction with a rectifier or a thermocouple, a-c measurements can be made. This subject is discussed later in this chapter.

mechanism. One great disadvantage of this type of mechanism would be the necessity of carrying with it a source of current for the stationary coil. Such a source would need to produce a constant current in the coil, a requirement which would be difficult to fulfill in a simple manner. To avoid this difficulty the stationary coil and the movable coil are connected in series, as shown in the figure, so that the current to be measured flows in both coils at the same time.

Assume that the current in the stationary coil produces a magnetic field of flux density B in the space within which coil M moves. Since the magnetic path is air,

$$B = ki, \tag{5-1}$$

where k is a proportionality factor and i is the current in coils SS and M. The force acting on the sides of the movable coil is proportional to the current in its turns and also to the flux density of the magnetic field; but the latter is also proportional to the current, and hence

$$\text{Force} = k_1 Bi = k_2 i^2. \tag{5-2}$$

The torque which produces motion is proportional to that component of this force which is normal to the plane of the movable coil. If β is the angle between the plane of the movable coil and the axis of the stationary coil, the torque on the movable coil is approximately expressed by

$$\text{Torque} = Ki^2 \cos \beta. \tag{5-3}$$

In the electrodynamometer mechanism, as in the D'Arsonval type, current is conducted to the movable coil through spiral springs. Since these springs produce a restraining torque that is directly proportional to the angular displacement of the movable coil from its zero position, a scale for use with an electrodynamometer mechanism is governed by equation (5-3). Because of the i^2 term in this equation, the scale is cramped at the zero end, with increasingly larger divisions as the scale progresses. The variation in the size of the succeeding scale divisions is also affected by the $\cos \beta$ term. However, by designing the mechanism so that β is not large when the pointer is in the zero position, the effect of this term can be made small.

A reversal of the current in the mechanism does not cause a reversal of the direction of the motivating torque. A reversal of the direction of the torque can take place only when either the current in the stationary coil or that in the movable coil is reversed, but not both. Since the stationary coil and the movable coil are connected in series, a reversal of current in one is coincident with the reversal of current in the other, and the torque is always in the same direction regardless of the direction of the current.   This type of mechanism can accordingly be used for making either d-c or a-c measurements.

Damping in the electrodynamometer type is generally obtained by the air friction produced in a closed air chamber by a very light aluminum vane attached to the shaft of the movable coil.

6. Thomson, or Inclined-Coil, Mechanism.   The instrument mechanism shown in Fig. 5-5 is the *inclined-coil* type.   Only a single stationary coil inclined at an angle of 45° with the horizontal is used.

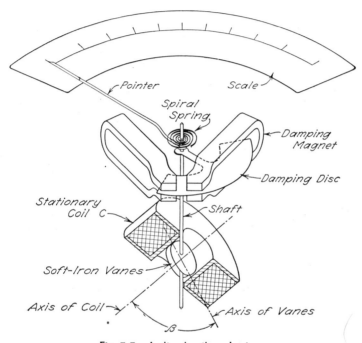

Fig. 5-5.   Inclined-coil mechanism.

Mounted on the pointer shaft are two parallel elongated soft-iron vanes.   The planes of these vanes make an angle of 45° with the shaft. Thus, if the shaft is turned, the vanes may be made to become parallel either to the plane of the coil or to the axis of the coil.

When current flows in a coil winding, the magnetomotive force produced sets up magnetic lines of force that link the coil and that in the coil are parallel to the coil axis.   When an elongated piece of iron is subjected to a magnetizing force having a component in the direction of its longest dimension, the piece becomes a magnet with unlike poles at its opposite ends.   Hence, when the current to be measured is introduced into the coil winding of the mechanism shown in Fig. 5-5, the magnetomotive force produced causes the parallel elongated soft-iron vanes to become magnetized. The resulting action is similar to that which takes place when a bar magnet is placed in a magnetic field. The vanes, whose axis is displaced from the axis of the coil by an angle β, if unrestrained, would turn until their axis became parallel to the axis of the coil and to the magnetic lines within the coil. Since the vanes are mounted on a pivoted shaft, they cause the shaft to turn with them, producing a deflection of the pointer along the scale. With the motion of the shaft restrained by the spiral spring shown in the figure, the movement of the shaft is restricted, and it turns until the restraining torque of the spiral spring is just equal to the motivating torque, at which point it comes to rest.

The torque acting to turn the shaft varies directly with the strength of the magnetic field of the coil and with the strength of the poles of the magnetized vanes. The strength of the field of the coil is proportional to the current in the coil. The strength of the poles induced in the vanes is also proportional to the coil current if the permeability of the vanes is constant. The permeability is nearly constant, since the magnetomotive force produced by the current in the coil is so small that the flux density in the vanes is low. Hence the torque is very nearly proportional to the square of the current in the coil. The torque is also a complex function of the position of the vanes—that is, of the angular displacement β between the axis of the vanes and the axis of the coil. The torque acting to turn the shaft can accordingly be expressed approximately as

$$\text{Torque} = kf(\beta)i^2. \tag{5-4}$$

Since the restraining torque of the spiral spring varies linearly with the deflection of the pointer, the deflection would be proportional to the square of the current in the coil if $f(\beta)$ remained constant. In such a case a scale for use with this type of mechansim would be cramped at the zero end, and each succeeding division would be larger than the preceding one. However, $f(\beta)$ is not constant. When β is appreciable, as is the case when the deflection is small, $f(\beta)$ does not vary appreciably with change of β, so that the torque is governed largely by the current-squared factor of the equation. Hence the scale follows the square law at the lower end. However, when appreciable current flows in the coil and the deflection of the pointer is large, in which case β is small, $f(\beta)$ decreases rapidly as the deflection is increased; and, as a result, the succeeding divisions diminish in size at the upper end of the scale. Accordingly, the scale of this type of mechanism is usually cramped at both ends. The amount of cramping at either end of the scale can be controlled to a certain extent by the placement of the vanes—that is, by the choice of β at zero and full deflection.

In this mechanism the direction in which the shaft will turn when current is introduced is independent of the direction of the current in the coil winding. A reversal of this current only reverses the direction of the magnetic lines of force. The force acting on the vanes is always in such a direction as to cause them to move toward a position which is parallel to the axis of the coil. The direction of the motion is determined, however, by the initial or zero position of the vanes. Since the direction of deflection is independent of the direction of the current, the inclined-coil type of mechanism can be used for making a-c or d-c measurements. Nevertheless, for reasons given later, this type of mechanism should not be used for making d-c measurements when accuracy is important.*

The inclined-coil mechanism may be damped by means of a light aluminum vane operating in a closed air chamber or by means of a very light aluminum disc rotating with the pointer shaft and moving between the poles of permanent horseshoe magnets as shown in Fig. 5-5. The motion of the disc in the field of the magnets produces eddy currents in the disc, the effect of which is to produce a torque which opposes the motion of the disc. The amount of damping is governed by moving the magnets toward or away from the center of the disc.

7. Weston, or Concentric-Vane, Mechanism. The activating elements of the *concentric-vane* mechanism are shown in Fig. 5-6. This mechanism consists of a fixed coil C, into which the current to be measured is introduced, and two concentric soft-iron vanes F and M located within the coil. Vane F, indicated in the figure by the heavily shaded area, and its nonmagnetic support are fixed, being cemented to the inside wall of the coil. Vane M is attached to the pointer shaft by means of supporting spokes, the assembly being free to move. The motion of the movable vane and attached pointer is opposed by the restraining torque of the spiral spring S.

When current is introduced into coil C, the magnetomotive force produced magnetizes both of the iron vanes in the same direction, the upper edges of the vanes becoming north poles and the lower edges south poles when the direction of current is counterclockwise in the coil. Since corresponding edges are magnetized alike, a force of repulsion exists between the vanes, causing the movable vane to move in a clockwise direction. This motion takes place not only

---

* This statement applies to all iron-vane mechanisms.

because of the existence of the force but also as a consequence of the zero position of the concentric vanes. Upon inspection of the figure it will be noted that the end of the movable vane extends in a clockwise direction beyond that of the fixed vane and that a corresponding displacement occurs at the other end. It should be obvious that only a force of attraction could cause the movable vane to move in a counterclockwise direction.

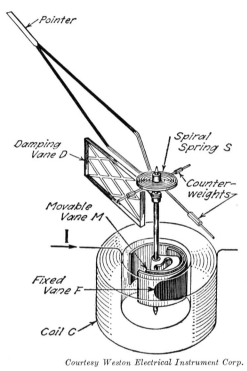

In this mechanism, as in the inclined-coil type, the strength of the poles induced in the vanes is very nearly proportional to the current. Since the force of repulsion is proportional to the product of the pole strengths, the torque acting on the movable element is proportional to the square of the current. Furthermore, the repelling force is a function of the displacement of the movable vane from the zero position, for, in effect, such a displacement is equivalent to increasing the distance between two magnets. Hence the motivating torque is also a function of the displacement from the zero position. The torque can be expressed approximately by

Courtesy Weston Electrical Instrument Corp.

Fig. 5-6. Concentric-vane mechanism.

$$\text{Torque} = kf(d)i^2, \tag{5-5}$$

d being the distance from the end of the fixed vane to the corresponding end of the movable vane. If $f(d)$ remained constant, then with the usual type of restraining spring the pointer deflection would be proportional to the square of the coil current, and the scale would follow a square law. In general, however, $f(d)$ is purposely controlled by shaping the vanes to give a scale that, although cramped at the lower end, is nearly uniform over the upper 50 per cent or more of its range.

Since a change in the direction of the current in the coil will change the direction of the induced magnetism in both vanes at the same time, the force between the vanes will remain one of repulsion, and the direction of displacement of the movable vane will not be affected by the change in the direction of the current. The concentric-vane mechanism can, therefore, be used to make measurements of alternating current and also direct current.*

This mechanism is damped by air friction in the same manner as the electrodynamometer.

8. Radial-Vane Mechanism. The *radial-vane* type of mechanism is shown in Fig. 5-7. The operating principle of this type of mechanism is similar to that of the concentric-vane mechanism. As in the latter type, the radial-vane mechanism has a fixed vane *F* and a movable vane *M* located within the fixed coil *C*. Both vanes are rectangular in shape, the movable vane being attached to the pointer shaft and the fixed vane being cemented to the inside surface of the coil.

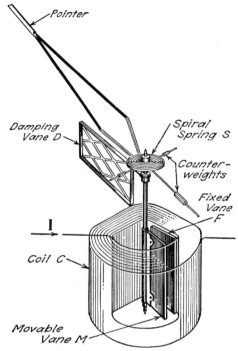

Courtesy *Weston Electrical Instrument Corp.*

Fig. 5-7. Radial-vane mechanism.

The motion of the movable vane is similar to that of a hinge. The movement of the pointer and shaft assembly is restrained by the spiral spring *S*, and damping is secured by the aluminum damping vane *D*.

When the current to be measured flows in the coil, the magnetomotive force produced magnetizes the fixed and movable vanes in the same manner as in the concentric-vane type. Therefore the force of repulsion between the vanes is proportional to the square of the coil current and is also a function of the angle through which the movable vane is displaced from its zero position. Owing to the opposing influences of an increase of coil current and the resulting increase of

---

* See the footnote on page 45.

displacement angle on the force of repulsion between the vanes, the torque developed does not increase as the square of the coil current but more nearly as the first power of the current. Thus with the usual type of restraining spring the deflection of the pointer is approximately proportional to the coil current, and the scale is nearly uniform.

The radial-vane type of mechanism has recently come into wide use as a result of the development of alloys for the vanes which are capable of producing extremely strong magnets.

9. Effective Value of an A-C Current and Voltage. When current flows in a resistance, the electrical energy supplied to the resistance is converted into heat energy. The instantaneous rate at which this conversion takes place—that is, the instantaneous power supplied to the resistance—is

$$p = i^2R, \tag{5-6}$$

where p is the instantaneous power in watts, i is the instantaneous value of the current in amperes, and R is the resistance in ohms.

When alternating current flows in a resistance, the average power, or the average rate at which heat is produced, is

$$\text{av } p = P = (\text{av } i^2)R, \tag{5-7}$$

(av i^2) being the average of the squares of the instantaneous values of current for one cycle. When the current is direct, the steady value $I_{\text{d-c}}$ and the instantaneous value i are the same, so that the average power is

$$P = I_{\text{d-c}}^2 R. \tag{5-8}$$

Equations (5-7) and (5-8) provide a basis for defining the effective value of an alternating current. An alternating current is said to have a value of one ampere when the average rate at which heat is produced in a resistance carrying the alternating current is the same as the rate at which heat is produced in an equal resistance by one ampere of direct current. On the basis of this definition, it follows that when the average power delivered to a resistance by an alternating current is the same as the power delivered by a direct current to an equal resistance, the effective value I of the alternating current in amperes is the same as the value $I_{\text{d-c}}$ of the direct current in amperes. The effective value of an alternating current can now be determined in terms of its instantaneous values. In accordance with the above, let P and R, respectively, be the same in equations (5-7) and (5-8). Then

$$(\text{av } i^2) = I_{\text{d-c}}^2.$$

Evidently (av i^2) is the square of an alternating current of quantity

I which has the same effect as $I_{\text{d-c}}$. The quantity I is therefore the effective value of the alternating current, and

$$I = \sqrt{(\text{av } i^2)}. \qquad (5\text{-}9)$$

The effective value is also known as the root mean square, or rms, value, since it is the square root of the average of the squares of the instantaneous values.

Similar considerations will show that the effective, or rms, value V of an alternating voltage is

$$V = \sqrt{(\text{av } v^2)}, \qquad (5\text{-}10)$$

where v is the instantaneous value of the voltage.

When dealing with a-c circuits and machines, the effective values of current and voltage are the values considered unless there is a definite statement to the contrary. It will become evident in the following sections that the effective value is the one measured by the types of a-c ammeters and voltmeters most generally used.

10. Deflection of Electrodynamometer and Iron-Vane Mechanisms When Carrying Alternating Current. In the discussion of the electrodynamometer mechanism it is shown that the direction of the motivating torque is independent of the direction of the current through the mechanism. It is also shown that the torque is directly proportional to the square of the current and to the cosine of the angle between the plane of the movable coil and the axis of the stationary coil.

When the mechanism carries alternating current, the direction of the current reverses at regular intervals, and the current magnitude changes from instant to instant. Thus the torque acting on the movable element also changes in magnitude from instant to instant but is always in the same direction. Since the instantaneous value of an alternating current is zero at regular intervals, the torque becomes zero at similar intervals. One might conclude that the pointer of the mechanism would oscillate between the zero position and one determined by the maximum instantaneous value of the current. If the alternations were slow—say, one a second—such would be the case. However, in the case of commercial alternating current having a frequency of 25 or 60 cycles per second, the alternations occur at the rate of 50 per second or more. The movable element cannot respond to such rapid variations in instantaneous torque because of its inertia and because of the effect of the damping mechanism, so it moves to a fixed position where the average torque produced by the current is equal to the counter torque of the restraining springs. The average torque produced by the current when the movable element is in the final position is

$$\text{Average torque} = K(\text{av } i^2) \cos \beta$$
$$= KI^2 \cos \beta, \qquad (5\text{-}11)$$

where I is the effective value of the alternating current and β is the angle between the axis of the stationary coil and the plane of the movable coil for its final position. Therefore the final pointer deflection depends upon the square of the effective value of the alternating current. Hence with a suitably calibrated scale the electrodynamometer mechanism can be used to measure the effective value of an alternating current. Since the instantaneous value i and the steady value $I_{\text{d-c}}$ of a direct current are the same, an electrodynamometer mechanism having a scale calibrated by the use of either direct or alternating current can be used for making both d-c and a-c measurements.

Considerations similar to the preceding show that when any one of the types of iron-vane mechanisms carries alternating current, the final pointer deflection also depends upon the square of the effective value of the alternating current. Accordingly, an iron-vane type of mechanism having a scale calibrated for use with alternating current can be used for measurements of either alternating or direct current. However, as previously intimated, the iron-vane types are intended mainly for a-c measurements.

11. Ammeters. In the D'Arsonval mechanism the current is conducted to the movable coil by the restraining springs. In order to obtain satisfactory sensitivity and to limit the mechanism to a convenient size, the mass of the movable coil must be kept small. For this reason the coil is wound of small-size wire and hence is not capable of carrying large currents. The coils of some D'Arsonval mechanisms are designed to carry but a few microamperes, and very seldom do they ever carry more than a few milliamperes. In order to adapt this type for use as an ammeter, a shunting element is used to provide a by-pass for the greater part of the current, so that only a very small proportion of the total current will pass through the coil. By proper selection of the shunt, the proportion of the total current which is by-passed can be controlled, and the mechanism can be made to give full-scale deflection at the desired total current. For example, let it be assumed that the resistance of the coil of a D'Arsonval mechanism is 5 ohms and that 10 milliamperes are necessary in the coil to cause full-scale deflection of the pointer. It is desired that full-scale deflection shall occur after a shunt has been applied and when the total current is 50 amperes.

Under these conditions the current flowing in the shunt will be

$$50 - .01 = 49.99 \text{ amp.}$$

The circuit of the coil and shunt is shown in Fig. 5-8. Since the coil and shunt are in parallel, the potential drop across each must be the same; thus

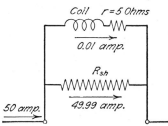

$$.01 \times r = 49.99 \times R_{sh}.$$

Substituting for r gives

$$.01 \times 5 = 49.99 \times R_{sh}.$$
$$R_{sh} = .001 \text{ ohm.}$$

By connecting a shunt of this resistance across the coil, the mechanism can be used to measure currents up to 50 amperes, and can be made to be direct reading by the use of a proper scale.

Fig. 5-8. Circuit of an ammeter showing the shunt, coil of the mechanism, and the division of the current being measured.

Shunts are usually made of manganin in order that their resistance will be nearly independent of temperature. It is general practice to include the shunt within the instrument case when the ammeter range does not exceed 25 amperes. Instruments having current ranges greater than 25 amperes are usually supplied with separate external shunts. Two typical shunts are illustrated in Fig. 5-9.

Shunts are not generally used in connection with mechanisms that are designed for measuring alternating currents. Complications arise since the opposition offered to current by the coil or coils of a mechanism is not constant when alternating current is used, but varies with frequency. Hence the proportion of the total current which would be by-passed by the resistance type of shunt would not be the same

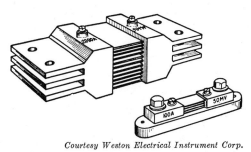

Courtesy Weston Electrical Instrument Corp.

Fig. 5-9. Ammeter shunts.

under different conditions of frequency. To remedy this situation a shunt can be designed so that it will have the same ratio of resistance to inductance as the circuit of the mechanism, in addition to having the correct opposition, so that it will divide the total current in the correct proportion. However, the practical attainment of such conditions is difficult.

A shunt of this type is sometimes used with an electrodynamometer mechanism. In such a case, the shunt is connected so that it by-passes the circuit of the movable coil and spiral restraining springs. A shunt is not required for the stationary coils since the wire can be of adequate size to carry the maximum current for which the instrument is designed. As a rule, however, when an electrodynamometer mechanism is used as a current-measuring instrument, it is usually as a milliammeter, in which case a shunt is not necessary.

In the iron-vane type of mechanism the current flows only in the stationary coil, the wire of which can be of a size that will safely carry any desired current. Hence a shunt is not required with this type of mechanism.

In order to measure very large alternating currents, electrodynamometer and iron-vane ammeters are used in conjunction with current transformers, and the ammeter indication is multiplied by the transformer ratio to determine the current being measured.

Good-grade portable ammeters of the types discussed in this section are usually accurate to within about 0.5 per cent of full-scale value. The upper frequency limit of the a-c types for this accuracy is generally 400 to 500 cycles per second.

12. Voltmeters. In an early paragraph of this chapter a statement is made to the effect that the same mechanisms are used for both ammeters and voltmeters. When a mechanism is intended for use as a voltmeter, it is provided with a high-resistance element connected in series with the coil or coils of the mechanism. Since the current through the mechanism is directly proportional to the voltage across the series combination of the coil (or coils) and the resistance element, the scale of the instrument can be calibrated in volts instead of amperes. The resistance element is usually made of manganin so that it will be very nearly independent of temperature. The resistance of the element is of such a value as to limit the current in the coil (or coils) to the value required to produce full-scale deflection when the voltage being measured is the upper limit of the voltage range of the instrument.

Since a voltmeter is connected across a circuit or an element of a circuit, the voltmeter current should be very small compared to that in the circuit or element across which it is connected. It should be apparent that the higher the resistance of a voltmeter, the less disturbance it will produce when connected in a circuit. In the case of instruments that are used to measure a-c voltages, it is desirable that the opposition to the flow of current caused by the inductance of the coil be made a very small portion of the total opposition, since it varies in proportion to the frequency. By adding a sufficiently high pure resistance the effect of the inductance of the coil can be made negligible, and the current in the coil will not be noticeably affected by changes of frequency which are within the limits specified by the manufacturer. In view of the above, it should be clear that it is desirable for voltmeters to be of high resistance.

A single instrument mechanism can be used in voltmeters of different ranges by the use of various series resistance elements. Also, by using more than one series resistance, one voltmeter can be designed for use on more than one range of voltage. As an example of the latter, let it be assumed that a current of 10 milliamperes is necessary in the coil of a given mechanism in order to produce a full-scale deflection. Let it be further assumed that the voltmeter is to have ranges of 0 to 150 and 0 to 300 volts. To fulfill the requirement of a full-scale deflection when the voltage is 150 volts, the total resistance R_t between the instrument terminals must be such as to limit the current to 10 milliamperes when 150 volts are applied to the terminals. By Ohm's law,

$$R_t = r + R = \frac{V}{I} = \frac{150}{.010} = 15,000 \text{ ohms,}$$

r being the resistance of the coil and R that of the series resistor. With the value of r known, the resistance of the series resistor is easily calculated. By adding another resistance of 15,000 ohms, the total resistance R_t is doubled, and it now requires 300 volts to produce the current of 10 milliamperes which is necessary to cause a full-scale deflection. If terminals are brought out at the junction of the two added resistances and at the end of the second

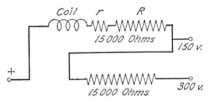

Fig. 5-10. Circuit of a voltmeter showing the series resistors and the coil of the mechanism.

resistance, as indicated in Fig. 5-10, the instrument becomes a double-range voltmeter, having a 0- to 150-volt and a 0- to 300-volt range. With two scales on the voltmeter, one for each range, direct readings can be made; otherwise the proper factor must be applied to the scale indication, this factor depending upon the scale. In the example used, a factor of two must be applied if the 300-volt terminal is used and there is only one scale of 0 to 150 volts. If there is but one scale of 0 to 300 volts, a factor of one half must be applied when the 150-volt terminal is used.

The series resistances are generally mounted within the voltmeter case. However, high-voltage instruments are sometimes provided with separate resistors connected externally to the instrument. Such external resistors are known as *multipliers*.

In general, good-grade voltmeters of the types discussed above are accurate to within about 0.5 per cent of full-scale value. In the a-c types, this accuracy is maintained if the frequency of the voltage being measured is within the range of 25 to about 150 cycles per second.

13. Hysteresis and Eddy Currents in Iron-Vane Instruments. Energy must be supplied to the vanes of an iron-vane instrument when they are carried through cycles of magnetization by the alternating current in the coil of the instrument. The rate at which energy is expended in this manner is known as *hysteresis loss*. The alternating flux caused by the alternating current in the coil also induces voltages which produce currents in the vanes. The circulation of these currents, which are called *eddy currents*, requires energy. The energy required by hysteresis and the eddy currents in the iron vanes must be supplied to the coil of the instrument and then transmitted magnetically to the vanes. The effect of these added energy requirements is to increase the apparent electrical resistance of the instrument. This effect is negligible when the instrument is used within the frequency limits specified by the manufacturer.

When an iron-vane type of instrument is used as a voltmeter, the energy requirements resulting from hysteresis and eddy currents cause an error that increases as the frequency is raised more and more above the upper limit specified for the particular voltmeter being used. The opposition to the flow of current in the coil is increased, among other things, by the increase in the apparent resistance resulting from the larger hysteresis and eddy-current energy requirements. The torque depends upon the current in the coil, and the current in turn upon the voltage being measured. Thus, with a constant voltage but changing frequency, the effect of the hysteresis and eddy-current losses in the vanes is to reduce the coil current and hence the pointer deflection as the frequency becomes greater and greater.

When an iron-vane type of instrument is used to make d-c measurements, two readings should be taken. One of these should be taken after the connections to the instrument terminals have been interchanged, thus reversing the current in the coil. The two readings should then be averaged. The necessity for reversing the current in the coil follows from the fact that the vanes may have retained some magnetism as a result of previous use. Although taking the average of the two readings will reduce the error resulting from residual

magnetism, it does not necessarily eliminate it, and hence the accuracy
of the iron-vane type of instrument is not consistent when used for
d-c measurements.   Instruments of this type are intended primarily
for making a-c measurements.

14. Rectifier Instruments.   Iron-vane and electrodynamometer
instruments are best suited for making a-c measurements at the commercial power frequencies.   Rectifier-type instruments, on the other
hand, are particularly important in the communication field since they
can be used for measurements in the frequency range from the power
frequencies up to and including the important audio frequencies.

Rectifiers depend for their operation upon the characteristic of
permitting current to flow through them freely in one direction only.

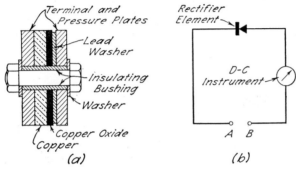

Fig. 5-11.   (a) Cross section of a copper-oxide rectifier element.   (b) Circuit in which
half-wave rectification is produced.

Rectifiers as a group include a variety of types.   The one most commonly used in connection with the rectifier instrument is the copper-
oxide type.   A cross-sectional illustration of a single copper-oxide
rectifier element is shown in (a) of Fig. 5-11.   Such an element offers a
much lower resistance to current flowing from the copper oxide to the
copper than to current flowing from the copper to the copper oxide.
In the circuit shown in (b) of the figure, the rectifier element is shown
symbolically by the block and the solid arrowhead.   The block
represents the copper and the arrowhead the copper oxide; thus the
arrowhead points in the direction in which current flows more freely.

If an a-c voltage is applied to terminals A and B, current will
flow freely in the circuit during that period when terminal B is $+$ and
A is $-$, but very little current will flow during the period when terminal
A is $+$ and B is $-$.   The average of these two currents will be one in
the direction indicated by the arrowhead, and the magnitude of its
average value will be indicated by the d-c instrument shown.

A rectifier may consist of one or more elements connected in series for half-wave rectification, or in the form of a bridge for full-wave rectification. The connection discussed in the preceding paragraph is that for half-wave rectification, since current flows freely during the period of only one half of each cycle. A bridge circuit made up of four rectifier elements is shown in Fig. 5-12(a). When an a-c voltage is applied to terminals A and B in this circuit, the current flows freely from F to D, through the milliammeter from D to E, and from E to C during the period when terminal A is $+$ and B is $-$. During this same period, very little current flows from F to E and from D to C. During the period that terminal B is $+$ and A is $-$, the current flows freely from C to D, through the milliammeter from D to E, and from E to F; but during this same period very little current flows from C to E and from D to F. It should be noted that regardless of which of the

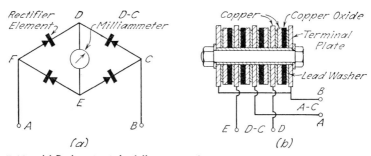

Fig. 5-12. (a) Bridge circuit for full-wave rectification. (b) Cross-sectional view showing the method of stacking the discs to form a bridge or full-wave rectifier.

terminals A and B is positive, the milliammeter is in the path of the free flow of current and that the current in the milliammeter is always from D to E. Thus, current flows freely through the milliammeter during both halves of the a-c cycle. For this reason the bridge circuit is called a *full-wave rectifier*. In a bridge circuit as shown, terminals A and B are called the a-c terminals and D and E the d-c terminals. The method of stacking the discs to form a bridge or full-wave rectifier is shown in (b) of the figure.

A rectifier-type instrument consists essentially of a bridge-type copper-oxide rectifier and a D'Arsonval-type milliammeter, both being contained in the same case. The connections from the milliammeter to terminals D and E of the rectifier are made within the instrument case. Only a pair of terminals corresponding to A and B are brought out. These are the instrument terminals. The bridge-type, or full-wave rectifier, is used because the half-wave type is not satisfactory for insertion in an a-c circuit as a current-measuring device since, in addition to rectifying the current to the milliammeter, it

would also rectify the circuit current.   Although half-wave rectification could be used in the case of a voltmeter, it is not practicable since
nearly full line voltage would be applied to the rectifier during the
part of the cycle when the rectifier would not freely pass current.   If
this voltage were more than a few volts per rectifier element, the elements would be destroyed.   These effects are eliminated by the use
of full-wave rectification.

When the current in the movable coil of a D'Arsonval mechanism
varies from instant to instant, the pointer deflection is directly proportional to the average value of the current.   The effective value
of the rectified current in the D'Arsonval milliammeter of a rectifier-
type instrument is $I = \sqrt{(\text{av } i^2)}$ and the average value is (av i).
Therefore the deflection of the pointer of a rectifier-type instrument
is not proportional to the effective value when the instrument is being
used to measure alternating current.   Both the effective value and
the average value of the current depend upon the shape of the wave
obtained when the instantaneous values of the current in the leads to
the bridge circuit are plotted as a function of time.   For a given wave
shape a definite numerical relation exists between the effective value
and the average value of the rectified wave, so that, although the
pointer deflection is proportional to the average value, the scale may be
calibrated in terms of the effective value.   However, two currents
having widely different wave shapes may have the same effective
values but different average values after being rectified.   Hence a
rectifier-type instrument indicates effective values only when the wave
shape of the current being measured is the same as that used to calibrate the instrument.   In circuits used in practice, most a-c currents
and voltages vary nearly sinusoidally with time.   For this reason, a-c
currents of this wave shape are used to calibrate rectifier-type instruments, and the scale is marked to read in terms of effective values of a
sine wave.   It should now be clear that, when such an instrument is
used in connection with a-c currents having wave shapes which are
widely different from a sine wave, a large error in the effective value
indicated by the instrument may result.   This error is called the
wave-form error.

A change in termperature affects the rectifying characteristic of a
copper-oxide rectifier.   With an increase of temperature the forward
resistance of the rectifier, the resistance in the direction of the free
flow of current, is decreased, as is also the back resistance, the resistance in the direction opposite to the forward resistance.   However, for
an increment of temperature rise the decrease in the forward resistance is less than the decrease in back resistance, the result of which is to

reduce the ratio of forward current to back current. Obviously, for an applied a-c voltage of constant value the average value of the current in the D'Arsonval milliammeter of a rectifier-type instrument is lowered as the temperature is increased. This effect causes a temperature error when the instrument is used in a place where the ambient temperature is appreciably different from that where the instrument was calibrated.

As the voltage applied to a copper-oxide rectifier is increased, the forward resistance drops off rapidly at first and then levels off to a fairly constant value. Under similar conditions, on the other hand, the back resistance increases rapidly at first and then levels off to a fairly constant value. As a result of these characteristics, the ratio of forward current to back current and hence the average value of current in the D'Arsonval milliammeter are not proportional to the applied voltage. Therefore, in the rectifier-type instrument, the scales of milliammeters and of voltmeters designed to measure voltages less than 10 volts are considerably compressed near the zero end.

The frequency range within which the rectifier-type instrument is suitable for use is limited by the effect of the capacitance between the discs of each rectifier element. In Fig. 5-13 these capacitances are indicated by C_1, C_2, C_3, and C_4. The effect of these capacitances is to form paths for the pulsating currents established by an a-c voltage applied to the terminals A and B. Thus, when terminal A is positive, the current flows from F to D. At D, part of this current is by-passed around the back resistance of the rectifier element in branch DC by the capacitance C_2, causing the current in the milliammeter to be less than it would be if the capacitance were not present. The other capacitances, C_1, C_3, and C_4, also affect the average current through the milliammeter. The by-passing effect of these capacitances is directly proportional to the frequency of the a-c voltage applied to terminals A and B. It should be clear, then, that a rectifier-type instrument should be used to make measurements of a-c voltages and currents only when the frequency does not exceed the value at which the by-passed currents are of significant magnitude. In general, the frequency error is about 0.5 per cent for each 1000 cycles per second up to 20,000

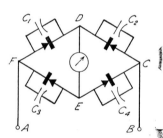

Fig. 5-13. Circuit showing the equivalent capacitances of the rectifier elements in the bridge circuit of a full-wave rectifier.

The outstanding advantages of rectifier-type instruments are their ruggedness and their high sensitivity; that is, they require little current and power for operation. Their accuracy, however, is not as good as that of the previously discussed types. Usually under favorable conditions rectifier instruments can be relied upon to within 2 to 5 per cent of full-scale value. Nevertheless, they are particularly well suited for measuring low a-c voltages and small a-c currents in the range of frequencies from the power frequencies to about 20,000 cycles, provided a frequency correction is made at the higher frequencies. When used as low-range a-c voltmeters, they disturb circuit conditions less than any of the other common types, since they require less current for operation. As milliammeters and microammeters they can be used to measure smaller currents than any of the other a-c types. In addition, their opposition to the flow of current is much less than that for similarly rated iron-vane and electrodynamometer instruments.

Rectifier-type current-measuring instruments are not usually made in ranges greater than about 15 milliamperes, since they are justifiable mainly because of their ability to operate on very small currents. They can, however, be obtained in ranges up to several hundred milliamperes from some manufacturers. Shunting the rectifier for higher current ranges is not satisfactory, since the opposition of the rectifier varies with current and frequency.

Rectifier-type voltmeters are made by connecting a resistance element in series with a rectifier-type milliammeter. A common resistance for such voltmeters is 1000 ohms per volt of range. They are usually made in ranges as low as 1 volt. Some rectifier milli-voltmeters use a transformer to step up the voltage applied to the rectifier. The frequency range of these instruments, however, is very limited.

15. Thermocouple Instruments. The thermocouple instrument consists primarily of a heater, a thermocouple, and a D'Arsonval-type milliameter. Instruments of this type offer the most practical means of measuring a-c currents at the radio frequencies. They can, however, also be used at the lower frequencies and for d-c measurements.

When two conductors X and Y of dissimilar metals or alloys are joined together at both ends, as shown in Fig. 5-14(a), and one of the junction points such as m is heated so that the temperature of this junction is different from that at n, a d-c current flows in the circuit. Evidently a d-c residual electromotive force is generated in the loop as a result of the difference between the temperatures of the two junctions m and n. The conductors X and Y are called a *thermocouple*, the heated junction m the *thermal junction*, and the residual emf the *thermal electromotive force.*

If junction n is opened and another piece of conducting metal C is inserted as shown in (b) of the figure, the action in the circuit is unaffected as long as there is no difference between the temperatures of the new junctions J and K. Thus, if junction n of (a) and junctions J and K of (b) are at the same temperature but junctions m of the

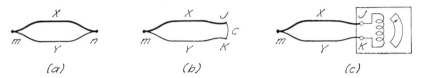

Fig. 5-14. (a) Thermocouple circuit consisting of two dissimilar metals. (b) Thermocouple circuit of (a) with third conductor inserted at junction *n*. (c) Thermocouple circuit after replacing conductor *C* in (b) by the coil of an instrument.

circuits are raised equal amounts above this temperature, equal thermal electromotive forces will be generated in the two circuits.

The element C can be the coil of a sensitive, permanent-magnet type of d-c instrument of which J and K are the terminals. There will be no current in the coil and hence no instrument pointer deflection as long as the temperatures at junctions m, J, and K are the same, such as the room or ambient temperature. If the thermal junction m

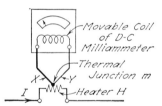

Fig. 5-15. Circuit of a thermocouple-type instrument.

is heated, raising its temperature above that at J and K, a deflection of the instrument pointer will be observed, indicating the presence of a d-c current in the thermocouple circuit.

The magnitude of the thermal electromotive force generated in a thermocouple depends upon the kinds of metals used and upon the temperature difference between the two junctions. Two combinations of metals commonly used in thermocouple instruments are (1) iron and advance and (2) platinum and platinum-iridium. Over a considerable range of temperature differences, the thermal emf increases with increase of the difference. This property is made use of in the thermocouple type of instrument by using the heat produced by the current being measured to raise the temperature of the thermal junction. In Fig. 5-15 is shown a thermocouple circuit in which is included a D'Arsonval milliammeter. The thermal junction m is heated by passing the current I, which is being measured, through the heater H. The energy supplied to H is a function of the square of the current I, and is dissipated as heat. Any change in this current causes a change in the heat energy supplied per unit time and in the temperature at the junction m. Thus, when the current I is changed, the temperature difference between junction m and the instrument coil is likewise altered, causing a similar variation in the thermal electromotive force and the current in the instrument coil. A change in the current being measured is accordingly indicated by a corresponding change in the deflection of the instrument pointer.

Two methods are commonly used to supply heat to the thermal junction of instruments of low current rating. Fig. 5-16(a) illustrates one of these methods. The two dissimilar metals of the thermocouple are welded together, forming the thermal junction at m. This junction is heated by passing the current being measured through the lower

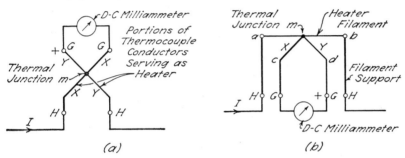

Fig. 5-16. Circuits of thermocouple-type instruments in which (a) portions of the thermocouple conductors are used as the heater element and (b) a separate filament is used as the heater element.

portions of XX and YY between terminals H. The other method is illustrated in (b) of the figure. A separate heater filament is employed. As shown, the heater filament ab is strung between the supports Ha and Hb. The thermal junction m is heated by passing the current being measured through this filament. The heater filament may be directly joined to the thermal junction at m or it may be electrically insulated from it. In the latter case, the heater filament and thermal junction are supported at m by being molded into a small glass bead. In either of the schemes illustrated in Fig. 5-16, the thermocouple and heater are enclosed in an evacuated glass envelope to avoid heat loss due to air convection currents, connections being brought out to external terminals corresponding to G and H.

The temperature of the heater reaches a stable value when the energy supplied to the heater is being removed at the same rate that it is being supplied. The heat loss due to air convection currents is very nearly eliminated by the use of the evacuated glass envelope. Furthermore, the temperature of the heater is low enough so that the loss due to radiation is small. Hence nearly all of the energy supplied to the heater must be removed by conduction. The rate at which heat is removed by conduction is directly proportional to temperature difference. Thus, when current is introduced into the heater, the temperature of the heater and the thermal junction will rise until the temperature difference between the thermal junction and the surroundings, which is the same as that between the two junctions of the thermocouple, is the value needed to cause the heat to be conducted from the thermal junction as fast as it is being supplied. At this stable condition,

Rate at which energy is supplied = Rate at which energy is removed.

$$I^2R = k(T_m - T).$$

In this equation I is the effective value of the current in the heater, R is the resistance of the heater, T_m is the final stable temperature of the heater and thermal junction, T is the temperature of the surroundings or the other junction of the thermocouple, and k is a proportionality constant. Solving for the temperature difference between the two junctions of the thermocouple,

$$(T_m - T) = \frac{I^2R}{k}.$$

Thus the temperature difference is proportional to the square of the effective value of the current in the heater.

Within the limited temperature operating range of the thermal junction, the thermal electromotive force is very nearly proportional to the difference between the temperatures of the junctions of the thermocouple—that is, to $(T_m - T)$. Accordingly, the current in the D'Arsonval milliammeter connected to terminals G in (a) or (b) of Fig. 5-16 will be very nearly proportional to the square of the effective value of the current being measured and will be independent of its wave form. Thus direct current can be used to calibrate the above types of thermocouple instruments, and they can then be used to measure current of any wave form. It should be noted that the scales of these instruments will not be uniformly divided if made for direct reading, but will follow a square law.

If a thermocouple instrument is calibrated by use of direct current or alternating current of the power frequencies, it will be in error at the higher frequencies owing to skin effect* and to capacitance between the leads connecting the terminals of the thermocouple

---

* See page 157.

device to its elements, such as *Ha*, *Hb*, *Gc*, and *Gd* in Fig. 5-16(b). Skin effect causes the resistance of the heater to increase with increase in the frequency of the current being measured. This results in a higher temperature of the thermal junction and a higher thermal electromotive force for a given effective value of the current being measured, causing a frequency error. In order to keep this error small, very fine wire is used for the conductors X and Y in (a) and the heater filament *ab* of Fig. 5-16. The frequency error due to capacitance between the leads can be made negligible by using special care in bringing out the various leads so as to make the capacitances small.

When a thermocouple instrument is used where the ambient temperature is different from that where the instrument was calibrated, a temperature error results. Part of this error is present because the rise in temperature of the heater for a given current is not independent of the ambient temperature, since the heater resistance varies with this temperature. This part of the temperature error is made negligible by making the heater of a metal with a low temperature coefficient* of resistance. The major part of the temperature error is due to the fact that for a given temperature difference between the thermocouple junctions the thermal electromotive force is not exactly the same for all temperatures of the cold junction.

Regardless of the errors discussed above, the accuracy of thermocouple instruments is fairly good. When used as current-measuring devices at usual room temperatures, they are accurate to within about 1 per cent of full-scale value at frequencies as high as 50 megacycles, 2 per cent at 75 megacycles, and 3 per cent at 100 megacycles.

Thermocouple instruments are manufactured for use in measuring currents from 2 milliamperes to 50 amperes. Instruments for use in measuring the high currents are of entirely different design than those described in the foregoing. One manufacturer uses a cylindrical tube for the heater element in order to obtain the needed current-carrying capacity and at the same time to reduce the skin effect. With high currents a considerable amount of heat has to be dissipated, and the entire instrument, including the D'Arsonval mechanism, must be designed to make the temperature gradient the same in both conductors of the thermocouple so that no temperature difference will exist between the two terminals of the coil of the D'Arsonval mechanism. A description of the construction of thermocouple instruments of high current ratings will be found in literature dealing more extensively with these instruments.

---

* See page 79.

A thermocouple milliammeter is converted to a voltmeter by adding a resistance element in series with the heater. Thermocouple voltmeters are not usually made for frequencies greater than 5000 to 15,000 cycles because of difficulties involved in the manufacture of accurate resistors which are not appreciably affected by changes in frequency and because vacuum-tube voltmeters are better suited for voltage measurements in low-power radio-frequency circuits, since they require but very minute currents for operation.

Thermocouple instruments must be used with great care because their ability to withstand overloads—that is, currents of greater than rated value—is much less than that of the other types of instruments discussed in this chapter. The usual thermocouple heater will carry a 50 per cent overload continuously, but such overloads should be avoided, since they raise the temperature of the heater to more than twice that at rated current, which may cause some evaporation of the metal in the heater to take place. Because of its low thermal capacity, the heater will burn out very quickly on a current in excess of the maximum rating.

16. Stray Magnetic Fields. When an instrument is inserted in an electric circuit, care should be taken to place it in a position where it is least likely to be affected by stray magnetic fields. Magnetic fields exist in the vicinity of permanent magnets, electromagnets, and coils and conductors carrying current. Such stray fields may add to or subtract from the field of the instrument mechanism and consequently may cause the instrument to give erroneous indications.

When an instrument carries direct current, it is usually much less affected by a stray magnet field produced by an alternating current than one produced by a direct current because of the compensating effect due to the reversal in the direction of the stray magnetic field. When an instrument carries alternating current and is in an alternating stray field, complexities are introduced by the time relations involved, and no general statement such as that given in the preceding case can be made.

Instruments of the iron-vane type are influenced more by stray magnetic fields than are the moving-coil types such as the electrodynamometer and D'Arsonval types because the motivating torque varies as the square of the strength of the magnetic field in the mechanism of the iron-vane types but varies only as the first power of the field strength in the moving-coil types. Both the electrodynamometer and iron-vane types are influenced more by stray magnetic fields than the D'Arsonval type because the moving coil of the latter operates in a field of much higher density than is produced in the other types, making any extraneous magnetic field less effective in changing the field of the mechanism. Furthermore, the moving coil of the D'Arsonval type is partly shielded by its permanent magnet.

By enclosing the instrument mechanism in a housing of ferrous metal, it can be effectively shielded from stray magnetic fields. Most instruments are now provided with such shields when manufactured. It is not safe, however, to depend entirely upon these shields. It is good practice even in the case of shielded instruments to place them as far as possible from any probable source of stray magnetic fields.

Laboratory Problem No. 5-1

AMMETER AND VOLTMETER TYPES AND THEIR USES IN MAKING MEASUREMENTS

Laboratory

1. Obtain 0- to 150-volt and 0- to 300-volt voltmeters of the following types: D'Arsonval, electrodynamometer, and iron-vane.

Examine each of these instruments carefully, giving special attention to the following:

(a) Type and general appearance.
(b) Manufacturer's name and serial number.
(c) Arrangement of the terminals and push button.
(d) Uniformity or nonuniformity of the scale divisions.
(e) Antiparallax mirror.
(f) Technical data found on the scale or on the cover or both.

Make a record of the observations on the data sheet.

2. If instrument parts are available for inspection, examine them, noting that many of the parts are small and delicate.

3. With each type of voltmeter, measure the voltage of the 115-volt d-c source. Make two measurements with each voltmeter, in each case making the second measurement with the connections from the instrument to the source reversed. Make a record of the readings and the behavior of each type.

4. Repeat 3, but measure the voltage of the 115-volt a-c source.

5. In Fig. 5-27 are shown circuit elements connected in a series-parallel combination.

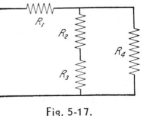

Fig. 5-17.

(a) On the data sheet draw the circuit diagram of this combination including in the diagram a circuit disconnect switch and the voltmeters and ammeters needed to measure the voltage and current of each circuit element and also the voltage impressed on the circuit. Show the 115-volt d-c source connected to the proper side of the disconnect switch.

(b) Using the circuit elements designated by the instructor, set up the circuit and make the measurements indicated by the instruments shown on the circuit diagram drawn in (a). If the pointer deflection of any instrument is less than 25 per cent of full scale when a measurement is being made, replace that instrument with one of a more suitable range and repeat the measurement.   •

(c) Connect two voltmeters in series; and with these voltmeters so connected, use them to measure the voltage impressed on the circuit. Make a record of the resistance of each voltmeter.

Report

A. Of the types of instruments used in **3,** which type is or which types are suitable for making accurate measurements of d-c voltages? Of a-c voltages?

B. If tests similar to **3** and **4** above were performed, but instead of measuring voltages measurements of d-c and a-c currents were made by the use of ammeters constructed on the same principles as the voltmeters used in **3** and **4,** would the behavior of a particular type of ammeter be similar to the behavior of the corresponding type of voltmeter?

C. From data obtained in **5**(b), determine the circuit resistance and the resistance of each of the circuit elements.

D. How does the sum of the measured values of the voltages across R_1, R_2, and R_3 compare with the measured value of the voltage impressed on the circuit? Does the result of the comparison check with theory? Explain.

E. How does the sum of the measured values of the branch currents compare with the measured value of the current in R_1 (circuit current)? Does the result of the comparison check with theory? Explain.

F. The voltage across a circuit is to be measured, and it is known that this voltage is less than 300 volts but exceeds 200 volts. Only voltmeters of the 0- to 150-volt range are available. How could the voltage be measured with the available instruments?

G. How does the measured value of the impressed voltage obtained in **5**(c) compare with the value obtained in **5**(b)?

How does the ratio of the two voltmeter indications obtained in **5**(c) compare with the ratio of the resistances of the voltmeters that were used? Should or should not these ratios be the same? Explain.

Laboratory Problem No. 5-2
A STUDY OF AMMETER AND VOLTMETER MECHANISMS

Laboratory

1. Examine the instruments that have been removed from their cases to permit inspection of the mechanisms and other parts. Note that the mechanisms are delicate and must be treated with care. For each instrument determine and record the following:

  (a) Type of mechanism.
  (b) Source of restraining torque.
  (c) Method of damping.
  (d) Method of balancing the movable element.
  (e) Whether there is a shunt or a series resistor.
  (f) Whether shielded or not.
  (g) Uniformity of the scale divisions.
  (h) Whether or not an antiparallax mirror is provided.

Record the data found on the instrument scale or on the lid of the instrument case or both.

2. (a) Obtain three ammeters of the same or approximately the same range, the group to consist of a D'Arsonval, an electrodynamom-

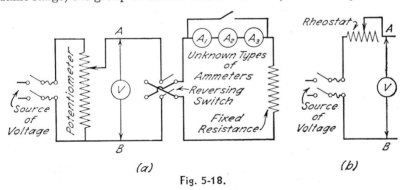

Fig. 5-18.

eter, and an iron-vane type. (Any markings or printed information on these instruments which might enable the student to identify the types should be removed or covered.)

Set up the circuit shown in (a) of Fig. 5-18, using a d-c voltage source. If a suitable potentiometer is not available, the scheme shown in (b) of the figure may be used. The fixed resistance should be such as to limit the current to a value which will not cause an off-scale deflection in the case of the lowest-range ammeter when the voltage between A and B is the same as that of the source.

Close the reversing switch to the side that causes an up-scale deflection of each ammeter. Adjust the voltage between points A and B in accordance with directions given by the instructor. Read and record the value of the circuit current as indicated by each of the ammeters. While data are being taken, care must be exercised to maintain the voltage between A and B constant. Use extreme care in reading all instrument indications. This is very important.

(b) Close the reversing switch on the side opposite to that used in (a) and take data as in (a), being careful to maintain the voltage constant between A and B at the value used in (a).

(c) Repeat (a) and (b), using an a-c voltage source.

3. (a) Obtain 0- to 150-volt voltmeters of the following types:

> (1) D'Arsonval type, shielded.
> (2) D'Arsonval type, not shielded.
> (3) Iron-vane type, shielded.
> (4) Iron-vane type, not shielded.

(b) Set up the circuit shown in Fig. 5-19. Place the unshielded iron-vane voltmeter in such a position that the mechanism coil will be in the magnetic field produced when d-c current flows in coil A. Close the double-pole double-throw switch in the d-c position and adjust the current in coil A so that an appreciable change takes place in the indication of the voltmeter when the coil-circuit disconnect switch is opened and closed.

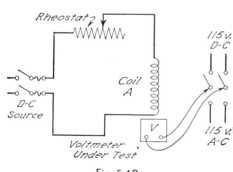

Fig. 5-19.

(c) Without disturbing the position of the voltmeter and with no current in coil A, read and record the voltmeter indication when the double-pole double-throw switch is in the d-c position. Close the coil-circuit disconnect switch and again read and record the voltmeter indication. Repeat the above procedure with the double-pole double-throw switch in the a-c position.

(d) Repeat the test procedure of (c), using each of the other three voltmeters. In each case place the voltmeter so that the mechanism is in approximately the same position as the mechanism was placed in (c). When using the D'Arsonval type, take data only for the d-c position of the double-pole double-throw switch.

Report

A. From an analysis of the data obtained in **2,** determine which of the ammeters is the D'Arsonval type, which the electrodynamometer type, and which the iron-vane type. In each case give the line of reasoning followed in making the selection.

B. Which of the two types of voltmeters tested in **3,** D'Arsonval or iron-vane, was most affected by the stray magnetic field? Why?

C. Was the iron-vane type affected by the magnetic field more when measuring d-c voltages or when measuring a-c voltages? Why?

D. Discuss the results obtained with shielded and unshielded instruments.

E. The coil of the D'Arsonval mechanism of a 5-amp ammeter has a resistance of 5 ohms, and the shunt has a resistance of 0.01002 ohm. What changes would need to be made to convert this ammeter to a 150-volt voltmeter?

CHAPTER 6
DROP-OF-POTENTIAL METHODS FOR MEASURING D-C RESISTANCE

1. Methods for Measuring D-C Resistance. D-c resistance, the resistance offered to direct current, can be measured by a number of methods. When accuracy is of paramount importance, one of a number of bridge methods should be used. Of these, the more common are the Wheatstone-bridge method, which is usually used for measuring resistances ranging from 1.0 ohm to 100,000 ohms, the Carey-Foster-bridge method for resistances of 0.01 ohm to 1000 ohms, and the Kelvin-double-bridge method for resistances of 0.0001 ohm to 1.0 ohm.

For d-c resistance measurements such as may be required in the study and testing of electrical circuits and machines, simpler and more direct methods may be used. Three of the more convenient ones, the voltmeter-ammeter method, the two-voltmeter method, and the single-voltmeter method, are discussed in this chapter. Since each of these methods requires that the drop of potential between the terminals of the unknown resistance be determined, they are usually classified under the general heading of *drop-of-potential methods*.

2. Voltmeter-Ammeter Method. When a fair degree of accuracy is satisfactory, the voltmeter-ammeter method is one of the most common methods used for measuring d-c resistances ranging approximately from 0.001 ohm to 100,000,000 ohms. This method is merely the application of Ohm's law. When a current of I amperes flows in a resistance element having a resistance of R ohms, a potential difference of V volts exists between the terminals of the element. In accordance with Ohm's law

$$V = IR,$$

or
$$R = \frac{V}{I}. \tag{6-1}$$

Hence it is necessary only to measure the current in an unknown resistance and the voltage between its terminals in order to obtain data for calculating its resistance.

In Fig. 6-1 is shown a test circuit for the voltmeter-ammeter method.   The current-limiting resistance is used to limit the current in the circuit to a value which the unknown resistance can safely carry. When it is desired to know the resistance of the unknown at a given temperature, the resistance is measured at room temperature, and the value obtained is converted to the value at the given temperature by the methods discussed in Chapter 7.   In these cases the current-limiting resistance is adjusted to give the highest value of current that can be used without causing an appreciable change in the temperature of the resistance under test.   In general, it will be found that this current will be from one-fourth to one-half the rated operating current of the unknown resistance.

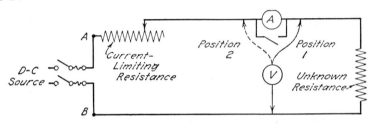

Fig. 6-1.   Test circuit for determining resistance by the voltmeter-ammeter method.

3. Factors Influencing Selection of Test Procedure in Applying Voltmeter-Ammeter Method.   In any given case the best test procedure to follow in applying the voltmeter-ammeter method depends upon the resistances of the voltmeter and ammeter as compared with that of the resistance being measured.   The best procedure also depends upon the ability of the power source to maintain a constant voltage.   Each case is a problem which must be studied before proceeding to take the data.

4. Voltmeter-Ammeter Method Test Procedures When Voltage Across Test Circuit Is Constant. *Preliminary Test.*   Consider that the voltage is known to be constant between points A and B of the circuit shown in Fig. 6-1.   Then with the ammeter shunting switch open, the preliminary test is to note the ammeter and voltmeter indications with the voltmeter connected first in position 1 and then in position 2.

(*1*) *No Change in Ammeter and Voltmeter Indications in Preliminary Test.*   If no appreciable change takes place in the ammeter and voltmeter indications when the preliminary test is made, the voltmeter can be placed in either of the positions shown without introducing appreciable error. and the instruments may be connected in the circuit one at a time or simultaneously when taking data.   When the preliminary test shows that this procedure may be followed, it will in general be found that the magnitude of the unknown resistance is large in comparison with the resistance of the ammeter but small in comparison with the resistance of the voltmeter.

(2) *Change in Ammeter Indication, but No Change in Voltmeter Indication in Preliminary Test.* If in the preliminary test an appreciable change takes place in the indication of the ammeter but not in that of the voltmeter, the voltmeter should be used in position 2. With the voltmeter in this position and both instruments connected in the circuit simultaneously, the ammeter indicates the actual current in the unknown resistance, and the voltmeter indicates the voltage across the unknown resistance with but a relatively small error due to the potential drop across the ammeter. The instruments may therefore be connected in the circuit simultaneously and their indications read simultaneously or one at a time. The instruments, however, should not be connected in the circuit one at a time and readings taken unless it is definitely shown that the current taken by the voltmeter does not produce an appreciable voltage drop across the current-limiting resistance. When this voltage drop is appreciable, the current in the unknown resistance will be greater when the voltmeter is disconnected than when it is connected in position 2. Thus, if the ammeter indication with the voltmeter in position 2 is the same as when the voltmeter is disconnected, the instruments may be connected in the circuit one at a time when the data are being taken.

In general, when there is an appreciable change in the indication of the ammeter but not in that of the voltmeter in the preliminary test, it is evidence that the magnitude of the unknown resistance is comparable to that of the voltmeter and is very high in comparison with the resistance of the ammeter.

(3) *No Change in Ammeter Indication, but Change in Voltmeter Indication in Preliminary Test.* If there is an appreciable change in the indication of the voltmeter but not in that of the ammeter when the preliminary test is made, the voltmeter should be used in position 1. With the voltmeter in this position and both instruments connected in the circuit simultaneously, the voltmeter indicates the actual voltage across the unknown resistance, and the ammeter indicates the current in the unknown resistance with but little error due to the current in the voltmeter. Since the voltmeter indication is different for the two positions shown in Fig. 6-1, the ammeter resistance is appreciable in comparison with that of the unknown resistance. Under such circumstances, opening and closing the ammeter shunting switch may change the current in the test circuit and the voltage across the unknown resistance. Therefore the shunting switch across the ammeter must be

left open while the instrument indications are read.   It is immaterial, however, whether or not the voltmeter is connected when the ammeter indication is read.

In general, when an appreciable change takes place in the indication of the voltmeter but not in that of the ammeter in the preliminary test, the unknown resistance is comparable in magnitude to the resistance of the ammeter and is very low in comparison with the resistance of the voltmeter.   In this case, the contact resistances at the terminals of the unknown resistance may be appreciable compared to the resistance of the unknown; and care must be taken to be certain that the voltmeter leads are connected to the permanent terminals of the unknown resistance and not to the temporary leads of the test circuit.

(4) *Change in Ammeter and Voltmeter Indications in Preliminary Test.*   Both instrument indications may change when the preliminary test is made if the unknown resistance, the ammeter resistance, and the voltmeter resistance tend to approach the same order of magnitude. This condition may exist even when high-grade instruments are used if the voltage across points A and B of the test circuit of Fig. 6-1 is relatively low and the circuit current is small.   When a change takes place in both instrument indications in the preliminary test, the best procedure is to connect the voltmeter in position 1, read the instrument indications with both instruments connected simultaneously in the circuit, and then correct the ammeter indication for the current taken by the voltmeter.   If V is the voltage indicated by the voltmeter when in position 1, R_V is the resistance of the voltmeter, and I_A is the current indicated by the ammeter, then the current I in the unknown resistance is

$$I = I_A - \frac{V}{R_V}.\qquad (6\text{-}2)$$

The voltmeter resistance R_V is usually given on the scale of the instrument or on the certificate fastened to the lid of the case.

5. Voltmeter–Ammeter Method Test Procedures When Voltage Across Test Circuit Is Not Constant.   Whenever the voltage of the d-c power source is not constant, the most reliable procedure is to connect the voltmeter in position 1 and take simultaneous readings of the indications of the voltmeter and ammeter.   The ammeter indication can then be corrected, when necessary, by using equation (6-2).   Many test men prefer this procedure under all conditions, regardless of whether the voltage across points A and B of the test circuit remains constant or not.

In cases in which the voltage across points A and B is not constant but the magnitude of the unknown resistance is known to be comparable to that of the voltmeter and is large in comparison with the resistance of the ammeter, the voltmeter may be connected in position 2 and simultaneous readings of the instrument indications taken without introducing appreciable error.

6. Two-Voltmeter Method. From the analysis of the two-voltmeter method which follows it will become apparent that the method will give fairly accurate results when the unknown resistance has a magnitude comparable to that of a voltmeter.   The higher the magnitude of the unknown resistance, the higher should be the resistance of the voltmeter if satisfactory results are to be obtained.

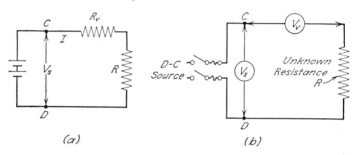

Fig. 6-2.   (a) Equivalent circuit of the test circuit shown in (b).   (b) Test circuit for determining resistance by the two-voltmeter method.

In Fig. 6-2(a), the potential difference V_S between terminals C and D is

$$V_S = I(R_V + R) = IR_V + IR. \qquad (6\text{-}3)$$

Let R be the resistance whose value is to be determined and R_V be the resistance of a voltmeter V_V, which has been connected in series with R, as shown in (b) of the figure.   Voltmeter V_V will indicate the difference in potential that exists between its own terminals.   With a current I in the circuit, the indication of voltmeter V_V is then $V_V = IR_V$.   If the difference in potential between terminals C and D is measured by voltmeter V_S, the potential difference IR between the terminals of resistance R can readily be determined by use of equation (6-3).

$$IR = V_S - IR_V = V_S - V_V. \qquad (6\text{-}4)$$

The value of R can now be determined in terms of the measured voltages and the resistance R_V of voltmeter V_V.   Dividing equation (6-4) by $IR_V = V_V$ gives

$$\frac{IR}{IR_V} = \frac{V_S - V_V}{V_V},$$

and

$$R = R_V \left(\frac{V_s - V_V}{V_V} \right) = R_V \left(\frac{V_s}{V_V} - 1 \right). \qquad (6\text{-}5)$$

Two voltmeters are used to measure the values of V_s and V_V in equation (6-5) because they permit simultaneous determinations of V_s and V_V. Thus the two-voltmeter method can be used regardless of how constant the d-c source voltage remains. The value of R_V required in equation (6-5) is usually readily available, since instrument manufacturers show this value either on the instrument scale or on the lid of the instrument case.

It should be observed that this method is most suitable for determining the values of unknown resistances when these values are comparable to the value of the resistance of the voltmeter V_V. If R is large compared to R_V, the voltage V_V will be small compared to V_s. In such a case an error of a fractional part of a volt in the read value of V_V may result in a large error in the calculated value of R. If, on the other hand, R is small compared to R_V, then V_s and V_V will be of nearly like magnitudes. Under this condition V_s/V_V in equation (6-5) may be only slightly greater than unity, in which case a small error in this ratio will make a large error in the term $[(V_s/V_V) - 1]$ and hence a large error in the calculated value of R.

7. Single-Voltmeter Method. A single voltmeter can be used to secure the data required for equation (6-5) provided that the source voltage is known to remain substantially constant and the potential difference between terminals C and D to be unaffected when the test circuit is opened. The test procedure in such a case is to measure the potential difference between terminals C and D before the test circuit is set up. The same voltmeter is then placed in series with R, and its indication V_V is noted. Thus both V_s and V_V are measured with only a single voltmeter. The accuracy of the results obtained when this test procedure is used depends upon how constant V_s remains during the entire procedure, for the value of V_s used in equation (6-5) must be the value of the potential difference at terminals C and D at the time V_V is being measured. Should V_s change between the time its value is measured and the time V_V is measured, there would obviously be an error in the calculated value of R. Hence, as a check when a single voltmeter is used to make the measurements of V_s and V_V, V_s should be remeasured immediately after V_V is measured and its value compared with that found at the start of the test.

An important application of the single-voltmeter method is found in the ohmmeter, an instrument used for measuring resistances directly.

Laboratory Problem No. 6-1

DETERMINATION OF D-C RESISTANCE BY DROP-OF-POTENTIAL METHODS

Laboratory

1. Using a constant-voltage d-c source, obtain data by the voltmeter-ammeter method from which the resistances of several unknown resistors can be determined. Use resistors in the range from about 0.01 ohm to 25,000 or more ohms and having a current-carrying capacity from 50 amperes or more to a few milliamperes. For each resistor perform the preliminary test for determining the most suitable voltmeter position and draw a complete circuit diagram showing the positions of the instruments. In order to show the effect of an appreciable current in the voltmeter, do not use voltmeters having resistances greater than about 100 ohms per volt of the voltmeter range.

2. Using the voltmeter-ammeter method and the test procedure which should be applied when the d-c source voltage fluctuates, obtain data from which the resistances of the same unknown resistors used in **1** can be determined.

3. Using the single-voltmeter method, obtain data from which the resistance values can be calculated for the resistors used in **1** to which the method is applicable.

4. Obtain data by the single-voltmeter method for determining the resistance between the 300-volt terminals of a voltmeter having a resistance of about 1000 ohms per volt of range. Also record the actual resistance given on the lid or scale of this voltmeter.

Report

A. Calculate the resistances of the unknowns from the data obtained in **1** and **2**. Discuss any discrepancies.

B. Calculate the resistances of the unknowns from the data obtained in **3**. How do these values compare with the values determined in **A?** Discuss any discrepancies.

C. Calculate the resistance between the 300-volt terminals of the voltmeter tested in **4**. How does this value compare with the value given on the lid or scale of the voltmeter?

D. Why is a current-limiting resistance used in the test circuit of the voltmeter-ammeter method?

E. Explain why the resistances of all the unknown resistors were not measured by the single-voltmeter method in **3**.

CHAPTER 7
CURRENT, RESISTANCE, AND HEAT

1. Joule's Law. When a current of I amperes flows through a conductor having a resistance of R ohms, the rate at which electrical energy is consumed, or the power in watts, is

$$P = I^2R. \tag{7-1}$$

If the current persists for the duration of t seconds, the electrical energy in watt-seconds, or joules, supplied during this period and manifesting itself as heat is

$$J = Pt = I^2Rt. \tag{7-2}$$

Experiment has shown that the amount of heat required to raise the temperature of 1 gram of water through 1° C is equivalent to 4.19 joules, this required amount of heat being by definition 1 calorie. Therefore the heat in calories that is developed when a current of I amperes flows through a resistance of R ohms for a time of t seconds is

$$H = \frac{I^2Rt}{4.19} = .24I^2Rt. \tag{7-3}$$

Equations (7-2) and (7-3) are the mathematical expressions of Joule's law, Joule having been the first to discover that the heating effect of a current in a resistance is proportional to the square of the current, to the resistance, and to the time the current flows.

Since heat is developed when current is introduced into a conductor having resistance, the temperature of the conductor will rise if the heat is not propagated away by conduction, convection, and radiation as rapidly as it is developed. Equilibrium, or constant conductor temperature, will be established only when the point is reached at which the heat is propagated away at the same rate that it is developed. The laws of heat propagation by conduction, convection, and radiation are complex. Thus no simple relation exists between the heat developed by current flowing in a conductor having resistance and the resulting temperature of the conductor.

2. Resistivity. At a constant temperature the resistance of a uniform conductor is directly proportional to its length l and inversely proportional to its cross-sectional area a, or

$$R = \rho \frac{l}{a}, \qquad (7\text{-}4)$$

ρ being the proportionality constant. The constant ρ is called the *resistivity*. Its value for a given material depends upon the temperature and the units in which the length and the cross-sectional area are measured. For engineering work the resistivity is usually given in ohms per circular mil foot, a circular mil foot being a cylindrical conductor .001 in. in diameter and 1 ft long. The International Annealed Copper Standard, which is the internationally accepted value for the resistivity ρ of annealed copper of standard purity, is 10.371 ohms per circular mil foot at 20° C. Not all commercial annealed copper agrees with this figure, but may be several per cent higher, depending on the purity. In the case of hard-drawn copper $\rho = 10.653$ ohms per circular mil foot at 20° C. Resistivity values for several of the more common conductors are listed in Table 7-1.

3. Effect of Temperature upon Resistance. The resistance of most unalloyed metals such as aluminum, copper, and silver increases as the temperature rises. Some alloys, such as constantan and manganin, increase very little in resistance with rise in temperature, and there-

TABLE 7-1

RESISTIVITY VALUES AND TEMPERATURE COEFFICIENTS FOR VARIOUS
CONDUCTORS

Material	Resistivity (ρ)		Temp. Coeff. (α)	
	Temp. (° C)	Ohms per Cir. Mil Ft	Temp. (° C)	Coeff.
Aluminum..................	20	17.01	18	.0039
Carbon....................	0	21,050	0	−.0005
Constantan (Cu 60, Ni 40)........	0	265.3	25	.000002
Copper (annealed)...............	20	10.371	20	.00393
Copper (hard-drawn).............	20	10.653	20	.00382
German Silver (Ni 18)...........	20	198.5	20	.0004
Iron (99.98 % pure)..............	20	60.2	0	.0062
Manganin (Cu 84, Mn 12, Ni 4)...	20	264.7	12	.000006
Nichrome.....................	20	601.6	20	.0004
Silver.......................	18	9.80	20	.0038
Tungsten.....................	20	33.15	18	.0045

fore are used in the resistance elements of measuring instruments, in which a change of resistance introduces error. The resistance of carbon, electrolytes, and most insulating solids has been found to decrease with a rise in temperature.

4. Temperature Coefficient and Its Use. Experiment has shown that graphs of resistance vs temperature for most conductors are approximately straight lines within the usual operating range of temperatures. This linear relationship between resistance and temperature has resulted in the use of the term *temperature coefficient of resistance*. The *temperature coefficient* at a given temperature is defined as the change in resistance per ohm per degree centigrade increase in temperature. The temperature coefficient is usually represented by the symbol α_t, the subscript t indicating the base temperature to which the coefficient applies.

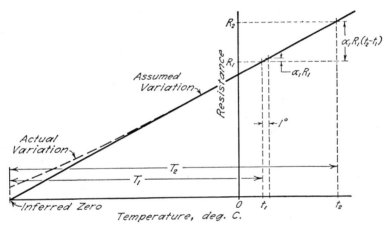

Fig. 7-1. Variation of the resistance of metallic conductors with temperature.

The use of the coefficient in the solution of resistance-temperature problems can best be illustrated by considering Fig. 7-1. Here the straight-line portion of the resistance vs temperature graph has been extended until it intersects the horizontal axis, or zero-resistance line. The negative temperature represented by this intersection is called the "inferred zero," since at this temperature ($-234.5°$ C for annealed copper) the resistance would be zero if the actual resistance vs temperature graph were the assumed straight line. Actually, the true graph departs from the assumed linear relationship when the temperature is low and theoretically would show zero resistance at absolute zero ($-273°$ C). An experiment has been performed in which a current was induced magnetically in a ring of mercury cooled down to nearly absolute zero. Upon removal of the inducing force the current continued to flow for several hours without any electromotive force whatsoever, thus showing that the resistance of the mercury ring was practically zero at this extremely low temperature.

The fact that the extended straight-line portion and the actual curve do not agree at lower temperatures does not detract from the usefulness of Fig. 7-1 for the purpose of determining resistances over the usual working range. The truth of this statement will become evident from the considerations that follow. Let R_1 be the resistance at a temperature $t_1°$ C. Then, according to the definition of temperature coefficient, α_1 is the change in resistance per degree (centigrade) temperature rise per ohm of resistance at t_1*; and the increase ΔR in resistance (α_1 assumed positive) for a temperature rise of 1° above t_1 is

$$\Delta R_{[t_1 \text{ to } (t_1+1)]} = \alpha_1 \cdot 1 \cdot R_1 = \alpha_1 R_1. \tag{7-5}$$

If the temperature increases from t_1 to t_2, the increase in resistance is

$$\Delta R_{(t_1 \text{ to } t_2)} = \alpha_1 R_1 (t_2 - t_1), \tag{7-6}$$

and the resistance R_2 at the temperature $t_2°$ C is therefore

$$R_2 = R_1 + \Delta R_{(t_1 \text{ to } t_2)} = R_1 + \alpha_1 R_1 (t_2 - t_1) = R_1[1 + \alpha_1(t_2 - t_1)]. \tag{7-7}$$

Equations (7-5) and (7-6) are illustrated graphically in Fig. 7-1.

Equation (7-4) can now be written to include the effect of a change in temperature. Thus the resistance in ohms at any temperature $t_2°$ C is

$$R_2 = \rho_1 \frac{l}{a} [1 + \alpha_1(t_2 - t_1)], \tag{7-8}$$

where

ρ_1 = resistivity of the conductor at $t_1°$ C in ohms per circular mil foot,

l = length of conductor in feet,

a = area of conductor in circular mils,

and α_1 = temperature coefficient at $t_1°$ C.

In using equations (7-7) and (7-8) it will be noted that the temperature coefficient must be known at the initial temperature $t_1°$ C. In most instances, however, the temperature coefficient will not be listed in a table (such as Table 7-1) at the required temperature $t_1°$ C but at some other temperature. Hence it is necessary to be able to calculate

---

* It should be noted that the temperature coefficient is not the slope of the straight line.

the temperature coefficient α_1 at a temperature $t_1°$ C from a known value α at $t°$ C taken from a table. Owing to the straight-line relationship between resistance and temperature, the change in resistance ΔR is always the same for each degree centigrade rise in temperature. Therefore, according to equation (7-5),

$$\Delta R = \alpha R = \alpha_1 R_1, \tag{7-9}$$

where R and R_1 are the resistances of the conductor and α and α_1 are the temperature coefficients at the temperatures t and t_1, respectively. Hence, from equations (7-7) and (7-9),

$$\frac{\alpha_1}{\alpha} = \frac{R}{R_1} = \frac{R}{R[1 + \alpha(t_1 - t)]} = \frac{1}{1 + \alpha(t_1 - t)},$$

or

$$\alpha_1 = \frac{\alpha}{1 + \alpha(t_1 - t)}. \tag{7-10}$$

Equation (7-10) thus provides a means for calculating the temperature coefficient α_1 at a temperature $t_1°$ C from a known value α at $t°$ C.

Changes of resistance with temperature can be calculated by the use of either equation (7-7) or equation (7-8) together with equation (7-10). However, a more direct method can be developed. In the following, when reference is made to "inferred zero," only the magnitude is under consideration. As indicated in Fig. 7-1, let

$$T_1 = \text{"inferred zero"} + t_1 \tag{7-11}$$

and

$$T_2 = \text{"inferred zero"} + t_2. \tag{7-12}$$

Then

$$\frac{R_2}{R_1} = \frac{T_2}{T_1}. \tag{7-13}$$

This equation follows as a consequence of the similar triangles resulting from the linear relationship between resistance and temperature.

To use the simple relationship expressed in equation (7-13), the value of the "inferred zero" must be determined. Since the change in resistance ΔR per degree centigrade increase in temperature is constant,

$$\Delta R \cdot T_1 = R_1,$$

or

$$T_1 = \frac{R_1}{\Delta R} = \frac{R_1}{\alpha_1 R_1} = \frac{1}{\alpha_1}. \tag{7-14}$$

Therefore

$$\text{"Inferred zero" (magnitude)} = T_1 - t_1 = \frac{1}{\alpha_1} - t_1. \tag{7-15}$$

The "inferred zero" can thus be calculated from any known value of the temperature coefficient and its base temperature. For example, Table 7-1 shows that annealed copper has a value $\alpha = .00393$ at 20° C. Substituting these values in equation (7-15) gives

$$\text{Annealed copper "inferred zero" (magnitude)} = \frac{1}{\alpha_1} - t_1 = \frac{1}{.00393} - 20$$

$$= 254.5 - 20 = 234.5,$$

$$(7\text{-}16)$$

denoting a temperature of 234.5° below the centigrade zero, or −234.5° C.

5. Determination of Temperature Coefficient. If the resistance of a conductor is known at two different known temperatures, the temperature coefficient for the conductor material can be calculated.

One of the required values can be secured by measuring the resistance of the conductor at room temperature by the voltmeter-ammeter method or any of the usual bridge methods. Care must be taken in order not to heat the conductor appreciably while readings are being taken.

A second value of resistance may be determined by placing the conductor in an oil bath and raising the temperature of the bath 40° or 50° C. The bath should be stirred constantly so as to keep all parts at the same temperature. The temperature of the conductor can then be secured by reading a thermometer placed in the bath.

The oil bath can be heated either externally or by sending an appreciable current through the conductor. If the voltmeter-ammeter method is used for the resistance measurement, current values that will not further increase the temperature of the conductor should be used.

In order to indicate the use of the above test data, consider the following:

Let $R_1 =$ resistance of the conductor at the room temperature of $t_1°$ C

and $\alpha_1 =$ temperature coefficient at $t_1°$ C.

The resistance R_2 of the conductor at the final temperature $t_2°$ C of the oil bath after heating is then

$$R_2 = R_1[1 + \alpha_1(t_2 - t_1)],$$

or

$$\alpha_1 = \frac{R_2 - R_1}{R_1(t_2 - t_1)}.$$

$$(7\text{-}17)$$

The temperature coefficient of the conductor for the room temperature $t_1°$ C can thus be calculated by equation (7-17). This coefficient may be converted to any other base temperature by the use of equation (7-10).

6. Resistance of Windings in Electrical Machines at Normal Operating Temperature. The windings of electrical machines are heated not only by the current flowing in them but also by the losses that occur in the iron linking the winding and in some cases by heat transferred from hotter portions of the machine. In the past, owing to insulation temperature limitations, machines have been designed so that this heating usually results in an average winding temperature of approximately 75° C when the machine is operated at rated load. With the development of new insulating materials, the trend is toward higher operating temperatures. If the ambient or room temperature is 20° C, the temperature rise to an operating temperature of approximately 75° C is, accordingly, about 55° C.

At the usual operating temperature the resistivity ρ of annealed copper is approximately 12 ohms per circular mil foot. In the discussion of resistivity it was pointed out that at 20° C ρ for this material is 10.371 ohms per circular mil foot. Thus, in a temperature rise of approximately 55° C the winding resistance increases a little over 15 per cent. The figure of 12 ohms per circular mil foot, as the resistivity of annealed copper at normal operating temperature, is often used in design work where a definite operating temperature for a winding is not known or easily calculated.

In securing data at no load for use in predicting electrical machine operating characteristics, winding resistances are usually measured by the voltmeter-ammeter method at room temperature. Before being used in calculations a resistance value so obtained should be converted to its 75° C value in accordance with standard practice. This conversion is easily made by use of equations (7-11), (7-12), and (7-13).

7. Determination of Temperature Rise in a Winding by the Increase-of-Resistance Method. The average temperature rise of a machine winding above ambient or room temperature, due to operation under load conditions, can be determined from two resistance measurements and a single temperature observation. This can be seen readily by inspection of equations (7-11), (7-12), and (7-13), for, if R_1 is the initial resistance taken at an ambient temperature $t_1°$ C, and R_2 is the resistance under operation, the operating temperature $t_2°$ C can be calculated easily and the temperature rise determined. This method of determining the temperature rise of a winding has become known as the *increase-of-resistance method*.

Laboratory Problem No. 7-1

CURRENT, RESISTANCE, AND HEAT—I

Laboratory

Caution: In the tests indicated below which involve the use of the shunt field winding of a d-c dynamo, be certain to *disconnect the voltmeter before opening the circuit disconnect switch.*

1. (a) Obtain data by the voltmeter-ammeter method from which the resistance of the shunt field winding of a d-c dynamo can be calculated for room temperature. Perform the test under conditions that will not cause the temperature of the winding to rise appreciably above the room temperature. Measure and record the room temperature.

(b) After completing (a), increase the current in the field winding until the voltage across the winding is 100 volts in the case of a 115-volt machine, or 200 volts in the case of a 230-volt machine. Allow the current to persist until parts **2** and **3** of this problem have been completed.

2. Obtain data from which a curve of resistance vs current can be plotted for a carbon-filament lamp.

3. Obtain data from which a curve of resistance vs current can be plotted for a nichrome heater element.

4. Obtain data from which the resistance of the field winding used in **1** can be redetermined.

Report

A. From data obtained in **1** and **4,** determine the temperature rise of the shunt field winding.

B. Plot the curves for which data were obtained in **2** and **3**.

C. What do the results obtained in **2** prove concerning the temperature coefficient of carbon? State fully the line of reasoning by which this conclusion was reached.

D. What do the results obtained in **3** prove concerning the temperature coefficient of nichrome? State fully the line of reasoning by which this conclusion was reached.

E. The resistance of a nichrome heater element is 18.1 ohms at a temperature of 28° C. If the heater is made of 162 in. of #23

(A.W.G.) nichrome wire having a temperature coefficient of 0.0003 at 20° C, determine the resistivity of the nichrome wire in ohms per circular mil foot at 20° C.

F. A 110-volt heating element has a resistance of 22 ohms when operated at rated voltage. It is used to heat a small vessel containing one quart of water. If the temperature of the water is 20° C when the heating element is connected to a 110-volt source and one half of the energy output of the element is lost, determine the temperature of the water at the end of 15 min. What is the temperature of the water at the end of 40 min?

Laboratory Problem No. 7-2

CURRENT, RESISTANCE, AND HEAT—II

Laboratory

Caution: In the tests indicated below which involve the use of the shunt field winding of a d-c dynamo, be certain to *disconnect the voltmeter before opening the circuit disconnect switch.*

1. Obtain data by the voltmeter-ammeter method from which the resistance of the shunt field winding of a d-c dynamo can be calculated for room temperature. Perform the test under conditions which will not cause the temperature of the winding to rise appreciably above the room temperature. Measure and record the room temperature.

With the d-c voltage impressed on the field winding maintained constant, obtain such additional data as are needed for determining the variation of the average temperature of the field winding with time by the change-in-resistance method. The voltage impressed on the field winding should be approximately 100 volts in the case of 115-volt machines and 200 volts in the case of 230-volt machines. Take instrument readings at intervals of approximately 10 min for a period of 2 hr.

2. Obtain data for determining the resistivity of a nichrome wire in ohms per circular mil foot for room temperature. Measure and record the room temperature.

3. (a) Connect a carbon-filament lamp to a 115-volt d-c source. Obtain data for determining its resistance.

(b) Connect a second carbon-filament lamp in series with the first lamp and connect this series combination to the 115-volt d-c source. Again obtain data for determining the resistance of the first lamp.

Report

A. Plot the curve for which data were obtained in **1.**

B. Discuss the shape of the curve plotted in **A.**

C. From the data obtained in **2,** determine the resistivity of the nichrome wire in ohms per circular mil foot for 600° F. An average value of the temperature coefficient of commercial nichrome wire at 20° C is 0.00025. How does the calculated resistivity compare with the average value for commercial nichrome wire, which is 722.3 ohms per circular mil foot at 600° F?

D. Determine the resistance of the carbon-filament lamp from data obtained in (a) and (b) of **3.** Discuss any difference in the two values of resistance.

E. An iron wire is 50 ft long and has a resistance of 0.368 ohm at 158° F. Determine the diameter of the wire.

F. A 110-volt heating element has a resistance of 22 ohms when operated at rated voltage. It is used to heat a small vessel containing 1 pt of water. If the heating element is connected to a 110-volt source and one half of the energy output of the element is lost, find the time required to raise the temperature of the water from 25° C to the boiling point.

CHAPTER 8

ELEMENTARY STUDY OF THE D-C SHUNT MOTOR

IN many laboratory circuit experiments it is desirable to use an a-c generator as a source of power. In nearly all laboratories the prime mover that drives the a-c generator is a d-c shunt motor. Therefore an elementary discussion dealing with the fundamental principles concerned in the operation and control of the d-c shunt motor follows in this chapter and a discussion of the operation and control of the a-c generator is presented in Chapter 9.

1. Motor Action. From the study of elementary magnetism and electricity, the reader will recall that when a conductor carrying cur-

Fig. 8-1. (a) Uniform magnetic field between two unlike poles. (b) Magnetic field surrounding a conductor carrying current. (c) Force acting on a current-carrying conductor placed in a magnetic field.

rent is placed in a magnetic field a force that tends to move the conductor is produced. When the direction of the magnetic field and the direction of the current in the conductor are known, the direction of the force can be determined by the application of Fleming's "left-hand rule." By reference to Fig. 8-1 and the use of a little imagination, the direction of the force can be determined without the application of this rule. In Fig. 8-1(a) the direction of the field is from the north to the south pole in accordance with convention. In the conductor shown in (b) of the figure the direction of the current is into the paper. This current produces a magnetic field around the conductor in the direction indicated by the arrowheads. When the conductor is introduced into the magnetic field between poles N and S, as shown in (c) of the figure, the magnetic lines due to the current in the conductor and those due to the poles are in the same direction in the region above the conductor, whereas below the conductor they are in the opposite direction. Accordingly, a greater number of lines per unit cross-sectional area is present above the conductor than below it.   It can be imagined that these lines do not like this crowded condition above the conductor and in an effort to spread out exert a force on it in a downward direction. It should be noted that the direction of this force is perpendicular to both the magnetic field and the conductor.

The magnitude of the force exerted on a current-carrying conductor placed perpendicular to a magnetic field is directly proportional to the strength of the field at the conductor position, to the length of the conductor, and to the magnitude of the current in the conductor. The force on the conductor can be expressed as

$$F = kBlI. \qquad (8\text{-}1)$$

In this expression B is the flux density at the conductor position, l the length of the conductor, and I the current in the conductor, k being the proportionality constant.

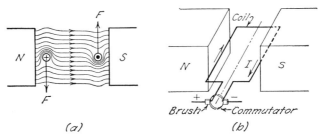

Fig. 8-2.   (a) Forces acting on current-carrying conductors placed in a magnetic field. (b) A single-turn coil and commutator.

If a second conductor carrying current in the opposite direction to that of the first is placed in the magnetic field as shown in Fig. 8-2(a), the force on the second conductor will obviously be upward. The two conductors can be mechanically joined together to form a loop or coil as shown in Fig. 8-2(b).   If such a coil were properly supported on pivots and free to rotate, it would move in a counterclockwise direction until it reached a vertical position.   If the coil were pushed past this point and at the same time the currents in the conductors were reversed, the coil would continue to rotate in the counterclockwise direction.   Reversal of the current can be accomplished by means of a commutator, as shown.   The torque developed by the rotating element can be made continuous by adding several coils having the same axis but angularly displaced from one another.

2. The Shunt Motor. The rotating element of a d-c motor consists of three parts, an iron cylinder with associated shaft, a winding, and a commutator. The winding is composed of a number of insulated coils spaced uniformly on the periphery of the iron cylinder. These coils may consist of several turns or a single turn, as indicated in Fig. 8-2(b). The coils are connected to the commutator, which is insulated from the shaft and has as many segments as there are coils. In the simplest case, the coil-to-commutator connections are made in such a manner that all of the coils are in series to form a closed circuit. This rotating element is called the *armature*. Current enters the armature by means of carbon blocks, called *brushes*, which rest under pressure on the surface of the commutator.

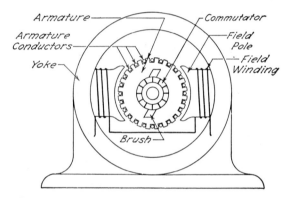

Fig. 8-3. Essential parts of a two-pole d-c shunt motor.

The frame or yoke of the d-c motor acts as a mechanical support for the field poles and in smaller machines for the end pieces which carry the bearings. The bearings support the armature so that it can rotate in a position between the field poles. On the core of each of the field poles is an insulated winding. These windings are connected in series in such a manner that when this circuit carries d-c current equal numbers of north and south poles are produced, adjacent poles always being opposite in kind. This complete winding is known as the *field winding*. Electromagnets are used to produce the magnetic field in a commercial d-c motor, instead of the permanent magnets shown in Figs. 8-1 and 8-2, because of the high-density field that can be produced and the ease with which it can be varied by simply adjusting the magnitude of the current in the field winding.

Fig. 8-3 is a schematic sketch showing the essential parts of a two-pole d-c motor.

As has been indicated in the foregoing, some source of power must be provided to supply the current in the field winding and also in the armature conductors. The field winding can be connected directly to the source of power as shown in Fig. 8-4. Likewise, the armature can be connected directly as shown. A d-c motor connected this way is called a *shunt motor* because the field winding is connected in parallel with the armature winding, thus shunting it.

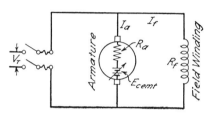

3. Torque. When current is introduced into the armature winding of a d-c motor by means of the brushes, the arrangement of the armature winding is such that all of the armature conductors under the influence of the north poles carry currents of equal magnitude, all of which flow in the same direction. The conductors under the influence of the south poles also carry currents of the same value as those under the north poles but opposite in direction. It is necessary that the current directions be opposite under poles of opposite kind in order that torque in the same direction be produced by the current in each conductor. If I is the current in an armature conductor and B_{av} is the average radial flux density in the air gap between the poles and armature, the average tangential force on an armature conductor is

$$F_{av} = kB_{av}lI. \tag{8-2}$$

For a given motor the radius of the armature, the length of the armature conductors, the number of conductors, and the number of parallel conducting paths through the armature are constant. In addition, the average radial flux density is dependent upon the total flux per pole ϕ. Therefore the average torque developed by a d-c motor is

$$T_{av} = K\phi I_a, \tag{8-3}$$

where I_a is the total current supplied to the armature and K is a constant determined by the design of the motor and the units used in the expression.

4. Counter Electromotive Force. If the conductor of Fig. 8-1(c) moved downward through the magnetic field so that it cut the lines of force, an electromotive force would be induced, or generated, in the conductor. This electromotive force would be in such a direction that, could a current be set up by it, the current would be in such a direction that the resulting force would oppose the motion of the conductor. Such a current would, obviously, be in the direction opposite to that shown in the figure. Hence the generated voltage must be in the direction opposite to that of the impressed voltage producing the current indicated in the figure.

As soon as the armature of a motor starts to rotate, electromotive forces are generated in the armature conductors which add together and oppose the current into the armature from the outside source. This generated voltage is called the *counter emf* or *back emf*. In order to determine the factors controlling the counter emf of a motor, consider the average voltage generated in an armature conductor as the armature rotates. In passing by one pole an armature conductor cuts ϕ magnetic lines, ϕ being the total flux per pole. The average rate at which these lines are cut by the conductor, or, in other words, the average voltage generated in the conductor, is directly proportional to the flux per pole ϕ and the speed n of the armature in revolutions per unit time. Owing to the arrangement of the armature winding and the position of the brushes, the voltages generated in the conductors composing one of the identical parallel paths between brushes of opposite polarity all add. Therefore the average voltage generated between brushes of opposite polarity, or the counter emf of the armature, is given by

$$E_{\text{cemf}} = k'n\phi. \qquad (8\text{-}4)$$

In this equation k' is a constant determined by the design of the machine and the units used in the expression. This relation must hold at all times and is the fundamental expression for the generated voltage in a dynamo whether it is used as a motor or as a generator.

5. Resistance of Armature and Field Winding. The fundamental circuit of the shunt motor is shown in Fig. (8-4), in which E_{cemf} represents the counter emf, R_a the resistance of the armature, R_f the resistance of the field winding, I_a the current in the armature winding, and I_f the current in the field winding.

Since no energy is required to maintain a magnetic field, the only energy required in the field winding is that used to supply the heat produced by the current acting against the resistance of the wire of which the winding is made. The expression for the power loss is

$$P_f = I_f^2 R_f. \qquad (8\text{-}5)$$

None of the power represented by this expression does any useful work. This power is entirely lost and, accordingly, is a waste. For this reason, d-c motors are designed to keep this loss as small as is economically sound from the standpoint of material and construction costs. Since this loss of power is proportional to the square of the current, the field winding is made of a large number of turns of small wire, giving the winding a relatively high resistance and thereby keeping the current low.

All the power supplied to the armature winding, on the other hand, is converted into mechanical power with the exception of that dissipated as heat due to the current acting against the resistance of the armature circuit. This dissipated power is determined by the equation

$$P_a = I_a{}^2 R_a. \tag{8-6}$$

This also represents waste power. It is a determining factor in the performance of the motor.

Since the torque required in a motor is determined by the mechanical load, the current I_a varies widely. In order to keep the heat loss in the armature as low as possible and to maintain good performance, the resistance of the armature winding is kept as low as is economically sound from the standpoint of material and construction costs. In motors of one horsepower and larger this resistance is only a fractional part of an ohm and decreases with increase in the size of the motor.

6. Starting Boxes. No generated voltage will be present ($E_{cemf} = 0$) in the armature of the motor shown in Fig. 8-4 as long as the armature is at a standstill. Hence, in accordance with Ohm's law, at the moment the power connection is made, but before the armature has started to rotate, the current in the armature will be

$$I_a = \frac{V_T}{R_a}. \tag{8-7}$$

Since R_a is very small, the current might be hundreds of amperes in the case of small motors and even thousands of amperes in the case

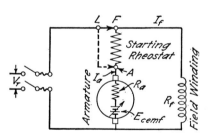

Fig. 8-5.   Circuit of a d-c shunt motor with a starting rheostat.

of large machines were not some means used to keep the current down to a safe value. This result is achieved by inserting in series with the armature a resistance that can be gradually decreased as the motor gains speed and as the current is limited by the increasing counter emf. Such a resistance is indicated by AF in Fig. 8-5. This resistance is usually of such a value as to limit the initial current to about rated value for the machine, and is rugged enough to carry this current for a brief period without overheating.

When the motor is being started, but before the line switch is closed, the movable contactor to the resistance AF should be in the position shown at F in order for the full resistance to be included in the armature branch of the circuit. Since the armature is at a standstill, the moment the switch is closed the initial current will be

$$I_a = \frac{V_T}{R_{sb} + R_a}. \tag{8-8}$$

In this equation and in equation (8-9) R_{sb} represents the resistance between the movable contactor and point A. Accordingly, R_{sb} will depend upon the position of the contactor.

As soon as the armature starts to rotate, a counter emf E_{cemf} will be generated which will increase in direct proportion to the speed. The counter emf being in a direction opposed to the applied voltage V_T, the current in the armature will decrease as the motor gains speed. The speed will increase until the electrical power input to the motor just balances the motor losses and the power requirements for any mechanical load that may be connected to the motor. Under this condition of equilibrium,

$$I_a = \frac{V_T - E_{cemf}}{R_{sb} + R_a}. \tag{8-9}$$

When the movable contactor is moved toward A, so as to reduce the resistance in the armature branch of the circuit, more current will flow and the speed will again increase until a new balance is reached. This process will continue until the movable contactor is at A, as shown by the dotted line, and none of the resistance is any longer in the armature branch of the circuit.

When a motor is started, it is desirable that it start quickly. This does not mean that the acceleration should be great, but that the motor should start immediately upon the closing of the line switch and should gain speed reasonably fast. To achieve this result, a good starting torque is required. As has been pointed out, the torque is directly proportional to the strength of the magnetic field. To get a strong field, the field winding is connected directly to the line, as shown in Fig. 8-5, allowing maximum current in the winding.

It will also be noted in Fig. 8-5 that, as the movable contactor of AF is moved toward A, the resistance of AF is removed from the armature branch of the circuit and becomes part of the field winding branch, causing current I_f to decrease. However, the resistance of AF is small in comparison with R_f, and the change in I_f will be inappreciable.

In practice the resistance element *AF* with accessories are incorporated in what is known as a *starting box*. Starting boxes may differ in details of construction and the accessories supplied, but fundamentally they are all very much alike. There are two common types of boxes. One is known as the *3-point* box, and the other is known as the

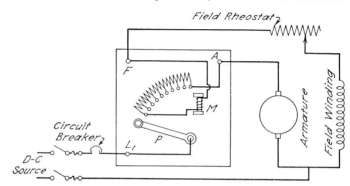

Fig. 8-6.   A 3-point starting box connected to a d-c shunt motor.

4-point box. Sketches of these two types are shown in Figs. 8-6 and 8-7, respectively.

It will be noted that the circuits shown in these figures are the same as that shown in Fig. 8-5 with the exception that in Figs. 8-6 and 8-7 the coil winding of magnet *M* is added. The function of the

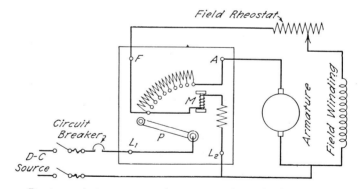

Fig. 8-7.   A 4-point starting box connected to a d-c shunt motor.

magnet is to hold the arm *P* in its final position after the motor has been started. This arm operates against a spring, the purpose of which is to return the arm to the starting position should the line voltage be interrupted, causing the motor to stop and the magnet to become de-energized.

The 4-point box differs from the 3-point box only in the manner in which the coil of the holding magnet M is connected in the circuit.   In the 3-point box, the holding coil is in series with the field winding. In the 4-point box, the holding coil is connected directly across the line.   This difference is clearly indicated in the figures.

To start the motor it is merely necessary to place the contactor P on the first tap on the resistor and close the line switch; and, as the motor gains speed, slowly move the arm toward and finally up against the holding magnet.

7. Speed Control.   The fundamental equation for the counter emf of a motor has been shown to be

$$E_{\text{cemf}} = k'n\phi.$$

From Fig. 8-4 it is evident that

$$E_{\text{cemf}} = V_T - I_a R_a. \tag{8-10}$$

Substituting in this equation the value of E_{cemf} given in equation (8-4) gives

$$V_T - I_a R_a = k'n\phi, \tag{8-11}$$

from which

$$n = \frac{(V_T - I_a R_a)k''}{\phi}. \tag{8-12}$$

In general, in the case of a shunt motor, $I_a R_a$ is very small in comparison with V_T, and equation (8-12) may, without appreciable error, be written as

$$n = \frac{k''V_T}{\phi}. \tag{8-13}$$

This equation shows that, if V_T is held constant, the speed of the motor will be inversely proportional to the flux ϕ.   This flux can be conveniently varied by the insertion of a rheostat in series with the field winding.   Cutting in rheostat resistance, thus decreasing the field current and consequently the flux, will cause the motor speed to increase.   Conversely, cutting out rheostat resistance will cause the speed to decrease.*   This method of controlling the speed of a motor is the one most commonly used.   For most of the motors found in electrical engineering laboratories, a 25-ohm rheostat connected in series with a rheostat having a resistance approximately equal to that

---

* When the resistance of the armature circuit is large and when $I_a R_a$ is not negligible, the opposite effect may occur.   Increasing the field current may cause the motor to speed up, and, conversely, decreasing the field current may cause a decrease in the speed.

of the field winding will usually provide fine control. In selecting these rheostats, consideration should be given not only to their resistances but also to their current ratings.

A magnetic circuit breaker which has an instantaneous trip should be placed in one of the line leads supplying a d-c shunt motor, as indicated in Figs. 8-6 and 8-7. The purpose of the circuit breaker is to protect the motor armature against the extremely high speeds that would be produced if the field circuit should become open-circuited when the motor is lightly loaded. Under this condition the motor armature would accelerate rapidly and in a few seconds reach a speed that might result in serious damage to the motor. The circuit breaker protects the armature against these excessive speeds because at the instant the field circuit becomes open-circuited, the counter emf is very small and an abnormally high armature current results. This excessive current will operate the circuit breaker and open the supply circuit. In general, a circuit breaker setting of 150 per cent of rated motor current will keep the breaker from operating during the starting period and will provide good protection. In any case, the setting should not exceed 250 per cent of rated motor current. On the basis of the foregoing it should be apparent that a field rheostat should always be given a continuity test before it is connected in a motor field circuit.

When a motor is being started, care should be exercised to see that the movable arms of the field rheostats are in such positions that none of the rheostat resistances are in the circuit. This is necessary in order to obtain the strong field required to produce a good starting torque.

8. Obtaining Low Speeds. *Method 1.* For some types of tests it will be found necessary to operate a shunt motor at speeds considerably less than the minimum speed obtained with the field rheostat resistance all cut out. An inspection of equation (8-12) shows that one way of reducing the speed below this minimum is to insert additional resistance in the armature circuit.

In Fig. 8-8 is shown a variable resistance R connected in series with the armature circuit of a shunt motor. In order to obtain a good starting torque, the resistance of R should be cut out while the motor is being started in the usual manner with the starting box. The desired low speed can then be obtained by adjusting the resistance of R. If the impressed voltage and field rheostat setting remain unchanged, increasing the resistance of R will decrease the speed; and by increasing it sufficiently, very low speeds can be obtained. If necessary, the field rheostat can be adjusted along with R to give finer control of the speed.

In order to obtain a low speed of approximately 100 rpm in the case of a lightly loaded shunt motor of the usual horsepower, voltage, and speed ratings* found in electrical engineering laboratories, R should be of the order of magnitude of 25 to 100 ohms and should be capable of continuously carrying the armature current under the lightly loaded condition. In case the motor is loaded so that it takes an armature current near rated value, R should be of the order of magnitude of 2 to 5 ohms and should be capable of continuously carrying rated armature current. In both of the cases cited above it is assumed that the field rheostat is set at about the position that gives rated speed for rated impressed voltage and zero resistance in R.

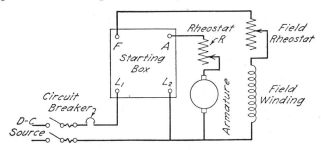

Fig. 8-8.   Circuit for obtaining low speeds by means of a rheostat inserted in series with the motor armature.

A rheostat of the lamp-bank type can be used for R in place of the conventional type. Before the motor is started, the switches of the rheostat should be in the positions for minimum resistance, and the terminals of the rheostat should then be short-circuited by means of a single-pole single-throw switch. After the motor has been started by means of the starting box, the shorting switch across the terminals of the rheostat can be opened and its resistance increased to reduce the speed of the motor to the desired value.

For the motor in Fig. 8-8 equation (8-12) may be written as

$$n = \frac{(V_T - I_a R_a - I_a R)k''}{\phi}. \tag{8-14}$$

If ϕ is assumed constant and since $I_a R_a$ is small compared to V_T, the voltage drop across R will be one-half that of the impressed voltage when the motor speed is approximately one-half that obtainable with zero resistance in R. For speeds less than this the drop across R becomes more than one-half V_T, and the lower the speed the more nearly it approaches V_T. Therefore, if the speed of a 230-volt motor

---

* Fifteen horsepower or less, 230 or 115 volts, and 1000 to 2000 rpm.

is to be reduced to a value such that the voltage across R is greater than 115 volts, a rheostat made up of 115-volt elements will need to be connected in the series-parallel arrangement, which will avoid exceeding the 115-volt rating of the elements. Even in cases in which it is not intended to reduce the motor speed sufficiently to cause a voltage in excess of 115 volts across the rheostat, the elements of the rheostat should not be put in parallel unless it is certain that there will not be any large fluctuations in load which might cause the motor speed to be less than the value intended.

In an electrical engineering laboratory, where test apparatus is usually set up only temporarily, adding resistance to the armature circuit of a shunt motor in order to obtain low speeds has the advantage

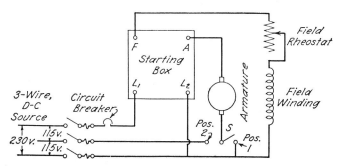

Fig. 8-9. Circuit for lowering the speed range of a 230-volt d-c shunt motor by using one half of rated voltage on the armature circuit.

of simplicity. It has a marked disadvantage in that, with a given amount of resistance in R, the speed of the motor changes considerably with moderate changes in load. Under these conditions, frequent adjustment of R is necessary to keep the speed even approximately constant. This method is fairly satisfactory, however, when the motor is lightly loaded. The method is seldom used for regular operation in industrial applications because of the poor speed regulation and because of the power loss in R, which under loaded conditions would be prohibitive.

Method 2. In Fig. 8-9 is shown a circuit that can be used to lower the speed of a 230-volt shunt motor to approximately one-half the speed obtained with rated impressed voltage and no resistance in the field rheostat. This circuit is a simple modification of the circuit in Fig. 8-7, and it should be apparent that the circuit of Fig. 8-6 can be similarly modified. In order to make use of the circuit it is necessary to have a 115- to 230-volt power source as indicated. This type of power source is usually available in an electrical engineering laboratory.

The motor shown in Fig. 8-9 is started in the usual manner regardless of the position of switch S. When S is in position 1, the motor connections are the same as those in Fig. 8-7. However, when S is in position 2, the field circuit is connected across 230 volts as before, but only 115 volts are impressed on the armature circuit. If the field rheostat setting is not changed, the speed for position 2 is approximately one-half that for position 1. This fact can be seen by considering equations (8-12) and (8-13), which show that, when the field flux is constant, the motor speed is nearly directly proportional to the voltage impressed on the armature terminals.

The field rheostat can be used to vary the motor speed in the same manner for position 2 of switch S as for position 1. A little thought will show that switch S should not be thrown from one position to the other while the motor is running. The motor should be stopped, the change in switch position made, and then the motor started again.

When the necessary power source is available and the range of speeds that this method can provide is sufficient, this method is preferable to the first method discussed because the speed regulation is good for either position of switch S.

Laboratory Problem No. 8-1

ELEMENTARY STUDY OF THE D-C SHUNT MOTOR

Laboratory

1. (a) Connect a d-c shunt motor so that it can be started by use of a starting box. Include in the circuit the auxiliary apparatus needed for protecting the circuit and for controlling the speed of the motor.

Start the motor. Make a record on the data sheet of the direction of rotation as viewed from the commutator end.

(b) Stop the motor. Make such changes in the motor-circuit connections as will cause the direction of rotation to be reversed. Make a record of the changes made. Start the motor and make a record of the direction of rotation.

(c) Stop the motor and make such changes in the motor-circuit connections as will cause the direction of rotation to be reversed to that in (b). Do not make changes similar to those made in (b). Make a record of the changes made. Start the motor and make a record of the direction of rotation.

2. (a) With the motor connected so that it will rotate in the proper direction and with power supplied from a source whose voltage is approximately that for which the motor is rated, obtain data from which a curve of motor speed vs motor field current can be plotted. The range of speed used should be from the minimum obtainable by adjustment of the field rheostat to a maximum value of 125 per cent of rated speed. At each step in taking the data, also read and record voltage across the motor armature.

(b) Make the necessary changes in the motor-circuit connections so that the motor can be operated with approximately rated voltage impressed on the field circuit but approximately one-half of rated voltage applied to the armature. When the motor is operating under these conditions, obtain data from which a curve can be plotted between motor speed and motor field current. Use approximately the same range of field currents as used in (a). At each step in taking the data, also read and record the voltage across the motor armature.

3. Insert a suitable variable resistance R between terminal A of the starting box and the motor armature terminal originally connected to A. Make whatever changes are necessary so that the motor can be operated with approximately rated voltage applied to its armature when all of the resistance of R is cut out. Start the motor. With all of the resistance of R out, adjust the motor field current to give rated speed. Maintaining the field current constant at this value, increase the resistance of R in several steps until the motor speed is about 25 per cent of rated speed. At each step read and record the motor speed, the voltage across the motor armature, and the motor field current.

Report

A. Plot the curves for which data were obtained in **2**(a) and (b). Use the same set of axes for both curves.

B. On another sheet and from the data obtained in **3,** plot a curve of motor speed vs motor armature voltage.

C. Discuss the curves plotted in **A.**

D. Discuss the curve plotted in **B.**

E. Why is a magnetic circuit breaker which has an instantaneous trip placed in one of the lines supplying a d-c shunt motor?

F. Will reversing the line connections from the power source to a shunt motor cause a reversal of the direction of rotation? Explain.

G. A certain starting box is suitable for use with a 10-hp, 230-volt, 38-amp, 1750-rpm d-c shunt motor. The terminals of the starting box were arbitrarily numbered 1, 2, 3, and 4; and measurements were

made from which the resistances between various pairs of terminals
were found to be as follows:

Between Arbitrarily Numbered Terminals	Resistance with Contactor in Off Position	Resistance with Contactor on First Active Tap
1 and 2	Infinite	4.5 ohms
1 and 3	2000 ohms	2000 ohms
1 and 4	4.5 ohms	4.5 ohms
2 and 3	Infinite	1995.5 ohms
2 and 4	Infinite	0 ohms
3 and 4	1995.5 ohms	1995.5 ohms

Draw a schematic sketch showing the internal connections of the
starting box and label each terminal with the number which was
arbitrarily assigned before the resistances were measured.

CHAPTER 9
ELEMENTARY STUDY OF THE A-C GENERATOR

1. Generation of A-C Voltage. When a conductor is passed through a magnetic field in such a manner as to cut the lines of force, a voltage is induced in the conductor, the magnitude of which in volts at any instant is equal to the number of lines (maxwells) cut per second $\times 10^{-8}$.

In (a) of Fig. 9-1 is shown a uniform magnetic field established by the poles N and S. Since the field is uniform, the same number of

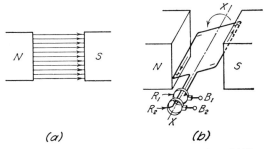

(a)   *(b)*

Fig. 9-1. (a) Uniform magnetic field between two unlike poles. (b) Elementary two-pole single-coil a-c generator.

lines of force pierce every square centimeter of the cross-sectional area of the field. Let a rectangular loop of conducting material be introduced into the field, as shown in (b) of the figure. Assume that the loop can be revolved about the fixed axis XX, the latter being horizontal and parallel to the faces of the poles. The ends of this loop are connected to two insulated rings R_1 and R_2, which revolve with the loop, connection to the external circuit being made possible by means of the stationary brushes B_1 and B_2.

Now, if the linear velocity of the sides of the loop in centimeters per second is v, the length of a side in centimeters is l, and the flux density in lines per square centimeter is B, the number of lines of force cut per second by a side of the loop is $Blv \sin \theta$, θ being the angle between the plane of the loop and a vertical plane passing through the axis. The electromotive force generated in the coil side is

$$e = Blv \sin \theta \times 10^{-8} \text{ volts.}$$

If the direction of rotation is counterclockwise, as indicated, the direction of the generated voltage in the side passing the N pole is such that, were the loop closed, current would flow in the direction shown by the arrow.   Thus, in this side of the loop the front end is at a higher potential than the back end, and in accordance with convention these ends are marked $+$ and $-$, respectively.   In the other side, the one passing the S pole, the front end is $-$ and the back end $+$.   Hence the voltages generated in the sides add around the loop, and current would flow in a counterclockwise direction around it were the loop closed.

Whenever the loop passes through the vertical plane, and a side of the loop moves from the face of one pole to the face of the next, the generated voltage reverses.   This is as should be expected, for it is a well-established fact that the direction of the voltage depends upon the direction of the lines of force and the direction of the component of the motion which is perpendicular to the lines of force.   If either is reversed, the direction of the voltage is also reversed.   In the example cited, the direction of the lines of force remains unchanged, but the direction of the component of motion perpendicular to the lines of force is reversed as the loop passes through the vertical plane.   When the conductor is passing the face of the N pole, the direction of the component is downward; when it is passing the S pole, it is upward.   It follows from this fact that in an external resistance connected to B_1 and B_2 the current will reverse with the reversal of the generated voltage. Thus the current to the external circuit is one that reverses in direction every time the loop passes through the vertical plane. The arrangement shown in (b) of the figure is, accordingly, a very simple form of an a-c generator, or alternator.

If a curve of the instantaneous potential of B_1 with respect to B_2 for one complete revolution of the loop is plotted against θ, the result is the sine curve shown in Fig. 9-2; the angle θ is taken as zero when the

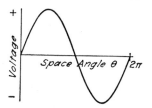

Fig. 9-2. Generated voltage in rotating coil of elementary two-pole a-c generator vs coil position.

side connected to B_1 is at the top.   For succeeding revolutions the curve is repeated.   Hence the curve of voltage shown in the figure is one of a series of connected and repeated curves; and for this reason it is called a *cycle*.

In (a) of Fig. 9-3 are shown two pairs of poles.   The general directions of the magnetic lines of force are also shown.   Let a loop of conducting material be introduced between the poles, as illustrated in (b) of the figure, and let this loop be revolved about the axis XX. As a side passes from the zone in front of one pole into that in front of the next pole, the direction of the motion with respect to the direction of the lines of force is reversed. Reversal of the generated voltage will, accordingly, occur four times per revolution. If θ is taken as

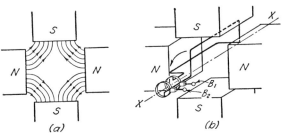

(a) (b)

Fig. 9-3. (a) General directions of the magnetic lines of force between the poles of a four-pole generator. (b) Elementary four-pole single-coil a-c generator.

zero when the loop side connected to B_2 is directly under the center of the top pole, the curve of the potential of B_1 with respect to B_2 as the loop revolves at a constant velocity in a counterclockwise direction is that shown in Fig. 9-4. In this case, the difference of potential between B_1 and B_2 and therefore the current in an external circuit connected to B_1 and B_2 goes through two complete cycles per revolution.

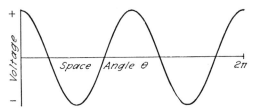

Fig. 9-4. Generated voltage in rotating coil of elementary four-pole a-c generator vs coil position.

2. Frequency. On the basis of the foregoing, it is now possible to establish a relationship between the rpm of the loop, the number of poles, and the number of cycles per second, the latter being known as the frequency. It should be clear that one cycle occurs for each pair of poles per revolution; hence

Cycles per sec = revolutions per sec $\times$ pairs of poles,

or

$$f = \frac{\text{rpm}}{60} \times \frac{p}{2} = \frac{\text{rpm} \times p}{120}. \tag{9-1}$$

In this equation p is the number of poles.

3. The Alternator.   In the simple alternators of Figs. 9-1 and 9-3 the source of the magnetic field is indicated by the poles marked N and S.   Theoretically it is possible for these to be the poles of permanent magnets.   However, the density of the field issuing from such a source is low and not easily varied.   For these reasons permanent magnets are not suitable for use in commercial generators.   Electromagnets, on the other hand, are ideal.   Magnets of this type can be designed to give fields of high density that can be readily and conveniently varied merely by adjusting the current in the winding of the magnet, or the *field winding*.   With very few exceptions, the magnetic fields of

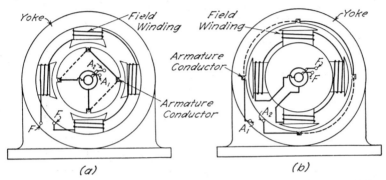

Fig. 9-5.   Elementary four-pole a-c generators (a) with revolving armature and (b) with revolving field structure.

generators are supplied by this type of magnet.   A 4-pole alternator having a field supplied in this manner is shown in (a) of Fig. 9-5.   The conductors in which the voltage is generated are placed in slots on the periphery of the revolving cylinder.

Since the only requirement for generating an electromotive force in a conductor is that lines of force be cut by the conductor, it does not matter whether the conductor itself moves and the field remains stationary or the conductor remains fixed and the field moves.   In (b) of Fig. 9-5 is shown an alternator in which the field structure and the associated field revolves, the conductors in which the electromotive force is generated being stationary and placed in slots in the yoke.

In alternators found in practice, the simple loops as shown in Figs. 9-1 and 9-3 are not used, but coils that may consist of many turns are formed and placed in slots on the periphery of the cylinder or on the inside surface of the yoke, as in (a) and (b) of Fig. 9-5.   These coils are connected in series, thus forming a continuous winding, which is called the *armature winding*.   The coil connections are made in such a manner that the summation of the instantaneous generated voltages in the coils gives the desired resultant voltage.

It should be obvious from the preceding study of the simple generator that the direction of the field issuing from a given pole must remain fixed with respect to the pole structure.   Direct current must accordingly be supplied to the field winding.   By increasing or decreasing the magnitude of the current in the winding, the density of the magnetic field will be similarly affected, as will the voltage generated in the armature winding.   Thus, by the use of rheostats, as shown in (a) and (b) of Fig. 9-6, a flexible and simple means for controlling the generated voltage of the alternator is obtained.   In this figure A_1 and A_2 are the output terminals of the armature winding.   It might occur to the reader

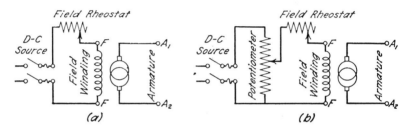

Fig. 9-6.   Circuits for controlling the field current of an a-c generator (a) by means of a field rheostat and (b) by means of a potentiometer and a field rheostat.

that the generated voltage could just as well be controlled by adjustment of the speed, since the generated voltage is determined by the rate at which the magnetic lines of force are cut.   It will be recalled, however, that the frequency of the generated voltage is directly proportional to speed.   As the student will learn in a later study of a-c circuits and machines, voltage of constant frequency is almost a necessity.   Hence the adjustment of the generated voltage by the use of speed control is never used in connection with the operation of a-c generators.

In the schematic diagram of Fig. 9-6 the armature terminals are shown connected to the brushes of the slip rings.   However, when connections are being made to an alternator, it should not be taken for granted that the armature winding is connected to the slip rings, since most a-c generators have revolving fields.   Hence connections from an external circuit to the field winding are almost always made to the brushes of the slip rings.   But, since generators in which the armature revolves are occasionally encountered, an inspection of the machine should be made in order to determine the proper external connections whenever the field winding and armature winding terminals are not properly marked.

Laboratory Problem No. 9-1
ELEMENTARY STUDY OF THE A-C GENERATOR

Laboratory

Use an M-G set consisting of a d-c shunt motor and an a-c generator.

1. Connect a suitable potentiometer and one or two suitable rheostats so that they can be used to control the d-c current in the field winding of the a-c generator.

Connect the d-c shunt motor in such a manner that it can be used to vary the speed of the generator from approximately 50 per cent to 125 per cent of rated generator speed.

2. Drive the generator at rated speed, and maintain the speed constant at this value while the measurements indicated below are being made. Measure and record the speed, field current, and generated voltage of the generator as the field current is progressively increased in increments from zero to a value that gives a generated voltage 125 per cent of rated voltage and then progressively reduced in decrements back to zero.

3. With the generator being driven at rated speed, adjust its field current until the value is such that the generated voltage is equal to the rated voltage of the generator. Measure and record this value of the field current; and during the remainder of the test maintain the field current constant at this value.

Reduce the speed of the generator to approximately one-half its rated value. Measure and record the speed, generated voltage, and field current of the generator as the speed is increased in increments to a value 125 per cent of rated speed.

Report

A. From the data obtained in **2**, plot the curves of generated voltage vs generator field current for progressively increasing values of field current and also for progressively decreasing values of field current. Use the same set of coordinate axes for both curves.

B. On another sheet and from the data obtained in **3**, plot a curve of generated voltage vs generator speed.

C. Discuss the curves plotted in **A.**

D. Discuss the curve plotted in **B.**

E. If the generator had been driven at a speed 50 per cent above its rated value in **2**, what would have been the generated voltage at a field current of 50 per cent of the maximum used (1) when this value was reached by progressively increasing the field current from zero value, and (2) when this value was reached by progressively decreasing the field current from the maximum used?

F. The 60-cycle water-wheel-driven generators at Boulder Dam run at a speed of 150 rpm. How many poles do they have?

Laboratory Problem No. 9-2

ELEMENTARY STUDY OF THE D-C SHUNT MOTOR AND THE A-C GENERATOR

Laboratory

Use an M-G set consisting of a d-c shunt motor and an a-c generator.

1. (a) Connect a d-c shunt motor so that it can be started by use of a starting box. Include in the circuit the auxiliary apparatus needed for protecting the circuit and for controlling the speed.

Start the motor. Make a record on the data sheet of the direction of rotation as viewed from the commutator end.

(b) Stop the motor and make such changes in the motor-circuit connections as will cause the direction of rotation to be reversed. Make a record of the changes made. Start the motor and make a record of the direction of rotation.

(c) Stop the motor and make such changes in the motor-circuit connections as will cause the direction of rotation to be reversed to that in (b). Do not make changes similar to those made in (b). Make a record of the changes made. Start the motor and make a record of the direction of rotation.

2. In series with the field winding of the a-c generator connect rheostats suitable for controlling the d-c current of the field winding.

With the motor rotating in the proper direction and driving the generator at the rated speed of the generator, adjust the generator field current so that a generated voltage equal to the rated voltage of the generator is obtained. In the test that follows maintain the field current at this value and at each step of the test record the value of the field current as proof that it was maintained constant.

Increase the speed of the generator to 125 per cent of rated speed. Now reduce the speed in steps to the lowest value obtainable with the motor field rheostat control and obtain data from which the following curves can be plotted:

(a) Motor speed vs motor field current.

(b) Generated voltage of the generator vs generator speed.

Report

A. Plot the following curves on the same set of coordinate axes:

(1) Motor speed vs motor field current from data obtained in **2**.

(2) Motor speed vs motor field current from calculated data based upon the assumption that the magnetic flux per pole of the motor is directly proportional to the field current and that the $I_a R_a$ drop of the armature is negligible. Make the initial point of this curve coincide with the maximum speed point of (1).

B. On another sheet and from data obtained in **2**, plot a curve of the generated voltage of the generator vs generator speed.

C. Discuss curves (1) and (2) plotted in **A**.

D. Discuss the curve plotted in **B**.

E. Will reversing the line connections from the power source to a shunt motor cause a reversal of the direction of rotation? Explain.

F. The 25-cycle water-wheel-driven generators at Niagara Falls have 28 poles. At what speed do the generators run?

CHAPTER 10

KIRCHHOFF'S LAWS

AMONG the most important fundamental principles applying to electric circuits are those credited to Kirchhoff and known as *Kirchhoff's laws*. These laws, one of which deals with current and the other with voltage, are stated below, and their applications are explained in the discussion that follows.

1. Kirchhoff's Law of Currents. *At any instant, the sum of the instantaneous values of the currents in the direction toward a junction point of two or more branches of an electric circuit is equal to the sum of the instantaneous values of the currents in the direction away from the junction point.*

2. Kirchhoff's Law of Voltages. *At any instant, the sum of the instantaneous values of the potential rises encountered in going around any closed electric circuit is equal to the sum of the instantaneous values of the potential drops.*

3. Symbols. In applying Kirchhoff's laws it is convenient to use a notation that distinguishes between the potential rise of a source and the potential drop across a circuit opposition element such as a resistor or a coil. Furthermore, in circuits in which the currents and voltages vary from instant to instant, as in the case of alternating currents, the system of notation must permit instantaneous values of current and voltage to be distinguished from effective values and the magnitude alone of an effective value to be distinguished from the complex or vector representation of the effective value. In this book lower-case letters are used to represent instantaneous values and upper-case, or capital, letters are used to represent effective values. The complex or vector representation of the effective value is designated by the capital letter with a line above it. The line is omitted when only the magnitude is to be considered. Thus i, I, and $\bar{I}$ represent an instantaneous value, the magnitude of the effective value, and the complex value, respectively, of a current. To distinguish the potential rise of a source from the potential drop across an opposition element, e, E, and $\bar{E}$ are used to represent potential rise and v, V, and $\bar{V}$ to represent potential drop.

4. Positive Directions of Currents and Voltages. In order to apply Kirchhoff's current law to a circuit it is necessary to choose for each conductor the direction in which the current is to be considered positive. Before applying Kirchhoff's voltage law it is also necessary to choose the direction to be considered positive for the potential rise of the generated or induced emf of each source and for the potential drop across each circuit opposition element. In the simpler circuits the positive direction of the potential rise of a source is usually assumed to be the same as the positive direction of current through the source. The potential drop across an opposition element is customarily considered positive in the same direction as the positive direction of current through the element. These choices of positive directions are entirely arbitrary and are made only so that the equations resulting from the application of Kirchhoff's laws can be written. It does not mean that the chosen positive directions are the actual directions of current, potential rise, or potential drop at a given instant but that, when these quantities are actually in the chosen directions, they will be considered positive. The physical meaning of these statements will become evident from the applications of Kirchhoff's laws discussed in this chapter.

5. Application of the Current Law. A simple circuit having two parallel branches and power supplied by a generator is shown in Fig. 10-1. The directions to be considered positive for the various currents, the potential drop between points c and d, and the potential rise of the generator are indicated by the arrows.

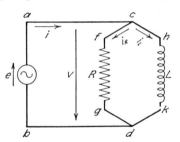

The application of Kirchhoff's current law to the currents at junction c of the circuit gives

$$i = i_R + i_L. \qquad (10\text{-}1)$$

Fig. 10-1. Two-branch parallel circuit supplied by an a-c generator.

In order to show the physical meaning of this equation and to illustrate its application, let it be assumed that the voltage supplied by the generator is such that the voltage drop, or potential drop, between terminals c and d varies sinusoidally with time and is defined by

$$v = V_{\text{max}} \sin \omega t. \qquad (10\text{-}2)$$

In this equation V_{max} is the maximum instantaneous value of the voltage drop, t is time in seconds, and ω is a constant determined by the time required to complete one cycle of variation.

A curve of v plotted against time is shown in Fig. 10-2. In the time interval during which v has positive values, the interval during which the curve is above the horizontal axis, point c is at a higher potential than point d, and hence there is a drop of potential from c to d. During the time interval in which values of v are negative, or the curve is below the horizontal axis, point c of the circuit is at a lower potential than d, and there is a drop of potential from d to c.

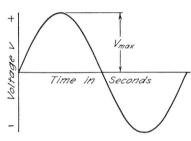

Now consider the branch $cfgd$ of Fig. 10-1. As shown, this branch contains only the pure resistance element R. When a voltage is impressed upon a pure resistance element, the current in the element is directly proportional to the voltage impressed on it and inversely proportional to its resistance.

Fig. 10-2. Variation with time of the instantaneous values of the voltage drop v in the circuit in Fig. 10-1.

Therefore, if the impressed voltage is one whose instantaneous values vary with time, the current in the resistance element will vary in an identical manner. In view of this fact, the equation relating the instantaneous values of the voltage drop

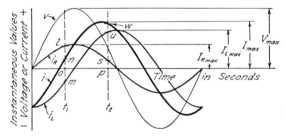

Fig. 10-3. Variation with time of the instantaneous values of the voltage and currents in Fig. 10-1.

v and the current i_R in Fig. 10-1 is

$$i_R = \frac{v}{R},$$

or

$$i_R = \frac{V_{max}}{R} \sin \omega t.$$

Since $\sin \omega t$ cannot be greater than unity, the maximum instantaneous value $I_{R_{max}}$ that i_R can have is V_{max}/R, so that

$$i_R = \frac{V_{max}}{R} \sin \omega t = I_{R_{max}} \sin \omega t. \qquad (10\text{-}3)$$

In Fig. 10-3 the curve of v is replotted. The curve of i_R is also plotted in this figure, the instantaneous values being determined by use of equation (10-3). These two curves are said to be in phase, since their positive maximum values occur at the same instant.

Now consider the branch *chkd*, which contains only the pure inductance element L. The relationship between the instantaneous values of the voltage drop v and the current i_L in Fig. 10-1 is expressed by the following equation:

$$v = L \frac{di_L}{dt}. \tag{10-4}$$

Solving this equation for i_L gives

$$di_L = \frac{v}{L} dt.$$

But, since

$$v = V_{\max} \sin \omega t,$$

then

$$di_L = \frac{V_{\max}}{L} \sin \omega t \, dt,$$

and

$$i_L = \frac{V_{\max}}{L} \int \sin \omega t \, dt$$

$$= - \frac{V_{\max}}{\omega L} \cos \omega t$$

$$= \frac{V_{\max}}{\omega L} \sin \left(\omega t - \frac{\pi}{2} \right).$$

Again, since $\sin [\omega t - (\pi/2)]$ cannot be greater than unity, the maximum value of i_L is $V_{\max}/\omega L$, and

$$i_L = \frac{V_{\max}}{\omega L} \sin \left(\omega t - \frac{\pi}{2} \right) = I_{L\max} \sin \left(\omega t - \frac{\pi}{2} \right). \tag{10-5}$$

From this equation it is seen that i_L is a current that varies sinusoidally with time but lags a quarter cycle behind the voltage drop v. The curve of i_L plotted against time is shown in Fig. 10-3.

It should be clear that during the part of the cycle in which i_R of Fig. 10-3 is positive and plotted above the horizontal axis the actual direction of the current in the resistance branch *cfgd* is from c to f. Likewise during the part of the cycle in which i_L is positive the actual direction of the current in the inductance branch *chkd* is from c to h. Conversely during the part of the cycle in which i_R is negative the actual direction of the current is from f to c in the resistance; and it is from h to c in the inductance branch during the part of the cycle in which i_L is negative. In view of the foregoing, at the instant t_1 indicated in Fig. 10-3, the current i_R is equal to $+ol$ and so is in the direction from c to f. At this same instant, the current i_L is equal to $-om$, indicating that the direction of the current is from h to c. The current i supplied by the generator can be determined from equation (10-1). Hence, at the instant selected,

$$i = ol + (-om) = on.$$

Since in magnitude ol is greater than om, on has a positive value, showing that the direction of the current i is toward point c at the instant t_1. In (a) of Fig. 10-4 the actual directions of the currents at the instant t_1 are indicated by the arrows.

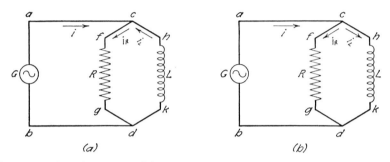

Fig. 10-4. Actual directions of the currents in the circuit of Fig. 10-1 (a) at the time t_1, shown in Fig. 10-3, and (b) at the time t_2, shown in Fig. 10-3.

If another instant such as time t_2 is selected, the current i_R is equal to $+ps$ and is from c to f in the circuit. At this same instant i_L is equal to $+pu$ and so is from c to h in the circuit. Therefore

$$i = ps + pu = pw.$$

Since i again has a positive value, it is still in the direction toward point c at the instant t_2. In (b) of Fig. 10-4 the actual directions of the currents at the instant t_2 are indicated.

By proceeding in a manner similar to the foregoing, enough points, such as n and w, can be determined to make it possible to plot a curve of i against time. Such a curve is shown in Fig. 10-3. During the period when the ordinates of this curve are positive, the direction of the current i supplied by the generator is actually from a to c; during the period in which the ordinates are negative the direction of the current is from c to a.

6. Application of the Voltage Law. A simple series circuit containing a pure resistance element R and a pure inductance element L is shown in Fig. 10-5. Power is supplied to the circuit by generator G. The current direction to be considered positive is indicated by an arrow. Also indicated by arrows are the directions to be considered positive for the potential rise of the generator and for the potential drops across the resistance, inductance, and the entire circuit.

The application of Kirchhoff's voltage law to the circuit gives

$$e = v_R + v_L = v. \qquad (10\text{-}6)$$

In order to show the physical meaning and use of this equation, let it be assumed that the current supplied to the circuit by the generator is one that varies sinusoidally with time and is defined by

$$i = I_{\max} \sin \omega t. \qquad (10\text{-}7)$$

A curve of i plotted against time in seconds is shown in Fig. 10-6. In the time interval during which values of i are positive, or the curve of i is above the horizontal axis, the current is in the direction from b to c. During

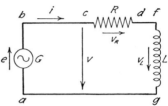

Fig. 10-5. Series circuit supplied by an a-c generator.

the time interval in which values of i are negative, or the curve of i is below the horizontal axis, the direction of the current is from c to b.

Now consider the resistance element R of the circuit. When a current flows in a resistance element, the voltage between the terminals of the element is directly proportional to the magnitude of the current and to the magnitude of the resistance of the element. Hence in Fig. 10-5 the potential drop v_R across the resistance element R at any instant is

$$v_R = i_R R,$$
or
$$v_R = R I_{\max} \sin \omega t.$$

Since $\sin \omega t$ cannot be greater than unity, the maximum instantaneous value of v_R is $R I_{\max}$, and therefore

$$v_R = R I_{\max} \sin \omega t = V_{R_{\max}} \sin \omega t. \qquad (10\text{-}8)$$

The curve of v_R is shown plotted in Fig. 10-6, the instantaneous values being determined by use of equation (10-8).

Now consider the inductance element L of the circuit in Fig. 10-5. In accordance with equation (10-4), the relationship at any instant between v_L, the potential drop across L, and i, the current in L, is

$$v_L = L \frac{di}{dt}.$$
But
$$i = I_{\max} \sin \omega t.$$

Therefore
$$v_L = L \frac{d(I_{max} \sin \omega t)}{dt}$$
$$= \omega L I_{max} \cos \omega t$$
$$= \omega L I_{max} \sin \left(\omega t + \frac{\pi}{2} \right).$$

Since $\sin [\omega t + (\pi/2)]$ cannot be greater than unity, the maximum value of v_L is $\omega L I_{max}$, and

$$v_L = \omega L I_{max} \sin \left(\omega t + \frac{\pi}{2} \right) = V_{L_{max}} \sin \left(\omega t + \frac{\pi}{2} \right). \qquad (10\text{-}9)$$

From this equation it is seen that v_L is a voltage that varies sinusoidally with time and is a quarter cycle ahead of the current i. The curve of v_L plotted against time is shown in Fig. 10-6.

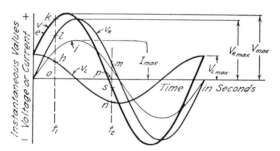

Fig. 10-6. Variation with time of the instantaneous values of the current and voltages in Fig. 10-5.

In Fig. 10-6, during the period of time in which the curve of v_R is above the horizontal axis there is a drop of potential from c to d in the circuit. Likewise during the parts of the cycle in which v_L is positive there is a drop of potential from terminal f to terminal g of the inductance element L. Conversely during the parts of the cycle in which v_R is negative there is a drop of potential from d to c; and when v_L is negative there is a drop of potential from g to f. Therefore, at the instant indicated by t_1 in Fig. 10-6, v_R is equal to $+ol$, and there is a drop of potential from c to d in the circuit. At the same instant, v_L is equal to $+oh$, and there is a drop of potential from f to g in the circuit. The potential difference between terminals a and b can be determined by use of equation (10-6). Thus

$$e = ol + oh$$
$$= ok = v.$$

The fact that e has a positive value indicates that there is a rise in potential from a to b of the circuit at the instant t_1. In accordance with Kirchhoff's voltage law, this rise must be equal to $v = ok$, the total drop of potential from c to g at the instant t_1. In (a) of Fig. 10-7 the actual directions of the potential rise of the generator and the potential drops across the resistance element, the inductance element, and the entire circuit at the instant t_1 are indicated. The actual current direction at this instant is also shown.

If another instant such as time t_2 in Fig. 10-6 is selected, v_R is equal to $+pm$, and there is a drop of potential from c to d in the circuit of Fig. 10-5. At this instant v_L is equal to $-pn$, and there is a drop of potential from g to f in the circuit. From equation (10-6)

$$e = pm +(-pn)$$
$$= -ps = v.$$

Since in magnitude pn is greater than pm, e has a negative value, which shows that the potential rise of the generator is actually from b to a

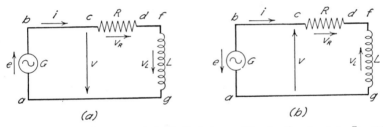

Fig. 10-7. Actual directions of the indicated quantities for the circuit in Fig. 10-5 (a) at the time t_1, shown in Fig. 10-6, and (b) at the time t_2, shown in Fig. 10-6.

at the instant t_2. In (b) of Fig. 10-7 are shown the actual directions of the potential rise of the generator and the potential drops across the resistance element, the inductance element, and the entire circuit at the instant t_2. The actual current direction at this instant is also shown.

By proceeding in a manner similar to the foregoing, enough points, such as k and s, can be determined to make it possible to plot a curve of e, the potential rise between the terminals of the generator. Such a curve is shown in Fig. 10-6. During the period when the ordinates of the curve are positive, there is a rise of potential from terminal a to terminal b. In the interval during which the ordinates of the curve are negative, there is a rise of potential from b to a.

7. D-C Circuits and Kirchhoff's Laws. In the discussion up to this point, the examples used are those in which the voltages and currents are not constant but vary in magnitude from instant to instant and in

which the directions of the rises and falls of potential, as well as the directions of the currents, reverse at regular intervals.

When the power sources in a circuit supply direct current and only the steady-state condition of the circuit is considered, the application of Kirchhoff's laws is simplified, because the magnitude and direction of the current in any branch and the difference of potential between the terminals of an element remain unchanged as long as no alterations occur in the circuit elements. Furthermore, in such a case the potential drop across a pure inductance element is always zero. This fact should be clear from an inspection of equation (10-4), for, if the current does not change in magnitude, di/dt is zero. Thus, if a branch of the

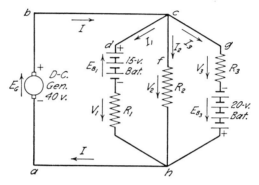

Fig. 10-8.   D-c network containing resistances, batteries, and a generator.

circuit contains a coil, only the resistance of the wire of the coil need be considered. A condenser in a branch of the circuit has the effect of a resistance of infinite magnitude; hence no current can flow in the branch, and the latter need not be considered as a part of the circuit when applying Kirchhoff's laws. For steady-state conditions, d-c circuits are therefore resistance circuits only.

In Fig. 10-8 a circuit network containing several branches is shown. The current directions to be considered positive are indicated by the arrows. Also shown are the directions to be considered positive for the potential rises of the generator and batteries and for the potential drops across the resistance elements. These choices for the directions are logical, since they are the same as the actual directions, each of which in this case can be determined by inspection. Not always can the actual directions of the currents be determined by inspection. In such instances the directions to be considered positive are arbitrarily chosen, and whenever the circuit solution gives a negative value for a current or potential drop the actual direction is opposite to that chosen as positive.

The application of Kirchhoff's current law to the currents at junction c gives

$$I = I_1 + I_2 + I_3.$$

Similarly at junction h

$$I_1 + I_2 + I_3 = I.$$

Now consider the loop $abcdha$. Progressing around this closed circuit in a clockwise direction and applying the voltage law, it is seen that

$$E_G - E_{B_1} = V_1,$$

or

$$40 - 15 = I_1 R_1.$$

Similarly for loop $abcgha$

$$E_G + E_{B_3} = V_3,$$

or

$$40 + 20 = I_3 R_3,$$

and for loop $hdcgh$

$$E_{B_1} + E_{B_3} = -V_1 + V_3,$$

or

$$15 + 20 = -I_1 R_1 + I_3 R_3.$$

It should be fully appreciated that the minus signs in the above equations are necessary because travel was opposite to the indicated positive directions for these quantities.

8. Double-Subscript Notation. The use of double subscripts in connection with the symbols for current and voltage has been found from experience to be a valuable aid in avoiding confusion in the solution of electrical circuits. However, unless the full meaning of the subscripts is thoroughly understood, their use generally leads to added confusion and incorrect solutions of the circuit problems.

Fig. 10-9. Simple circuit for use in the interpretation of double-subscript notation.

In connection with the circuit shown in Fig. 10-9, the symbols i_{CD} and i_{DC} refer to the instantaneous values of the current in the element between terminals C and D. The order in which the subscripts occur is of great importance, since the first of the two letters designates which of the two terminals has been chosen as the reference. Hence, in the case of the symbol i_{CD}, terminal C is the reference terminal. The symbol i_{CD} is a brief method of indicating that the current is considered positive in the direction from terminal C to terminal D. It should be understood and fully appreciated that i_{CD} has both positive and negative values. This may be seen by referring to the graph of i_{CD} plotted against time in (a) of Fig. 10-10. In the time interval from t_0 to t_1, the current is positive and is actually in the direction from terminal C to terminal D. In the time interval from t_1 to t_2, the current is negative and is actually in the direction from terminal D to terminal C.

The vector $\bar{I}_{CD}$, representing the effective value of i_{CD}, is shown in (b) of the figure. On the basis of the foregoing discussion and the use of a vector for representing a sine wave, it should be apparent that the subscripts of the symbol $\bar{I}_{CD}$ indicate that the instantaneous values of the current in the element between terminals C and D are considered positive in the direction from terminal C to terminal D.

Now consider the symbol i_{DC}, in which the subscripts are in the reverse order. This symbol indicates that terminal D is the reference

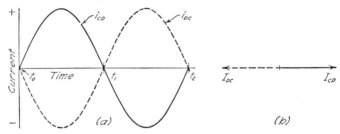

Fig. 10-10. Graphical illustrations of the significance of double-subscript notation (a) applied to instantaneous values of current and (b) applied to vector values of current.

terminal and that the current is considered positive in the direction from terminal D to terminal C. As pointed out above, the current is actually in the direction from terminal C to terminal D in the time interval from t_0 to t_1 and is in the direction from terminal D to terminal C in the interval from t_1 to t_2. Hence in the latter interval i_{DC} has positive values, and in the interval from t_0 to t_1 it has negative values. In the figure the time variation of i_{DC} is shown by the dotted curve. By comparing this curve with that for i_{CD}, it will be noted that the two are opposite in phase. Therefore the effective value I_{DC}, when represented as a vector, must be drawn in the opposite direction to $\bar{I}_{CD}$, as shown in (b) of the figure. It follows from the preceding discussion that

$$i_{CD} = -i_{DC},$$
$$i_{DC} = -i_{CD},$$
$$\bar{I}_{CD} = -\bar{I}_{DC},$$
and
$$\bar{I}_{DC} = -\bar{I}_{CD}.$$

In reference to Fig. 10-9 the symbol v_{CD} represents the instantaneous values of the potential drop across the element connected to terminals C and D; likewise the term v_{DC} also represents the instantaneous values of the potential drop between these same two terminals.

But, again, the order in which the subscripts occur has a very definite meaning. When the subscript C precedes subscript D, then terminal C is the reference terminal. The symbol v_{CD} indicates that the potential drop between terminals C and D is considered positive in the direction from terminal C to terminal D. The graph of v_{CD} plotted against time is shown in (a) of Fig. 10-11. Thus, in the time interval between t_0 and t_1, v_{CD} has positive values, indicating that terminal C is at a higher potential than terminal D and that there is actually a fall of potential from C to D during this interval. In the time interval between t_1 and t_2, terminal C is at a lower potential than terminal D, and there is actually a rise of potential from C to D. However, a rise of potential is a negative drop; hence v_{CD} has negative values in this interval, as indicated by the graph.

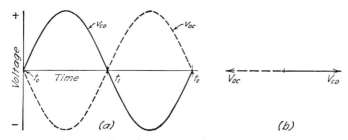

Fig. 10-11. Graphical illustrations of the significance of double-subscript notation (a) applied to instantaneous values of voltage drop and (b) applied to vector values of voltage drop.

The vector $\bar{V}_{CD}$, representing the effective value of v_{CD}, is shown in (b) of the figure. It should be apparent from the preceding discussion that the subscripts of the symbol $\bar{V}_{CD}$ indicate that the instantaneous values of the potential drop between terminals C and D are considered positive in the direction from terminal C to terminal D.

Now consider the term v_{DC}, in which the order of the letters of the subscript is reversed. When the subscript is written in this form, terminal D is indicated as the selected reference terminal, and the symbol v_{DC} means that the potential drop between terminals C and D is considered positive in the direction from terminal D to terminal C. From (a) of Fig. 10-11 it is obvious that, since terminal C is at a higher potential than terminal D in the time interval t_0 to t_1, there is actually a rise of potential, or a negative drop, from terminal D to terminal C during this same interval. Hence, the graph of v_{DC} between t_0 and t_1 has negative values, as indicated in the figure by the dotted curve. On the other hand, in the time interval from t_1 to t_2, v_{DC} has positive values, for, as has been shown, there is actually a drop of potential from terminal D to terminal C in this interval. The curve representing the voltage v_{DC}, accordingly, is opposite in phase to the curve of v_{CD}. The effective value V_{DC}, therefore, when represented as a vector, must be drawn in the opposite direction to $\bar{V}_{CD}$, as shown in (b) of the figure. In view of the foregoing

$$v_{CD} = -v_{DC},$$
$$v_{DC} = -v_{CD},$$
$$\bar{V}_{CD} = -\bar{V}_{DC},$$

and
$$\bar{V}_{DC} = -\bar{V}_{CD}.$$

In connection with the circuit shown in Fig. 10-9, the symbol e_{AB} represents the instantaneous value of the emf between terminals A and B, and the order of the subscripts indicates that the potential rise is considered positive in the direction from terminal A to terminal B. The symbol $\bar{E}_{AB}$ is the vector representation of the effective value of e_{AB}. Relations similar to those established for the currents and the potential drops in the circuit can also be established for the potential rises. Thus

$$e_{AB} = -e_{BA},$$
$$e_{BA} = -e_{AB},$$
$$\bar{E}_{AB} = -\bar{E}_{BA},$$

and
$$\bar{E}_{BA} = -\bar{E}_{AB}.$$

Double subscripts can also be applied to the symbols used for the currents and voltages in d-c circuits, the order of the subscripts having the same significance as in a-c circuits.

9. Single-Subscript Notation. The use of single subscripts with symbols representing instantaneous and d-c values of currents and voltages is illustrated in preceding sections of this chapter. When single subscripts are applied to the vector representation of a current or voltage, the direction in which the instantaneous values are considered positive must be indicated by an arrow on the circuit diagram. Thus, for Fig. 10-12 the following notations are equivalent:

$$\bar{E}_1 = \bar{E}_{BA}.$$
$$\bar{I}_2 = \bar{I}_{AC}.$$
$$\bar{I}_3 = \bar{I}_{DC}.$$
$$\bar{I}_4 = \bar{I}_{DB}.$$
$$\bar{V}_2 = \bar{V}_{AC}.$$
$$\bar{V}_3 = \bar{V}_{DC}.$$
$$\bar{V}_4 = \bar{V}_{DB}.$$

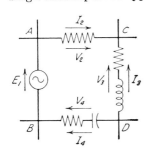

Fig. 10-12. Portion of a network for use in the interpretation of single-subscript notation.

10. Adaptation of Kirchhoff's Laws to Vector Quantities. As originally stated, Kirchhoff's laws apply to instantaneous values of current and voltage. However, in the case of currents and voltages that vary sinusoidally with time, the laws are of more practical use when considered with respect to their effective values represented in vector form.

It can be shown that, if a relation involving algebraic addition or subtraction exists between the instantaneous values of several sine waves, the same relation exists vectorially between their effective values. Therefore Kirchhoff's laws may be restated for sinusoidally varying currents and voltages as follows:

CURRENT LAW: *The vector sum of the currents in the direction toward a junction point of two or more branches of an electric circuit is equal to the vector sum of the currents in the direction away from the junction point.*

VOLTAGE LAW: *The vector sum of the potential rises encountered in going around any closed electric circuit is equal to the vector sum of the potential drops.*

11. Use of Double-Subscript Notation in the Application of Kirchhoff's Laws. Consider the circuit of Fig. 10-13. The application of Kirchhoff's voltage law for instantaneous values gives

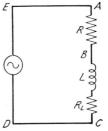

$$e_{DE} = v_{AB} + v_{BC} = v_{AC}. \qquad (10\text{-}10)$$

Application of the voltage law for vector quantities gives

$$\bar{E}_{DE} = \bar{V}_{AB} + \bar{V}_{BC} = \bar{V}_{AC}. \qquad (10\text{-}11)$$

Equations (10-10) and (10-11) are illustrated graphically in (a) and (b), respectively, of Fig. 10-14.

Fig. 10-13. Series circuit for use in applying double-subscript notation when using Kirchhoff's voltage law.

The instantaneous values of the current in the circuit are plotted in (a) of the figure. In accordance with the meaning of double subscripts and the significance of their order, the actual direction of the current i_{AB} in the resistor R of the circuit is from A toward B in the time interval from t_0 to t_1. Since element R consists of resistance only, there must be a drop of potential from terminal A to terminal B during this same time interval. Hence the curve of v_{AB} has positive instantaneous values in the interval from t_0 to t_1, as shown in the figure.

In the case of the inductance element between terminals B and C of the circuit, there is actually a potential drop from terminal B to terminal C during a portion, t_2 to t_3, of the time interval during which the current i_{BC} is negative, or actually in the direction from C to B. This follows from the fact that in an element containing inductance the current lags the voltage drop across the element, or, conversely, the voltage drop leads the current. Hence in the figure the curve of v_{BC} is shown leading the curve of i_{BC}.

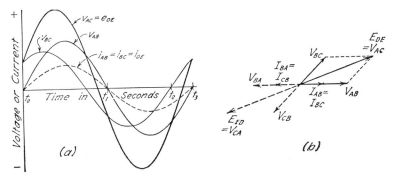

Fig. 10-14. Graphical representations of the relations between the current and voltages in Fig. 10-13 (a) by means of instantaneous values and (b) by means of vector values.

The curve of e_{DE} was determined by the use of equation (10-10). When the values of e_{DE} are positive, there is actually a rise in potential from terminal D to terminal E of the generator. When the values are negative, there is actually a rise in potential from E to D.

The vector $\bar{I}_{AB} = \bar{I}_{BC}$, representing the effective value of $i_{AB} = i_{BC}$,

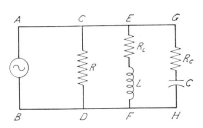

Fig. 10-15. Parallel circuit for use in applying double-subscript notation when using Kirchhoff's current law.

is drawn in (b) of the figure as the reference vector. Since v_{AB} is in phase with i_{AB}, the vector $\bar{V}_{AB}$, representing the effective value of v_{AB}, is drawn in phase with $\bar{I}_{AB}$. Since v_{BC} leads $i_{BC} = i_{AB}$, the vector $\bar{V}_{BC}$, representing the effective value of v_{BC}, is drawn leading $\bar{I}_{BC} = \bar{I}_{AB}$ by the phase angle represented by the time interval between the maximum values of v_{BC} and i_{BC}.

The vector $\bar{E}_{DE}$, representing the effective value of e_{DE}, was determined by the use of equation (10-11).

In a manner similar to that discussed above, double subscripts can be used in writing the voltage and current equations for a multi-branch circuit. Thus, in the circuit shown in Fig. 10-15,

$$e_{BA} = v_{CD} = v_{EF} = v_{GH},$$

and
$$\bar{E}_{BA} = \bar{V}_{CD} = \bar{V}_{EF} = \bar{V}_{GH}.$$
Also

and
$$i_{AC} = i_{CD} + i_{CE} = i_{CD} + i_{EF} + i_{GH}, \qquad (10\text{-}12)$$
$$\bar{I}_{AC} = \bar{I}_{CD} + \bar{I}_{CE} = \bar{I}_{CD} + \bar{I}_{EF} + \bar{I}_{GH}. \qquad (10\text{-}13)$$

The above equations are illustrated graphically in (a) and (b) of Fig. 10-16.

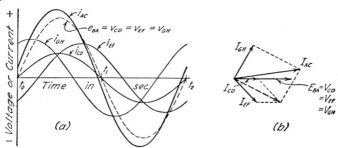

Fig. 10-16. Graphical representations of the relations between the currents and voltages in Fig. 10-15 (a) by means of instantaneous values and (b) by means of vector values.

Since branch CD of the circuit contains resistance only, the graph of i_{CD} is drawn in phase with that of v_{CD} in Fig. 10-16(a). The graph of i_{EF} is shown lagging that of v_{EF}, since the branch contains inductance as well as resistance. The branch GH contains capacitance as well as resistance, and hence the graph of i_{GH} must be shown leading that of v_{GH}. The vectors representing the effective values of the voltage and currents are shown in (b) of the figure. The curve of i_{AC} and the vector $\bar{I}_{AC}$ were determined by use of equations (10-12) and (10-13), respectively.

As an example of the use of double subscripts in writing the voltage and current equations for a complex a-c circuit, consider the circuit shown in Fig. 10-17. In this circuit the various opposition elements are

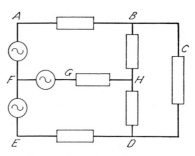

Fig. 10-17. Network for use in applying double-subscript notation when using Kirchhoff's laws.

indicated by the blocks and the generators by the usual symbol. By use of vector quantities in applying Kirchhoff's laws to the indicated junction points and loops, the following equations are obtained:

Junction F: $\bar{I}_{EF} + \bar{I}_{AF} + \bar{I}_{GF} = 0.$
Junction B: $\bar{I}_{AB} + \bar{I}_{HB} + \bar{I}_{CB} = 0.$

Junction H: $\bar{I}_{GH} + \bar{I}_{BH} + \bar{I}_{DH} = 0$.

Junction D: $\bar{I}_{HD} + \bar{I}_{CD} + \bar{I}_{ED} = 0$.

Loop $FABHGF$: $\bar{E}_{FA} + \bar{E}_{GF} = \bar{V}_{AB} + \bar{V}_{BH} + \bar{V}_{HG}$.

Loop $EFGHDE$: $\bar{E}_{EF} + \bar{E}_{FG} = \bar{V}_{GH} + \bar{V}_{HD} + \bar{V}_{DE}$.

Loop $BCDHB$: $0 = \bar{V}_{CD} + \bar{V}_{DH} + \bar{V}_{HB}$.

Laboratory Problem No. 10-1

KIRCHHOFF'S LAWS APPLIED TO A D-C CIRCUIT

Laboratory

Set up the circuit shown in Fig. 10-18, using the circuit constants designated by the instructor. Make only the measurements indicated

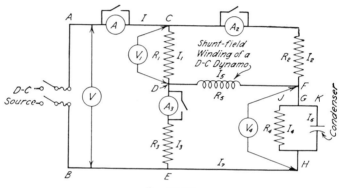

Fig. 10-18.

by the instruments shown in the diagram. If the voltage of the source fluctuates, either simultaneous readings of the instrument indications should be made or some form of voltage control should be used to maintain the voltage across A and B constant. After the instruments are connected so that up-scale deflections are obtained, show on the data-sheet diagram which terminal of each instrument is marked with a + sign.

Report

A. On the circuit diagram in the report designate the various currents as indicated in Fig. 10-18. Draw solid-line arrows to indicate the current directions in those branches in which the directions are actually known. Use dashed-line arrows in those branches in which the current directions are unknown and must be assumed.

B. Write the current equations for junction points C, D, E, F, and G. From these equations and the experimental data determine I_1, I_4, I_5, and I_7.

Adjacent to the dashed-line arrows originally drawn, draw solid-line arrows indicating the actual directions of the currents.

C. Using the symbol V_1 to represent the voltage drop across R_1, V_2 that across R_2, and so forth, write the voltage equations for loops $ACDFGHEBA$, $ACDEBA$, and $ACFGHEBA$. From these equations and the experimental data calculate V_2, V_3, and V_5.

Check the correctness of the calculated values by writing the voltage equation for loop $ACFDEBA$ and substituting the calculated values of V_2, V_3, and V_5 and the measured value of V in the equation.

D. Determine the power loss in each branch of the circuit. From these values calculate the total power input to the circuit.

Check this value of input power with that obtained when the measured values of impressed voltage and line current are used.

E. Write in symbol form the current equations for junction points C, D, E, F, and G, using double-subscript notation.

F. Write in symbol form the voltage equations for loops $ACDFGH-EBA$, $ACDEBA$, and $ACFGHEBA$, using double-subscript notation.

Laboratory Problem No. 10-2

KIRCHHOFF'S LAWS APPLIED TO A-C CIRCUITS IN TERMS OF INSTANTANEOUS VALUES

Laboratory

If the voltage of the source to be used in this problem fluctuates, either simultaneous readings of the instrument indications should be

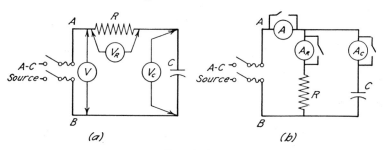

(a)   (b)

Fig. 10-19.

made or some form of voltage control should be used to maintain the voltage across A and B in the circuits of Fig. 10-19 constant.

1. Set up the circuit shown in (a) of the figure. R and C should be of such values that the voltages V_R and V_C will be of comparable magnitude. Read and record the indications of the three voltmeters.

2. Set up the circuit shown in (b) of the figure, using the same R and C as used in 1. Record the indications of the three ammeters.

Report

A. On a schematic diagram of the circuit used in 1, indicate the directions to be considered positive for the instantaneous current i in the circuit, the instantaneous voltage drop v_R across R, the instantaneous voltage drop v_C across C, and the instantaneous voltage drop v across the circuit.

Assuming that the instantaneous values of the circuit current varied sinusoidally with time ($i = I_{max} \sin \omega t$), make a table of the values of v_R and v_C based upon the measured values V_R and V_C. Calculate values of v_R and v_C for increments of 15° from $\omega t = 0$ to $\omega t = 360°$. Using Kirchhoff's voltage law, determine the value of v for each value of ωt previously used and include them in the table. From the values in the table plot curves of v_R, v_C, and v vs ωt.

B. On a schematic diagram of the circuit used in 2, indicate the directions to be considered positive for the instantaneous voltage drop v across the circuit, the instantaneous current i in the line supplying the parallel branches, the instantaneous current i_R in R, and the instantaneous current i_C in C.

Assuming that the instantaneous values of the voltage drop across the circuit varied sinusoidally with time ($v = V_{max} \sin \omega t$), make a table of the values of i_R and i_C for increments of 15° from $\omega t = 0$ to $\omega t = 360°$. Using Kirchhoff's current law, determine the value of i for each value of ωt previously used and include them in the table. From the values in the table plot curves of i_R, i_C, and i vs ωt.

C. From the curve of v obtained in **A**, determine the effective value V. How does this calculated value compare with the value measured in 1?

D. From the curve of i obtained in **B**, determine the effective value I. How does this calculated value compare with the value measured in 2?

Laboratory Problem No. 10-3

KIRCHHOFF'S LAWS APPLIED TO AN A-C CIRCUIT IN TERMS OF VECTOR VALUES

Laboratory

In order to obtain good results a well-regulated source of power should be used.

Set up the circuit shown in Fig. 10-20, using the circuit elements designated by the instructor. Measure all of the line voltages and currents. Also measure the current and voltage of each circuit element.

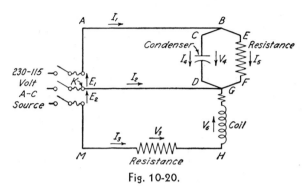

Fig. 10-20.

Report

A. In Fig. 10-20 the currents and voltages are identified by means of single-subscript notation. For each of these quantities, set up in symbol form an equation using single-subscript notation on one side and double-subscript notation on the other; for example, $\bar{I}_1 = \bar{I}_{AB}$, $\bar{V}_4 = \bar{V}_{BG} = \bar{V}_{CD} = \bar{V}_{EF}$, and so forth.

B. Using single-subscript notation, write the following:

(1) Kirchhoff's current-law equations for junction points B and G.

(2) Kirchhoff's voltage-law equations for loops $MKABEGHM$ and $MKGHM$.

C. Using the data obtained in the laboratory, draw to scale the following:

(1) Common-origin vector diagram showing the currents entering and leaving point G. Use the vector $\bar{V}_4$ for reference. Clearly show all construction lines.

(2) Common-origin vector diagram showing vectors $\bar{V}_3$, $\bar{V}_6$, and $\bar{E}_2$. Use the vector $\bar{I}_3$ for reference. Clearly show all construction lines.

CHAPTER 11
THE ELECTRODYNAMOMETER WATTMETER

1. Theory of Operation. An instrument to be useful as a means for measuring power should be one that will indicate average power. Such

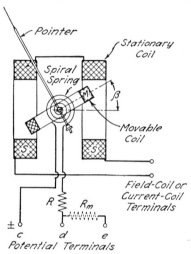

an instrument is shown schematically in Fig. 11-1. This instrument, which is an electrodynamometer type, consists of a stationary coil or set of stationary coils SS and a movable coil M, to which a pointer is attached. The coil set SS is called the *field*, or *current, coil* and coil M the *potential coil*. As is the case in nearly all indicating instruments, spiral springs provide the restraining force against which the moving element acts.

To measure the power delivered to a circuit or part of a circuit, the coils of the instrument are connected in the circuit as shown in Fig. 11-2.

Fig. 11-1. Schematic diagram of an electrodynamometer-type wattmeter.

In this circuit the wattmeter is shown connected in such a manner as to measure the power delivered to the load indicated, a load being any circuit or part of a circuit to which energy is supplied. In the branch containing coil M, r denotes the resistance of the potential coil and R is a high-resistance element that is noninductive. The resistor R is part of the instrument and is contained within the instrument case.

In order to simplify the analysis that follows, let it be assumed for the present that R is so great compared to the opposition offered to current by the

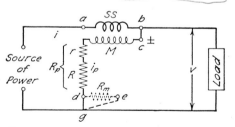

Fig. 11-2. Wattmeter coils connected in a circuit for making a power measurement.

130

load that the current in the potential coil M is negligible compared with that in the load. Under this condition the current in coil SS is the same as that in the load. The effect of this assumption on the wattmeter indication is discussed in detail in a following section of this chapter. Also for the sake of simplicity, let it be assumed that the magnetic field produced by the stationary coil SS is uniformly distributed and parallel to the axis of coil SS in the space within which coil M moves. It will become evident from the following discussion that any deviation from this condition in a particular instrument is taken care of in the calibration of the instrument scale. Since the magnetic field produced by coil SS is assumed to be uniformly distributed and parallel to the axis of the coil, the active sides of the movable coil M will be in a field of constant flux density regardless of the position of the coil. The force acting on each side of the movable coil M at any particular instant is proportional to the product of the current i_p in the movable coil and the flux density of the magnetic field produced by the current i in coil SS. The flux density of the magnetic field is directly proportional to the current i, and hence the instantaneous force acting on the movable coil can be expressed as

$$\text{Instantaneous force} = k i_p i. \qquad (11\text{-}1)$$

The inductance of coil M is so small compared to the sum $r + R$ that its effect on the instantaneous current i_p in coil M is generally negligible. Under this condition, the current i_p in coil M is directly proportional to v, the instantaneous potential difference between the terminals of the load. Accordingly, the instantaneous force on each side of coil M is

$$\text{Instantaneous force} = k' v i. \qquad (11\text{-}2)$$

On the basis of the assumptions made regarding the magnetic field produced by coil SS, the instantaneous torque acting on the movable coil M is given by

$$\text{Instantaneous torque} = k'' v i \cos \beta, \qquad (11\text{-}3)$$

where β is the angle between the plane of the movable coil and the axis of the stationary coil at the instant under consideration.

Because of the inertia and damping of the moving element, it cannot follow rapid periodic variations in instantaneous torque but will take a fixed position at the point at which the average torque is equal to the counter torque of the restraining springs. Since the counter torque is usually directly proportional to the angle through which the movable coil has moved—that is, to the pointer deflection—the final pointer deflection varies directly with the average torque acting on the movable coil.

In a d-c circuit the instantaneous values of v and i do not change for any fixed set of circuit conditions. Thus, when the instrument shown in Fig. 11-1 is connected in a d-c circuit, the average and instantaneous torques acting on the movable coil are equal. Also, since v and i are constant, the product vi is equal to the d-c power. Then, in accordance with equation (11-3), the average torque acting on the movable coil when it has come to rest is

$$T_{av} = k''vi \cos \beta = k''P \cos \beta, \qquad (11\text{-}4)$$

where β is the angle between the plane of the movable coil and the axis of the stationary coil. Thus, the final pointer position depends upon the d-c power. By supplying the instrument with a suitably calibrated scale, it can be used to measure d-c power directly.

When the instrument is used in connection with an a-c circuit, the instantaneous torque acting on the movable coil will not be constant, owing to the variations in v and i, even though the circuit conditions remain fixed. However, because of the inertia and damping of the moving element, it cannot respond to the variations in instantaneous torque when these variations occur as rapidly as they do in circuits supplied with power of commercial frequency. Under this condition the movable element assumes a position determined by the average torque. According to equation (11-3), the average torque acting on the movable coil in the final position is

$$T_{av} = k'' \, (\text{av } vi) \cos \beta, \qquad (11\text{-}5)$$

where β is the angle for the final position. In the above equation (av vi) is the average power delivered to the circuit, so that

$$T_{av} = k''P_{av} \cos \beta, \qquad (11\text{-}6)$$

and the final pointer deflection depends upon the average a-c power. The electrodynamometer instrument shown in Fig. 11-1 can therefore be used as a wattmeter for making measurements of either d-c or a-c power.

2. Wattmeter Rating. Since the current coil SS is connected in series with the circuit, its opposition to the current in the circuit must be kept low. For this reason, it is made of as few turns as practicable and of a size of conductor that is large enough to carry safely the current in the circuit. In order to keep the mass of the movable coil small, coil M, on the other hand, is constructed of a small-size conductor.   In view of these facts, it is only logical that a wattmeter of given construction must be rated so that overloading of either coil is not likely to occur.   The value of current that the current coil can carry safely is determined, among other things, by the size of the wire with which it is wound.   Hence each wattmeter must have a current rating. By the same logic, since the current in the potential coil is proportional to the voltage applied to the potential terminals of the instrument, the value of voltage that may be applied safely is limited by the size of the potential-coil conductor and of the conductor of which the resistance element R is made.   Accordingly, every wattmeter has a voltage rating.   In addition to the current and voltage ratings, the instrument also has a watt rating.   Referring to Fig. 11-2, let it be assumed that the current coil SS has been designed to carry a current of 20 amperes and that the potential coil M and resistor R have been so designed that 150 volts can safely be applied to the potential terminals c and d.   Let it further be assumed that a full-scale deflection of the instrument pointer occurs when a d-c current of 20 amperes flows in coil SS and 150 volts are applied to the potential terminals.   In such an event, the power supplied to the load would be $P = VI = 150 \times 20 = 3000$ watts.   This instrument would, then, have the following rating:

20 amp

150 volts

3000 watts

The reader should not be misled by the above example into thinking that the watt rating is always determined by the product of the voltage and current ratings.   In a-c circuits the power supplied to a circuit is not necessarily equal to the product of the effective values of voltage and current.   In order to calculate the power delivered to an a-c circuit, the above-mentioned product must be multiplied by a number between zero and one called the *power factor*.   Usually the power factor is less than one, its value being determined by the circuit conditions.   If the voltage impressed on the load of Fig. 11-2 were 150 volts, the current taken by the load 20 amperes, and the power factor of the load 0.2, the power delivered to the load would be $P = 150 \times 20 \times .2 = 600$ watts.   If the wattmeter discussed above were used to measure this power, the wattmeter indication would be 600 watts. This reading would be but one fifth of full scale.   In this lower part of the scale, the instrument and observational errors might result in an observed value having a percent error too high to be tolerated.   For this reason, wattmeters are designed and constructed with like voltage and current ratings but widely different watt ratings. For the case just discussed, an instrument having the following rating would be satisfactory:

20 amp
150 volts
1000 watts

This type of wattmeter is commonly referred to as a *low-power-factor wattmeter*, this designation meaning that it is designed primarily for use in low-power-factor circuits. It should be noted that such an instrument will show a full-scale deflection whenever the power is 1000 watts, regardless of the values of current, voltage, and power factor. Hence this wattmeter cannot be used to measure power in circuits in which the current is 20 amperes and the voltage 150 volts unless the power factor of the load is equal to or less than 0.33. It can, however, be used in circuits in which the current or voltage or both are less than rated values and the power factor greater than 0.33, provided that the power is equal to or less than 1000 watts.

3. Multiple Rating and Multiplying Factors. The resistance between the potential terminals c and d of the wattmeter shown in Fig. 11-2 is

$$R_p = r + R.$$

Now let another resistance R_m equal to R_p be added in series with the potential coil, as indicated by the dotted lines in Figs. 11-1 and 11-2. The resistance between terminals c and e is twice that between c and d. If connection is made from g to e instead of to d in Fig. 11-2, and the voltage across the load remains unchanged, the current in the potential coil M will be only half its former value, and the deflection of the instrument pointer will be reduced so that it indicates only half as much power as it formerly did. Changing the connection to the wattmeter has not, however, changed the amount of power delivered to the load. Therefore when terminal e is used, a multiplying factor of two must be applied to the wattmeter indication unless the instrument has two scales, one for use when the connection is to terminal d and the other when the connection is to terminal e.

Since the resistance between terminals c and e is twice that between terminals e and d, twice as much voltage can be safely applied to the potential terminals of the instrument when terminal e is used as could be applied before the resistance R_m was added. Hence the wattmeter will now have two voltage ratings, one applying to terminal d and the other applying to terminal e. Thus, if such a resistance as R_m were added to the wattmeter used as the first example in the discussion of ratings, the new rating would be

20 amp

150/300 volts

3000/6000 watts

If a resistance R_m were added to the wattmeter of the second example the new rating would be

20 amp

150/300 volts

1000/2000 watts

The added resistance R_m is called a *voltage multiplier,* or just a *multiplier.* It is usually contained within the instrument case, one end being permanently connected to the resistance R and the other to a terminal post, as indicated in Fig. 11-1. It is not unusual for multipliers to be self-contained. In such cases all connections to the multiplier are made externally by the user. In view of the foregoing,

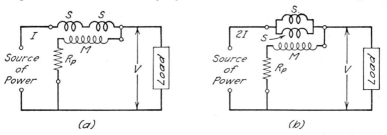

Fig. 11-3.   Sections of the current coil of a wattmeter (a) connected in series and (b) connected in parallel.

it should be clear that by the introduction of additional multipliers the voltage and power ratings can be further extended.

In Fig. 11-1 the stationary sections SS of the current coil are shown connected in series. If these sections were connected in parallel, the current capacity would be doubled, for each section would still be capable of carrying the same current as when the sections were connected in series. Thus, if facilities are provided to allow the coil sections to be connected either in series or in parallel, the instrument can be given two current ratings, one for the series connection and the other for the parallel connection.

Let it be assumed that each coil is capable of safely carrying a current of I amperes. With the two sections of SS connected in series the wattmeter can be used in a circuit in which the current is I amperes, as shown in (a) of Fig. 11-3. With the two coil sections connected in parallel, as shown in (b) of the figure, the current in the circuit can be doubled without having the current in each coil section exceed I amperes.   In the latter case, however, the magnetic field set up by the current in the coil sections will be no greater than when the sections are connected in series.   This follows from the fact that the magneto-motive force is the same in each instance, for the current per coil section is the same in both instances and the number of turns per section has remained unchanged.   Thus the deflection of the instrument pointer will be the same when the coil sections are connected in parallel and the current in the circuit is $2I$ as it is when the sections are connected in series and the current in the circuit is only I amperes. However, in the case of the parallel connection twice as much power is delivered to the load as in the case of the series connection.   A multiplying factor of two must therefore be applied to the pointer indication when sections SS are connected in parallel unless the instrument has a second scale for use under this condition.   That twice as much power is supplied when the current is $2I$ is based upon the assumption that the character of the load and the impressed voltage remain unchanged.

As an example of a wattmeter with both multiple current and multiple voltage ratings, assume that the 20-amp, 150-volt, 3000-watt instrument originally considered has its current and voltage ratings doubled by the methods discussed.   The new rating will then be

20/40 amp
150/300 volts
3000/6000/12000 watts

The correct scale to read or the scale-multiplying factor to use for various connections of the current and potential terminals are given below:

Terminals Used	Scale to Be Read If Instrument Has Scales of 3000, 6000, and 12,000 Watts	Multiplying Factor K If Instrument Has One Scale of 3000 Watts	Multiplying Factor K If Instrument Has One Scale of 6000 Watts	Multiplying Factor K If Instrument Has One Scale of 12,000 Watts
20 amp and 150 volt....	3000	1	$\frac{1}{2}$	$\frac{1}{4}$
20 amp and 300 volt....	6000	2	1	$\frac{1}{2}$
40 amp and 150 volt....	6000	2	1	$\frac{1}{2}$
40 amp and 300 volt....	12,000	4	2	1

It should be noted that the scale-multiplying factors for a given wattmeter depend upon the watt scale of the instrument.

It is common practice among manufacturers of wattmeters to state the multiplying factors in print on the instrument scale or on the instrument lid if and when such factors need to be applied. As previously indicated, some wattmeters are provided with several scales, so that the necessity for multiplying factors is eliminated.

4. Power Loss in the Wattmeter. In the explanation of the principle of operation of the wattmeter it was assumed that the current in the potential circuit cd of Fig. 11-4 was so small in comparison with that in the load that it need not be considered. This assumption was made at the time only for the purpose of simplifying the discussion. It should, however, be quite evident that at any selected instant the current i in coil SS is the sum of the current i_L in the load and the current i_p in the potential coil M.

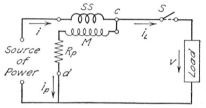

Fig. 11-4. Wattmeter coils connected so that the true power delivered to a load can be obtained by making a correction for the power loss in the wattmeter potential circuit.

In order to determine the effect of i_p on the wattmeter indication, let the switch S in Fig. 11-4 be opened. In this case the current in coil SS is i_p; and, as indicated by equation (11-2), the instantaneous force on the movable coil M is determined by the product $i_p v$, v being the instantaneous voltage across the potential terminals of the instrument. It has been shown that the deflection of a wattmeter pointer depends upon the average torque acting on the movable coil. According to equation (11-5), the average torque is directly proportional, among other things, to the average of the instantaneous forces acting on the sides of the movable coil. Hence, with switch S open, the wattmeter indicates the average of $i_p v$, which is the average power supplied to the potential circuit cd. Since the effect of the inductance of coil M is negligible compared to that of the resistance R_p of the potential circuit, $i_p = v/R_p$, and the average power supplied to the potential circuit is

$$(\text{av } i_p v) = \frac{(\text{av } v^2)}{R_p} = \frac{V^2}{R_p}, \tag{11-7}$$

where V is the effective value of the voltage across terminals c and d of the potential circuit. Thus, although no power is delivered to the load, the instrument pointer is deflected, the power indicated being that which is supplied to the potential-coil circuit of the instrument.

Now let the switch S be closed. The instantaneous current in coil SS will now have been increased by the amount i_L, the current in the load. The instantaneous force acting to move the instrument pointer is now determined by the product iv, and hence the wattmeter now indicates the power represented by the average of iv. Since $i = i_L + i_p$,

$$\text{(av } iv) = \text{(av } i_L v) + \text{(av } i_p v). \tag{11-8}$$

The first term on the right-hand side of this equation represents the power supplied to the load, and the second term represents the power supplied to the potential circuit of the wattmeter. If W is used to represent the power indicated by the wattmeter—that is, the actual wattmeter indication multiplied by any necessary multiplying factor— and P is used to represent the power supplied to the load, then from equations (11-7) and (11-8)

$$W = P + \frac{V^2}{R_p}, \tag{11-9}$$

or

$$P = W - \frac{V^2}{R_p}.$$

Thus, the true power delivered to the load can be determined by subtracting the power loss in the potential circuit of the wattmeter from the power indicated by the wattmeter.

In many instances the V^2/R_p loss is quite an appreciable part of the wattmeter power indication. In such cases the correction indicated in equation (11-9) must be made. To obtain the data needed for making this correction, the resistance R_p can be measured by the use of a Wheatstone bridge or other suitable bridge and the voltage impressed across terminals c and d can be measured by means of a voltmeter. However, it is rarely necessary to make the resistance measurement, since it is common practice among instrument makers to state the value of R_p somewhere on the instrument. Sometimes it is stated on the instrument scale but usually is printed on the certificate fastened to the instrument lid. When the instrument has more than one voltage rating, the value of R_p to be used should obviously be the one corresponding to the voltage terminal being used. Thus, when point g is connected to terminal d of the wattmeter shown in Fig. 11-2, $R_p = r + R$, whereas, when g is connected to terminal e, $R_p = r + R + R_m$.

It may occur to the reader that the error caused by power loss in the wattmeter can be eliminated by connecting the instrument as shown in

Fig. 11-5.   With this connection, however, the wattmeter indication is too great by the amount of the power loss in the coil SS, for here the voltage applied to the potential branch cd is greater than that applied to the load because of the voltage drop across coil SS.   Hence, in order to determine the power supplied to the load, it would be necessary to determine the power loss in coil SS and subtract it from the wattmeter power indication.   Since the resistance of coil SS is extremely low, its accurate determination may be difficult.   Furthermore, this re-sistance is not constant.   It is affected by the temperature changes resulting from the heat developed by the current in the coil.   Since this current may vary widely and since the heat devel-oped is a function of the current squared, the temperature of the coil, and hence its resistance, may

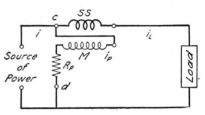

Fig. 11-5. Wattmeter coil connec-tions requiring a correction for the power loss in the current coil in order to obtain the true power delivered to a load.

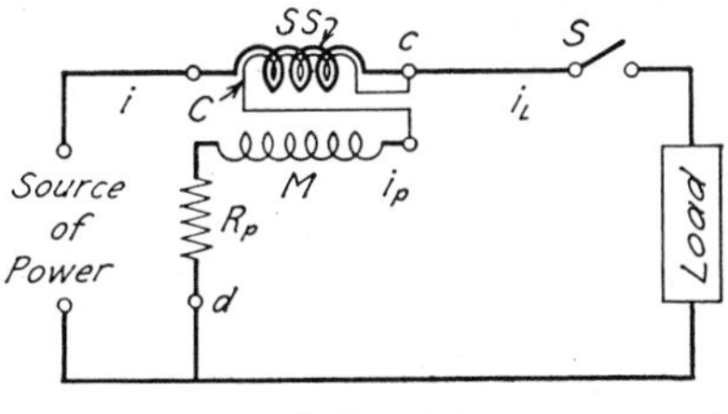

vary appreciably.   In most test circuits the applied voltage does not change appreciably, and the current in the potential circuit of the wattmeter remains fairly constant.   In addition, the resistor R in series with coil M is wound with a conductor that has a very low temperature coefficient.   Hence the resistance R_p remains substan-tially constant.   In view of these facts, the wattmeter connection shown in Fig. 11-4 should gener-ally be used, with a correction being made for the power loss in the potential circuit of the instrument.

5. Compensated Wattmeter.
In some wattmeters a third coil is introduced for the purpose of eliminating the effect of the power loss in the potential circuit on the pointer deflection.   The action of

Fig. 11-6. Coils of a compensated wattmeter connected in a circuit for making a power measurement.

this coil can be readily understood by considering Fig. 11-6.   This coil is called the *compensating coil* and is indicated by C.   It is closely wound over the sections SS of the current coil but is connected in series with the potential coil M and included between the potential terminals c and d.   The connections to coil C are made in such a manner that the magnetomotive force set up by the current i_p in it opposes that set up by the component i_p of i in the coil SS.   By proper adjustment of the number of turns in coil C the effect of the component i_p upon the instantaneous force on the wattmeter coil M is entirely neutralized, and the wattmeter power indication is the power delivered to the load and does not include the power loss in the potential circuit of the instrument. Wattmeters that have compensating coils are usually supplied with a switch by means of which the coil can be either included in or excluded from the circuit.

Before using a compensated wattmeter, it is customary practice to test the instrument in order to determine whether or not the compensation is correct. This test can be made by connecting the circuit of Fig. 11-6 to the source of power with the switch S open. If the compensation is correct, the wattmeter indication will be zero. In performing this test and also in using a compensated wattmeter for power measurements, care must be taken to connect the potential circuit on the load side of the current coil, and, in the case of multiple-current-range instruments, to set the compensating-coil switch to the current range for which the current-coil sections are connected. This precaution must be observed because for correct compensation the two sections of the compensating coil must be connected in series when the current-coil sections are connected in series and must be connected in parallel when the current-coil sections are connected in parallel.

6. Potential-Coil Connection and Polarity Markings. It will be readily understood from a consideration of Fig. 11-1 that the direction of the deflection of the pointer is determined by the direction of the magnetic field set up by the current in coil SS and by the direction of the current in the potential coil M. Hence, when a wattmeter is connected in a circuit as shown in Fig. 11-2, it is quite possible that the deflection of the pointer will be backward instead of up scale. By interchanging the connections to either the current terminals or potential terminals of the instrument, but not both, the pointer can be made to deflect in the proper direction. However, although such an arbitrary choice will produce the desired effect, it may result in an appreciable error in the wattmeter indication. When voltage is impressed on the potential terminals of the wattmeter, most of it appears as a drop across the series resistor R because the inductance and resistance of coil M are extremely small. Since coil M in (a) of Fig. 11-7 is connected directly to the line in which the current coil SS is connected, coil M is at the same electric potential as SS. In (b) of the figure, however, the potential of coil M is that of line 2, and, since most of the voltage v appears across resistor R, the potential of coil M differs from that of coil SS by the voltage v. As a result, an electric field of considerable magnitude may be established between these coils, depending upon the magnitude of the potential difference v. As constructed and placed in the instrument, the coils are in close proximity to each other, and the physical location of one with respect to the other is not changed by making the change in connections as indicated in Fig. 11-7. Because of their nearness to each other, a considerable force may be exerted between them if the electric field is of appreciable strength. In some wattmeters this force is of sufficient magnitude to influence the pointer deflection, thus introducing an error in the wattmeter indication. In order to avoid the possibility of such an error, the connections to the potential circuit of the wattmeter should be those shown in (a) of Fig. 11-7, that is, the connections should be such that the coil M is

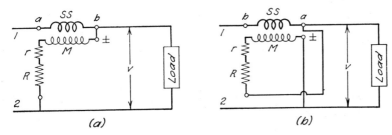

Fig. 11-7. (a) Correct connection of a wattmeter potential circuit, and (b) incorrect connection.

connected directly to the line in which the current coil is located. The electric potential of both the current coil and the potential coil will then be very nearly the same, and there will be practically no electric field between them. From an inspection of the wattmeter it is not evident which of the potential terminals connects directly to coil M. Since this information is necessary if the connections are to be made in accordance with (a) of the figure, most manufacturers connect the zero or $\pm$ potential terminal directly to coil M. Accordingly, the zero or $\pm$ potential terminal should be connected to the line in which the current coil is located. Then, if the pointer deflection is backward, the connections to the current coil SS should be reversed.

It is now standard practice for the instrument manufacturers to use a $\pm$ mark to identify the current-coil terminal that should be placed toward the source side of a two-wire circuit so that there will be an up-scale pointer deflection when the potential circuit is properly connected. Thus, in Figs. 11-2 and 11-7(a) the current-coil terminal a would have a $\pm$ mark if the connections shown produce an up-scale deflection. Wattmeter polarity markings are further discussed in Chapter 19 in connection with the measurement of polyphase power.

7. Error in Wattmeter Indication at Very Low Power Factors. In the foregoing discussion of the theory of the electrodynamometer type of wattmeter it has been assumed that the instantaneous value of the current in the potential coil is directly proportional to the instantaneous value of the voltage applied to the potential terminals of the wattmeter. In the case of alternating current this means that the current in the potential coil is assumed to be in phase with the voltage applied to the potential terminals of the instrument. It was argued that the resistance placed in series with the potential or movable coil was so great compared to the inductance of the coil that, for all practical purposes, the assumption was justified. It will now be shown that in special cases this assumption may result in an error that is not negligible.

It has been shown that the instantaneous force acting on the movable coil is directly proportional to the product of the instantaneous value of the current in the stationary coil and that in the movable coil. Referring to Fig. 11-4, let the current in the stationary coil be $i = I_{\max} \sin \omega t$ and that in the movable coil be $i_p = I_{p_{\max}} \sin (\omega t \pm \phi)$. The instantaneous force acting on each side of the movable coil is

$$
\begin{aligned}
f &= k i i_p \qquad\qquad\qquad\qquad\qquad\qquad\qquad (11\text{-}10)\\
&= k \left[I_{\max} \sin \omega t \times I_{p_{\max}} \sin (\omega t \pm \phi) \right]\\
&= k I_{\max} I_{p_{\max}} [\sin \omega t \sin (\omega t \pm \phi)]\\
&= k I_{\max} I_{p_{\max}} [\sin \omega t (\sin \omega t \cos \phi \pm \cos \omega t \sin \phi)]\\
&= k I_{\max} I_{p_{\max}} [\sin^2 \omega t \cos \phi \pm \sin \omega t \cos \omega t \sin \phi].
\end{aligned}
$$

The average value of the torque acting on the movable coil determines the final position of the wattmeter pointer. The average torque is, among other things, directly proportional to the average of the instantaneous forces. The average force acting during one cycle of the alternating current is

$$
\begin{aligned}
f_{av} &= \frac{k I_{\max} I_{p_{\max}}}{2\pi} \int_0^{2\pi} (\sin^2 \omega t \cos \phi \pm \sin \omega t \cos \omega t \sin \phi) d\omega t\\
&= \frac{k I_{\max} I_{p_{\max}}}{2\pi} \left[\cos \phi \left(-\frac{1}{2} \cos \omega t \sin \omega t + \frac{\omega t}{2} \right) \pm \frac{\sin \phi}{2} \sin^2 \omega t \right]_0^{2\pi}.
\end{aligned}
$$

Since $\sin \omega t = 0$ when ωt is 0 or 2π, all terms containing $\sin \omega t$ as a factor are zero in the last equation. Therefore

$$
\begin{aligned}
f_{av} &= \frac{k I_{\max} I_{p_{\max}}}{2\pi} \left[\frac{\omega t}{2} \cos \phi \right]_0^{2\pi}\\
&= k I I_p \cos \phi. \qquad\qquad\qquad\qquad (11\text{-}11)
\end{aligned}
$$

In this equation I and I_p are the effective values of the respective currents in the current coil SS and the potential coil M, and ϕ is the phase angle between the two current waves.

Inasmuch as I_p is directly proportional to the effective value of the voltage applied to the potential terminals, equation (11-11) may be written

$$f_{av} = k_1 IV \cos \phi. \qquad (11\text{-}12)$$

Since the various proportionality factors are taken care of in the calibration of the instrument, the wattmeter indication of the power at terminals AB in Fig. 11-8(a) is

$$W = IV \cos \phi. \qquad (11\text{-}13)$$

The actual power at the terminals AB, however, is

$$P = VI \cos \theta, \qquad (11\text{-}14)$$

θ being the phase angle between the $\bar{V}$ and $\bar{I}$.

Let α represent the phase angle between $\bar{I}_p$ and $\bar{V}$, as shown in Fig. 11-8(b). Since the potential circuit of the wattmeter is inductive,

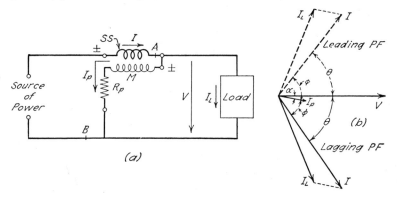

Fig. 11-8. (a) Wattmeter coils connected in a circuit for making a power measurement. (b) Vector diagram of the voltage and currents indicated in (a).

$\bar{I}_p$ lags $\bar{V}$. Therefore, with $\bar{V}$ as reference, the angle ϕ between $\bar{I}$ and $\bar{I}_p$ is $(\theta + \alpha)$ when $\bar{I}$ leads $\bar{V}$ and is $(\theta - \alpha)$ when $\bar{I}$ lags $\bar{V}$. These relations are shown graphically in Fig. 11-8(b). Equation (11-13) may now be written

$$W = IV \cos \phi = IV \cos (\theta \pm \alpha) \qquad (11\text{-}15)$$
$$= IV (\cos \theta \cos \alpha \mp \sin \theta \sin \alpha).$$

The error can now be determined.

$$\text{Error} = W - P = IV (\cos \theta \cos \alpha \mp \sin \theta \sin \alpha) - IV \cos \theta$$
$$= IV [(\cos \alpha - 1) \cos \theta \mp \sin \theta \sin \alpha]. \qquad (11\text{-}16)$$

Let R_p, X_p, and Z_p be the resistance, reactance, and impedance,[*] respectively, of the potential circuit. Equation (11-16) may then be written

$$\text{Error} = IV\left[\left(\frac{R_p}{Z_p} - 1\right)\cos\theta \mp \frac{X_p}{Z_p}\sin\theta\right]. \quad (11\text{-}17)$$

In general α is a very small angle, being of the magnitude of only two or three degrees at the most. In view of this fact, it is clear from a study of equation (11-15) that α has an appreciable effect only when θ is a very large angle—say, from 85 to 90 degrees—because the cosine changes rapidly with very small changes of the angle only when it lies in this range.

Since α is only two or three degrees, $\cos\alpha$ may be set equal to unity in equation (11-16). The equation then becomes

$$\text{Error} = \mp IV \sin\alpha \sin\theta = \mp IV \frac{X_p}{Z_p}\sin\theta. \quad (11\text{-}18)$$

Now, as pointed out, this error is insignificant except when θ is very large, in which case $\sin\theta$ may be set equal to unity. Hence, as a close approximation at very low power factors,

$$\text{Error} = \mp IV \sin\alpha = \mp IV \frac{X_p}{Z_p}. \quad (11\text{-}19)$$

An inspection of equation (11-15) and Fig. 11-8(b) shows that the − sign in equation (11-19) is applicable to leading power factors and the + sign to lagging power factors. Therefore, at very low power factors the wattmeter indication is too low for leading power factors and too high for lagging power factors.

8. Protection. Before a wattmeter is selected for installation in a circuit, the probable maximum value of current should be known, as should the probable maximum value of potential difference between the points to which the potential terminals of the wattmeter are to be connected. With these facts and some idea of the amount of power to be measured, a wattmeter having suitable current, voltage, and watt ratings can be chosen.

A wattmeter should never be used in a circuit except in conjunction with an ammeter and voltmeter, as indicated in Fig. 11-9. These instruments are the only means of determining whether the current and voltage ratings of the wattmeter are being exceeded. It is obvious that when the watt rating is exceeded the pointer will go off scale.

---

[*] See page 155.

However, in the case of circuits of low power factor, it is possible to exceed the current or voltage rating or both and yet have a pointer deflection that is only a fraction of full scale. Thus, the pointer deflection of the wattmeter is not an indication as to whether or not the current and voltage ratings are being exceeded. Consequently, an ammeter and voltmeter should always be used in conjunction with a wattmeter.

In order to protect the current coil of the wattmeter from abnormal currents due to accidental overloads or short circuits, a switch should be used to shunt this coil except when a reading is being taken. Such a switch is shown in Fig. 11-9. It will be a temptation to use a single short-circuiting switch for protecting both the ammeter and wattmeter

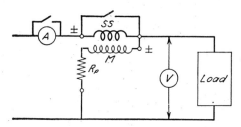

Fig. 11-9. Ammeter, voltmeter, and shunting switch in a circuit for the protection of a wattmeter against overloads.

together. Although a single switch will protect the instruments as long as the switch is closed, damage to both instruments may occur when the switch is opened if a load fault or an unexpected increase in the load causes excessive current in the circuit and the circuit protective devices fail to operate. On the other hand, if separate short-circuiting switches are used for each of the instruments, damage would occur, in case of abnormal conditions, to only one when one of the switches is opened. If the ammeter switch is opened first, it will be evident at once whether or not the current in the circuit is excessive. Furthermore, since the ammeter is the less expensive of the two instruments, opening the ammeter switch first will result in the least loss if damage is destined to occur.

In order to protect the potential circuit of the wattmeter from abnormal voltages, this circuit should not be left connected after readings have been taken. In some wattmeters push-button switches for opening the potential circuit are included in the instrument. When such a switch is not provided, one of the leads to the potential terminals of the wattmeter should be disconnected at the circuit end—not at the instrument end.

Laboratory Problem No. 11-1
THE WATTMETER

Laboratory

1. Obtain an uncompensated, multiple-rating wattmeter suitable for measuring the power in the circuit designated by the instructor.

Summarize on the data sheet the information found on the wattmeter lid and on the scale of the wattmeter.

2. Using the rating of the wattmeter and its scale range or ranges, determine the scale-multiplying factors or the scales, whichever is applicable, that should be used with the various current and potential terminal combinations. Check these results with any similar information found in **1**.

3. (a) Connect the wattmeter and a suitable ammeter and voltmeter in the circuit as shown in Fig. 11-10. If the voltage of the

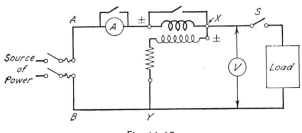

Fig. 11-10.

supply fluctuates, some form of voltage control should be used to maintain the voltage across A and B constant in all of the remaining tests of this problem.

(b) With the circuit disconnect switch closed, the wattmeter current-coil-shunting switch open, switch S open, the voltmeter disconnected, and the wattmeter potential circuit connected (push button also held down if there is one), record the power indicated by the wattmeter.

(c) Under the same conditions as in (b), record the indication of the wattmeter when

　(1) The potential circuit is opened at X but is connected at Y.
　(2) The potential circuit is opened at Y but is connected at X.

4. Using the wattmeter connections as shown in the circuit of Fig. 11-10, obtain data for determining the power delivered to the load.

5. Move the potential circuit of the wattmeter to the source side of the current coil and again obtain data for determining the power delivered to the load.

6. (a) Replace the wattmeter with a suitable one that is compensated. Repeat **3**(b).

(b) Obtain data for determining the power delivered to the load.

Report

A. Determine the power delivered to the load in **4, 5,** and **6**(b). Discuss any discrepancies in the values obtained.

B. Discuss the results obtained in **3**(b) and **6**(a).

C. Explain any pointer deflection observed in either of tests (1) or (2) of **3**(c). If no pointer deflection was observed, explain why a deflection is frequently encountered when test (1) is performed.

D. A current of 4 amperes flows in a coil when it is connected to a 100-volt 60-cycle source. The resistance of the coil is 6 ohms. Which of the wattmeters listed below would be the best to use for measuring the power supplied to the coil when it is connected to the 100-volt source? Give reasons for the selection made.

Wattmeter	Ampere Rating	Volt Rating	Watt Rating
1	5/10	150/300	750/1500/3000
2	10/20	75/150	300/600/1200
3	2.5/5	75/150	37.5/75/150
4	5	150/300	500/1000
5	5/10	30/60	60/120/240

E. If wattmeter 2 in **D** has only one scale of 1200 watts, determine the scale-multiplying factors to use with the various current and potential terminal combinations.

CHAPTER 12
MEASUREMENT OF VOLTAGE, CURRENT, AND POWER

1. Instrument Locations. In the laboratory study of the behavior of electrical circuits it will be necessary in many instances to measure the voltage, current, and power of a circuit or circuit element. For any test circuit that is set up to measure these quantities, the instrument locations and the test procedure should be such that the values of the quantities determined by measurement are as close to the actual existing values as can be obtained. In Fig. 12-1 is shown one arrangement of the instruments that can be used. This test circuit has an

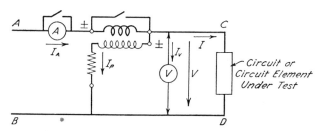

Fig. 12-1. Arrangement of the instruments in a circuit which makes possible convenient and accurate corrections of the ammeter and wattmeter indications.

advantage over other test circuits having different arrangements of the instruments in that the ammeter and wattmeter indications can be conveniently and accurately corrected when necessary.

2. Factors Influencing Selection of Test Procedure. In any particular case, the best procedure to follow when the arrangement shown in Fig. 12-1 is used depends upon the resistance and inductance of the ammeter, voltmeter, and each coil circuit of the wattmeter as compared with the resistance, inductance, and capacitance of the circuit or circuit element being tested. The best procedure also depends upon the ability of the source of power to maintain a constant voltage. Each particular case is an individual problem that must be investigated before an attempt is made to take the data. The cases analyzed in this chapter will serve to indicate the best test procedures.

Unless stated to the contrary, the following discussion is appli-

148

cable to the test circuit of Fig. 12-1 whether the current is direct or alternating.

3. Test Procedures When Voltage Across Test Circuit Is Constant. *Preliminary Test.* Consider that the ammeter and wattmeter current-coil-shunting switches in Fig. 12-1 are open and that the wattmeter potential circuit and the voltmeter are disconnected. With the voltage across points A and B constant, the preliminary test is to note the effect on the ammeter indication of connecting the wattmeter potential circuit and the voltmeter separately and then connecting them simultaneously.

(1) Ammeter Indication Not Affected in Preliminary Test. If the ammeter indication is not noticeably affected, the three instruments can all be connected in the test circuit, and (with the shunting switches open) the indications can be read one at a time or simultaneously without introducing appreciable error. In either case, however, it will be necessary to correct the power indication of the wattmeter because of the power loss in the wattmeter potential circuit and in the voltmeter whenever either of these losses or their sum is an appreciable part of the wattmeter power indication. By disconnecting the voltmeter before reading the wattmeter, the necessity for making a correction for the power loss in the voltmeter is eliminated.

Another possible procedure when the ammeter indication is not appreciably affected in the preliminary test is to have only one instrument in the circuit at a time. It should be remembered that even in this case the wattmeter power indication will usually need to be corrected for the potential-circuit loss. Care must be taken in following this test procedure, however, for the opposition offered to the current by the circuit or circuit element under test might be so low that it is comparable to that offered by the ammeter, the wattmeter current coil, or both. Then, opening and closing the shunting switches would make an appreciable change in the current and hence in the voltage across terminals C and D of the circuit or circuit element. In order to determine whether these oppositions are an appreciable part of the total opposition, it is necessary only to open and close the shunting switches and note the effect on the voltmeter indication. If the indication of the voltmeter is appreciably affected, the wattmeter current coil and the ammeter must be left in the circuit while all the instrument indications are read. A rather convenient procedure in this case is to read the ammeter, then connect the voltmeter in the circuit only until its indication is read, and lastly connect the wattmeter potential circuit and read the wattmeter indication. It should be apparent that this procedure can also be used when the opposition of the wattmeter current coil and that of the ammeter are a negligible part of the total opposition.

(2) *Ammeter Indication Affected in Preliminary Test.* If connecting the wattmeter potential circuit and the voltmeter appreciably affects the indication of the ammeter when the preliminary test is made, the three instruments shown in Fig. 12-1 should not be simultaneously connected in the circuit unless a correction of the ammeter indication is made for the currents in the wattmeter potential circuit and the voltmeter.

For the time being let it be assumed that the circuit of Fig. 12-1 carries alternating current which varies sinusoidally with respect to time. Then, since vector relations are involved, the correction can be understood best from an analysis of Fig. 12-2, which is the vector diagram for the test circuit of Fig. 12-1. On the vector diagram V is the voltage indicated by the voltmeter, I_A is the current indicated

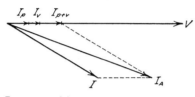

Fig. 12-2.   Vector diagram for the circuit of Fig. 12-1.

by the ammeter, I is the current in the circuit or circuit element under test, and I_{p+v} is the sum of the currents in the wattmeter potential circuit and the voltmeter. The vector $\bar{I}_{p+v}$ is in phase with $\bar{V}$, since the oppositions offered by the voltmeter and the potential circuit of the wattmeter are nearly pure resistance. $\bar{I}$ is arbitrarily taken as lagging $\bar{V}$.

The true power in the circuit or circuit element under test is

$$P = W - \frac{V^2}{R_p} - \frac{V^2}{R_v} = W - V^2\left(\frac{1}{R_p} + \frac{1}{R_v}\right) = W - \frac{V^2}{R}, \quad (12\text{-}1)$$

where W is the wattmeter indication multiplied by the proper scale-multiplying factor, R_p is the resistance of the wattmeter potential circuit, R_v is the resistance of the voltmeter, and

$$\frac{1}{R} = \frac{1}{R_p} + \frac{1}{R_v}. \quad (12\text{-}2)$$

The component of $\bar{I}$ which is in phase with $\bar{V}$ is

$$I_{\text{in phase}} = \frac{P}{V} = \frac{W - \dfrac{V^2}{R}}{V} = \frac{W}{V} - \frac{V}{R},$$

and the component of $\bar{I}_A$ which is in phase with $\bar{V}$ is

$$I_{A_{\text{in phase}}} = \frac{W}{V}.$$

Since the components of $\bar{I}$ and $\bar{I}_A$ which are in quadrature with $\bar{V}$ are the same, then

$$I_{\text{quadrature}} = I_{A_{\text{quadrature}}} = \sqrt{I_A{}^2 - \left(\frac{W}{V}\right)^2}.$$

The correct value of the current in the circuit or circuit element under test is

$$I = \sqrt{I^2_{\text{in phase}} + I^2_{\text{quadrature}}} = \sqrt{\left(\frac{W}{V} - \frac{V}{R}\right)^2 + \left(I_A{}^2 - \frac{W^2}{V^2}\right)}$$

$$= \sqrt{I_A{}^2 + \frac{V^2}{R^2} - \frac{2W}{R}}, \qquad (12\text{-}3)$$

where R is the value determined from equation (12-2).

Investigation will show that equation (12-3) can be used to obtain the correct current in the circuit or circuit element under test even when the circuit of Fig. 12-1 carries direct current. Under this condition, however, it is much simpler to use the equation

$$I = I_A - \frac{V}{R}, \qquad (12\text{-}4)$$

in which the various symbols represent the same quantities as before. The true d-c power supplied to the circuit or circuit element is calculated by means of equation (12-1) just as in the a-c case.

Another procedure that can be used for a majority of the cases encountered when the ammeter indication is appreciably affected in the preliminary test is to open the ammeter and wattmeter current-coil-shunting switches and read the ammeter, then connect the voltmeter only long enough to read its indication, and lastly connect the wattmeter potential circuit and read the wattmeter indication. When this procedure is followed, correct data will be obtained unless the voltage across points C and D is affected appreciably by any change in the voltage drop across the ammeter and the wattmeter current coil that is caused by connecting either the voltmeter or the potential circuit of the wattmeter. In general, such a change in voltage across C and D is only likely to take place when the voltage across A and B is relatively low.

In the cases in which the test procedure just discussed can be used, the only instrument indication that may require a correction is that of the wattmeter. The power indication will usually need to be corrected for the potential-circuit loss. When the procedure cannot be used because of the change produced in the voltage across the circuit or circuit element under test, then all three instruments must be connected in the circuit simultaneously and the necessary corrections made.

4. Test Procedure When Voltage Across Test Circuit Is Not Constant. The voltage across points A and B of the test circuit in Fig. 12-1 may not be constant because (1) the source of power may have poor voltage regulation or (2) connecting the wattmeter potential circuit or the voltmeter in the test circuit may disturb a more complex circuit of which the circuit under test is only a part. Whenever the voltage across points A and B is not constant, simultaneous readings of the indications of the three instruments and the use of equations (12-1) and (12-3) in the case of alternating current or equations (12-1) and (12-4) in the case of direct current is the only reliable method of securing the correct values of the required quantities.

5. Summary of Test Procedures. A review of the entire discussion regarding the test procedures to be followed in the use of the test circuit shown in Fig. 12-1 will show that, except when the voltage across points A and B is not constant or when connecting the wattmeter potential circuit or the voltmeter causes the voltage across points C and D to change appreciably, the most convenient procedure that can be followed may be summarized as follows:

(1) Be certain that the wattmeter potential circuit and the voltmeter are not connected in the test circuit.

(2) Open the switches shunting the ammeter and the wattmeter current coil and read the ammeter indication.

(3) Connect the voltmeter only long enough to read its indication.

(4) Connect the wattmeter potential circuit and read the wattmeter indication.

This procedure becomes even more convenient when the wattmeter potential circuit and the voltmeter are equipped with push-button switches, in which case connecting and disconnecting these elements can be accomplished by merely pushing and releasing the push buttons.

Whenever this procedure is not applicable, simultaneous readings of the three instruments must be taken and the necessary corrections applied to the ammeter and wattmeter indications. It should be remembered that equation (12-3), which gives the correct value of the a-c current in the circuit or circuit element under test when simultaneous instrument readings are taken, is based upon sinusoidal time variations of voltage and current.

The disturbing effects of the wattmeter potential circuit and the voltmeter can be reduced to a minimum by using high-resistance voltmeters and wattmeters having high-resistance potential circuits.

In any event, each particular case must be investigated, and judgment must be used in selecting the best test procedure.

Laboratory Problem No. 12-1

MEASUREMENT OF VOLTAGE, CURRENT, AND POWER

Laboratory

1. Obtain suitable instruments for measuring the voltage, current, and power of the a-c circuit designated by the instructor. Connect the instruments in the circuit as shown in Fig. 12-3. If the voltage of the

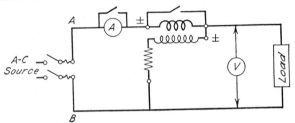

Fig. 12-3.

supply fluctuates, some form of voltage control should be used to maintain the voltage across A and B constant in parts **2** and **3** below.

2. Using a test procedure that will permit the minimum number of instrument corrections, obtain data for determining the voltage, current, and power of the load.

3. Read all three instrument indications simultaneously. Record the instrument indications and also the resistance of the voltmeter and the resistance of the wattmeter potential circuit.

4. Repeat **1, 2,** and **3,** but use the d-c circuit designated by the instructor.

Report

A. From the data obtained in **2,** determine the voltage, current, and power of the load.

B. From the data obtained in **3,** determine the voltage, current, and power of the load.

C. Discuss any discrepancies in the results of **A** and **B.**

D. Draw the current-voltage vector diagram for the conditions that existed in **3.** Draw the vector diagram to scale. Use the vector representing the voltage drop across the load as the reference vector.

E. Repeat **A, B,** and **C,** using the data obtained in **4.**

CHAPTER 13

OHMIC AND EFFECTIVE RESISTANCE

1. Ohmic Resistance. The relation between the d-c impressed voltage, the current, and the resistance of a circuit or a circuit element is given by Ohm's law. This relation is expressed mathematically by

$$R = \frac{V}{I}, \tag{13-1}$$

in which R is the resistance in ohms, V is the voltage in volts, and I is the current in amperes. The resistance R is usually referred to as either the *d-c resistance* or the *ohmic resistance*. It is a measure of the opposition offered to a direct current, and it depends only upon the material, physical dimensions, and temperature of the circuit element or elements.

When direct current flows in a circuit or a circuit element, the total power supplied by the source is dissipated in the ohmic resistance. This power loss is equal to the current squared multiplied by the ohmic resistance. Therefore ohmic resistance can be found by measuring the power absorbed when a known current exists. If P is the power in watts when a current of I amperes flows, then the ohmic resistance R in ohms is

$$R = \frac{P}{I^2}. \tag{13-2}$$

The power loss in a circuit or a circuit element carrying direct current is also equal to the product of the impressed voltage and the current. Substituting the product VI for P in equation (13-2) gives

$$R = \frac{P}{I^2} = \frac{VI}{I^2} = \frac{V}{I}, \tag{13-3}$$

which shows that the values of ohmic resistance determined by equations (13-1) and (13-2) are the same.

2. A-C Opposition. When the impressed voltage and current of a circuit or a circuit element vary sinusoidally with time, an a-c version of Ohm's law may be written as follows:

$$I = \frac{V}{Z},$$

or

$$Z = \frac{V}{I},$$ (13-4)

in which V is the effective value of the impressed voltage in volts, I is the effective value of the current in amperes, and Z, known as *impedance*, is the total opposition in ohms.

The impedance Z can be shown to have a value

$$Z = \sqrt{R_e{}^2 + X^2},$$ (13-5)

in which X is the *reactance* of the circuit or circuit element and R_e is the apparent or *effective resistance*. Both X and R_e are measured in ohms.

The value of the reactance X depends upon the circuit element or elements making up a circuit. For example, if a coil is the only circuit element, then $X = 2\pi f L$, where f is the frequency of the alternating current in cycles per second and L is the inductance of the coil in henrys. If the element is a condenser, $X = 1/2\pi f C$, C being the capacitance in farads.

The effective resistance R_e is not the same as the ohmic resistance. Usually it is appreciably larger and in some instances is many times greater. Furthermore, the effective resistance is not usually constant but will vary with frequency and the value of the alternating current if magnetic materials are near the circuit or circuit element. The reasons for this variation will become evident from the following discussion.

3. Losses in a Circuit Element Carrying Alternating Current. As previously stated, there is a power loss in a circuit element when it carries a direct current. Likewise, when an alternating current of the same value flows in the same circuit element there is also a power loss, which, in general, is greater for the alternating current than for the direct current. The additional loss in the case of alternating current is due to (1) the local losses caused by the varying magnetic field associated with the alternating current, (2) the non-uniform current density over the cross section of the conductors, and (3) the so-called dielectric-hysteresis loss in the insulation of the conductors.

(1) Local Losses. The local losses caused by the varying magnetic field set up by an alternating current consist of eddy-current and hysteresis losses in adjacent magnetic materials, eddy-current losses in adjacent conducting materials, and eddy-current loss in the conductor itself. If the conductor should be magnetic, there would also be hysteresis loss in the conductor.

If the magnetizing force acting on a magnetic material is increased from some value to a higher one and then reduced, it is found that the values of flux produced by the decreasing values of magnetizing force are greater than those produced by corresponding values of increasing magnetizing force. This phenomenon of flux lagging behind the magnetizing force is known as *hysteresis*. When an alternating magnetizing force acts upon a magnetic material, values of flux plotted against magnetizing force form a closed curve called a *hysteresis loop*. The area of the hysteresis loop is a measure of the amount of energy required to carry the magnetization of the magnetic material through one complete cycle. The rate at which energy is expended in this fashion is known as *hysteresis loss*.

In a homogeneous sample of iron in which the flux density is uniform and the change of flux between the positive and negative maximums is continuous without reversal, a general empirical expression for hysteresis loss is

$$P_h = K_h f B_m^{1.6}. \tag{13-6}$$

In this equation K_h is a constant that depends upon the quality of the iron, the dimensions of the particular sample under consideration, and the units used for the various quantities. B_m is the maximum flux density produced in the sample, and f is the number of cycles per second through which the magnetization is carried. The exponent 1.6 was determined experimentally by C. P. Steinmetz and has become known as the *Steinmetz exponent*. Although more recent experiments have shown that the exponent may vary from 1.4 to 2.0, the value 1.6 is usually used when definite information is not available concerning the exponent.

If the flux within an electrically conducting material varies, there may be a change in the number of flux linkages of local closed circuits within the mass of the conductor. When such a change of flux linkages does occur, emfs are induced which produce currents in these local circuits. These currents are called *eddy currents*. Since they flow through paths in the mass of the conductor which have resistance, they cause I^2R losses that result in considerable heating of the conducting material. The rate at which energy is thus expended is known as *eddy-current loss*. This loss is kept at a low value in the magnetic circuits of electrical machines by constructing the affected portions of these circuits of thin, electrically insulated sheets of steel called *laminations*. These laminations are placed so that their planes are parallel to the direction of the flux. Laminating any electrically conducting material in this manner not only reduces the emf induced in a local circuit but also results in an increase in the resistance of the local circuit because of the reduced area.

If the flux within a homogeneous electrically conducting material varies with time and the flux density is uniform* in the material, a general expression for eddy-current loss is

$$P_e = K_e f^2 B_m^2. \qquad (13\text{-}7)$$

In this equation K_e is a factor that depends upon the wave form of the flux variation, the conductivity of the material, the units used for the various quantities, the thickness of the laminations, and other physical dimensions. B_m is the maximum flux density produced in the material, and f is the frequency in cycles per second. It should be noted that the value of K_e will usually change whenever the wave form of the flux variation is altered. Therefore the eddy-current losses produced by two flux variations having the same maximum values and frequency but different wave forms will not usually be equal.

(*2*) *Loss Due to Non-Uniform Current Density in a Conductor.* When a steady-state direct current flows through a homogenous conductor, the current density is uniform over the cross section of the conductor. With alternating current in the conductor, however, the current is not distributed uniformly, but the current density is greater in portions of the conductor near the surface than in portions near the center.

The crowding of an alternating current toward the conductor surface is called *skin effect* and is caused by the time rate of change of the magnetic flux lines set up by the current in the conductor. The flux lines not only surround, but also exist in, the conductor. Consequently an elemental filament of the conductor near the center of the conductor is linked by more flux lines than is a like elemental filament near the surface. Thus, when the current alternates and produces an alternating flux, the electromotive force that is induced in each of the many elemental filaments and that opposes the flow of current is greater in the filaments near the center of the conductor than in those near the surface, causing the current to be crowded into the outer portions of the conductor.

For a given current in a given conductor the power loss is least when the current is uniformly distributed throughout the cross-sectional area of the conductor. This is true because the increase in the power loss produced when the current in a conductor is increased by a definite amount is greater than the decrease in power loss that results when an equal current in a like conductor is reduced by the

---

* This assumes that the magnetomotive force of the eddy currents is negligible, a condition that is approached at the low power frequencies when thin laminations are used.

same amount. Thus, when the distribution of a given current within a conductor is changed by skin effect from one that is uniform to one that is not, the power loss is increased. The power loss being the product of the resistance and the current squared, the increased power loss must be due to a greater resistance.

The skin effect is negligible at low frequencies for conductors of small cross-sectional area but is very appreciable for large conductors or high frequencies. At the high frequencies used in radio communication, the resistance of a cylindrical tube may be nearly as low as the resistance of a solid conductor of equal outside radius and made of the same material.

(3) *Dielectric-Hysteresis Loss.* A loss known as *dielectric hysteresis* occurs in the dielectrics of condensers and in the insulation of conductors. This loss is caused by the varying stresses produced in dielectric materials when subjected to alternating voltages. The dielectric-hysteresis loss is negligible for most dielectrics at low voltages and at the power frequencies. It becomes appreciable, however, at high voltages or high frequencies.

4. Effective Resistance. The foregoing discussion has shown that the power loss in a circuit element is greater when the circuit element is carrying alternating current than when it is carrying a direct current of the same value. Because of this greater loss, the apparent resistance of the circuit element when alternating current is used is greater than when direct current is used. This follows from the fact that resistance is the only circuit parameter causing a power loss. Since the apparent resistance is the value that must be used to account for all the losses in the circuit element, it has become known as the *effective resistance.* Accordingly, if P is the power in watts absorbed by a circuit or circuit element that carries a current having an effective value of I amperes, the effective resistance R_e in ohms is then

$$R_e = \frac{P}{I^2}. \tag{13-8}$$

Although the ohmic resistance of a circuit element is constant at a fixed temperature, the effective resistance usually is not unless the frequency, effective value of the current, and the current wave form remain unchanged. The effective resistance changes with frequency because all of the losses that make the effective resistance greater than the ohmic resistance vary with frequency although other conditions do not change. A change in the effective value of current changes the maximum flux density of the magnetic field produced by the current. Hence an inspection of equation (13-6) shows that a change in the effective value of current changes the ratio P_h/I^2, and thus the effective resistance, if the circuit element is near any magnetic material. The ratio P_e/I^2 is not affected by a change in the effective value of current when a linear relationship exists between current and maximum flux density, as can be seen by an inspection of equation (13-7). However, when this relationship is not linear, the ratio P_e/I^2 will change, causing a change in effective resistance. A change in the current wave form will alter the shape of the flux vs time curve and may change the maximum flux density, resulting in a change in the hysteresis and eddy-current losses, although the effective values of the current and frequency remain unchanged.

5. Determination of Ohmic and Effective Resistance. Equation (13-3) shows that the resistance of a circuit or circuit element with direct current—that is, the ohmic resistance—is equal to either the impressed voltage divided by the current or to the power divided by the current squared. As indicated by equation (13-8), the effective resistance with alternating current is equal to the power divided by the square of the current. However, equations (13-4) and (13-5) show that the effective resistance is not equal to the impressed voltage divided by the current except when the reactance is zero. Since this condition rarely occurs, it is generally necessary to measure the power in a circuit or circuit element in order to determine the effective resistance.

The use of equation (13-1) in determining the ohmic resistance requires the application of the voltmeter-ammeter method for obtaining the necessary data. This method is discussed in Chapter 6. Data needed for the determination of the ohmic resistance by equation (13-2) or the effective resistance by equation (13-8) can be obtained by the test procedures discussed in Chapter 12.

Laboratory Problem No. 13-1

OHMIC AND EFFECTIVE RESISTANCE—I

Laboratory

In all parts of this problem use an inductance coil into which a solid-iron core or a laminated-iron core can be inserted.

In parts **2** and **3**, an a-c generator driven by a d-c shunt motor is a convenient means of obtaining the required constant ratio of voltage to frequency.

1. Use a d-c source of power for this test. Set up a circuit consisting of the coil and a suitable means for controlling the d-c current in the coil. Using a voltmeter, an ammeter, and a wattmeter, obtain data from which the voltage, current, and power of the coil can be determined for the following conditions:

(a) Coil without an iron core.
(b) Coil with a solid-iron core.
(c) Coil with a laminated-iron core.

2. In this test impress on the coil an a-c voltage having the magnitude and frequency designated by the instructor. Obtain data from which the effective resistance of the coil can be determined for conditions (a), (b), and (c) of **1.**

3. Repeat **2,** but with the frequency and the voltage across the coil reduced to 50 per cent of the values used in **2.** *Note*: A constant ratio of coil voltage to frequency is required to keep the maximum flux density in a given core approximately the same regardless of the frequency.

Report

A. From the data obtained in the laboratory, calculate the values indicated in the table below. In the table V, I, and P refer, respectively, to the voltage drop across the coil, the current in the coil, and the power supplied to the coil for the test condition indicated. Tabulate the calculated results in a copy of the table shown.

		D-C		A-C Part 2	A-C Part 3
		$\dfrac{V}{I}$	$\dfrac{P}{I^2}$	$\dfrac{P}{I^2}$	$\dfrac{P}{I^2}$
		1	*2*	*3*	*4*
Coil without an Iron Core	*a*				
Coil with Solid-Iron Core	*b*				
Coil with Laminated-Iron Core	*c*				

B. Compare and discuss fully the following:

(1) *1* and *2* for *a*, *b*, and *c*.
(2) *2* and *3* for *a*.
(3) *3* for *a* and *b*.
(4) *3* and *4* for *b*.
(5) *3* for *b* and *c*.

Laboratory Problem No. 13-2
OHMIC AND EFFECTIVE RESISTANCE—II

Laboratory

In all parts of this problem use an inductance coil with a laminated-iron core.

In order to meet the voltage and frequency requirements of parts **2**(b) and **3,** an a-c generator driven by a d-c shunt motor can be used.

1. Obtain data from which the ohmic resistance of the coil can be calculated.

2. (a) Impress on the coil an a-c voltage having the magnitude and frequency designated by the instructor.   Obtain data from which the effective resistance of the coil can be determined.

(b) Maintaining the ratio of coil voltage to frequency constant at the value used in (a), obtain data from which a curve of effective resistance of the coil vs frequency can be plotted.   The range of frequency should be from the value used in (a) to a value approximately 50 per cent of that value.

3. Maintaining the frequency constant at the value used in **2**(a), obtain data from which a curve of effective resistance of the coil vs coil voltage can be plotted.   The range of coil voltage should be from the value used in **2**(a) to a value approximately 50 per cent of that value.

Report

A. Calculate the ohmic resistance of the coil from the data obtained in **1** and the effective resistance from the data obtained in **2**(a).   Completely explain the difference in the calculated values.

B. Plot the curve for which data were obtained in **2**(b).

C. Plot the curve for which data were obtained in **3**.

D. Discuss the curve plotted in **B.**

E. Discuss the curve plotted in **C.**

CHAPTER 14

DETERMINATION OF IMPEDANCE
AND ITS COMPONENTS

1. Impedance. In Chapter 13 it is pointed out that an a-c version of Ohm's law is applicable to a circuit or circuit element when the impressed voltage and the current vary sinusoidally with time. In this case the opposition is called *impedance* and is denoted by the letter Z. Accordingly,

$$Z = \frac{V}{I}. \tag{14-1}$$

Z is in ohms when V, the effective value of the voltage drop across the terminals of the circuit or circuit element, is in volts and I, the effective value of the current in the circuit or circuit element, is in amperes.

Since the voltage drop across an impedance may not be in phase with the current through it, the impedance will in general be a complex quantity when the voltage drop across the impedance and the current in the impedance are expressed as vector quantities. Thus

$$\bar{Z} = \frac{\bar{V}}{\bar{I}}, \tag{14-2}$$

the lines over the letters being used to indicate vector or complex quantities.

2. Determination of Impedance Magnitude by the Voltmeter-Ammeter Method. From a consideration of equation (14-1) it should

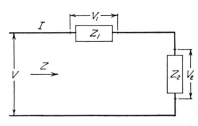

Fig. 14-1. Series circuit consisting of two impedances.

be clear that the voltmeter-ammeter method can be applied in order to obtain data from which the impedance of a circuit or circuit element can be calculated. The test procedures for the voltmeter-ammeter method discussed in Chapter 6 with regard to d-c circuits can also be used in a-c circuits except in those cases in which it is necessary to correct the ammeter indication for the current taken by the voltmeter. In these cases it is necessary to use the test procedure and ammeter correction discussed in Chapter 12 for such conditions.

162

If the values of I, V, V_1 and V_2 shown in Fig. 14-1 are measured, the indicated impedances can be determined, since

$$Z = \frac{V}{I}, \tag{14-3}$$

$$Z_1 = \frac{V_1}{I}, \tag{14-4}$$

and

$$Z_2 = \frac{V_2}{I}. \tag{14-5}$$

It is important to note that, when the measured values of the current and voltages are substituted in equations (14-3), (14-4), and (14-5), the resulting values of the impedances are the absolute values, or magnitudes, only.

3. Determination of the Magnitudes of the Components of an Impedance. *Method 1.* Impedance consists of two components, reactance and effective resistance. In complex notation it may be expressed as

$$\bar{Z} = R_e \pm jX. \tag{14-6}$$

The effective resistance R_e and the reactance X are measured in ohms. The plus sign in equation (14-6) is used when the reactance is inductive and the minus sign when it is capacitive.* As indicated by equation (14-6), impedance is the quadrature sum of the effective resistance and the reactance. Hence, in magnitude

$$Z = \sqrt{R_e^2 + X^2}. \tag{14-7}$$

If the voltage, current, and power supplied to a circuit or circuit element are measured, the impedance of the circuit or circuit element can be separated into its components. The effective resistance can be calculated from the current and power supplied to the circuit or circuit element, for in accordance with the definition of effective resistance

$$R_e = \frac{P}{I^2}. \tag{14-8}$$

The magnitude of the impedance can be determined by use of equation (14-1). Then, with Z and R_e known, the magnitude of the reactance

---

* Many authors write the general expression for impedance (equation 14-6) with only the $+$ sign and assign an algebraic sign to the quantity X, a $+$ sign being used when X is known to be inductive and a $-$ sign when it is known to be capacitive.

can be calculated, since equation (14-7) can be written in the form

$$X = \sqrt{Z^2 - R_e^2}. \tag{14-9}$$

Method 2. An alternative method of determining the components R_e and X requires no data other than that necessary in Method 1 and has the advantage of being more direct. Consider the impedance Z in (a) of Fig. 14-2. The available data determined by measurement are the power P supplied to Z and the magnitudes I and V.

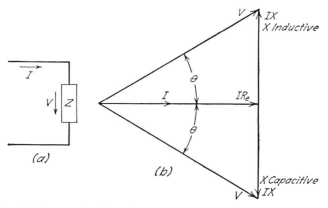

Fig. 14-2. (a) Current and voltage drop in an impedance. (b) Voltage-current vector diagram for (a).

For convenience, let the vector representing the current in Z be taken as a reference; that is, let the vector be drawn horizontally. Then

$$\bar{I} = I + j0.$$

This vector is shown in the vector diagram in (b) of the figure.

By Ohm's law
$$\bar{V} = \bar{I}\bar{Z}$$
$$= (I + j0)(R_e \pm jX).$$
$$\bar{V} = IR_e \pm jIX. \tag{14-10}$$

Accordingly the vector $\bar{V}$ is made up of the two components IR_e and $\pm jIX$. When X is inductive, the plus sign is used before jIX, and, when it is capacitive, the minus sign is used. The two possible positions of vector $\bar{V}$ as determined by equation (14-10) are shown in the vector diagram.

The power supplied to Z is

$$P = I^2 R_e. \tag{14-11}$$

From the vector diagram

$$IR_e = V \cos \theta. \tag{14-12}$$

Substitution of this value of IR_e in equation (14-11) gives

$$P = VI \cos \theta, \tag{14-13}$$

or

$$\cos \theta = \frac{P}{VI}. \tag{14-14}$$

The term $\cos \theta$ is called the *power factor*.

From an inspection of the vector diagram it is apparent that

$$IX = V \sin \theta. \tag{14-15}$$

Dividing equations (14-12) and (14-15) by I results in

$$R_e = \frac{V}{I} \cos \theta = Z \cos \theta, \tag{14-16}$$

and

$$X = \frac{V}{I} \sin \theta = Z \sin \theta. \tag{14-17}$$

Method 3. Methods 1 and 2 require the determination of the power delivered to the circuit element or circuit whose impedance components are to be determined. In the method described below a power measurement is not needed, all necessary data being obtained from ammeter and voltmeter measurements.

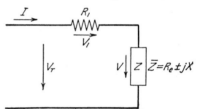

In Fig. 14-3, the impedance Z and its resistance and reactance components are to be determined. R_1 in this circuit is a pure resist-

Fig. 14-3. A resistor in series with an impedance for determining the components of the impedance.

ance. That R_1 be a pure resistance is important, for the method is based upon this premise. The impedance of the circuit including R_1 is*

$$\frac{\bar{V}_T}{\bar{I}} = \bar{Z}_T = R_1 + \bar{Z} = R_1 + R_e \pm jX,$$

and the magnitude of this impedance is

$$\frac{V_T}{I} = Z_T = \sqrt{(R_1 + R_e)^2 + X^2}. \tag{14-18}$$

The magnitude of Z is

$$\frac{V}{I} = Z = \sqrt{R_e^2 + X^2}. \tag{14-19}$$

---

* See page 172 for the method of determining the impedance of a circuit made up of elements connected in series.

Equations (14-18) and (14-19) may be solved simultaneously to determine R_e and X, the components of Z. From equation (14-18)

$$\left(\frac{V_T}{I}\right)^2 = R_1{}^2 + 2R_eR_1 + R_e{}^2 + X^2. \qquad (14\text{-}20)$$

From equation (14-19)

$$\left(\frac{V}{I}\right)^2 = R_e{}^2 + X^2. \qquad (14\text{-}21)$$

Subtraction of equation (14-21) from (14-20) gives

$$\frac{V_T{}^2 - V^2}{I^2} = R_1{}^2 + 2R_eR_1.$$

$$R_e = \frac{V_T{}^2 - V^2 - I^2R_1{}^2}{2I^2R_1}. \qquad (14\text{-}22)$$

If R_1 is known, R_e can be determined, since V_T, V, and I can be measured. If R_1 is not known, it can readily be determined by measuring the voltage drop across the resistance R_1. Let this voltage drop be represented by V_1. Then $R_1 = V_1/I$. Substitution of this value for R_1 in equation (14-22) gives

$$R_e = \frac{V_T{}^2 - V^2 - V_1{}^2}{2IV_1} = \frac{V_T{}^2 - (V^2 + V_1{}^2)}{2IV_1}. \qquad (14\text{-}23)$$

X can now be determined by substituting in equation (14-19) the value of R_e as determined from equation (14-23).

In the development of equation (14-23) it has been assumed that the current in the circuit is always the same. When this equation is to be used to determine R_e, it is necessary that the current I in the circuit and in the elements of the circuit does not change when measurements of V, V_1, and V_T are made. To conform with this requirement, the voltage V_T must be constant, or must be maintained constant by auxiliary apparatus.

When the voltage V_T cannot be depended upon to remain constant and it is not possible to maintain it constant by auxiliary apparatus, the current in Z should be measured simultaneously with a measurement of V. Let this measured value of current be designated by I'. Then

$$\frac{V}{I'} = Z = \sqrt{R_e{}^2 + X^2}. \qquad (14\text{-}24)$$

Now let V_T and the current be measured simultaneously also. Let the current in this case be designated by I''. Then

$$\frac{V_T}{I''} = Z_T = \sqrt{(R_1 + R_e)^2 + X^2}. \tag{14-25}$$

Solving equations (14-24) and (14-25) simultaneously gives

$$R_e = \frac{\left(\frac{V_T}{I''}\right)^2 - \left(\frac{V}{I'}\right)^2 - R_1{}^2}{2R_1} = \frac{Z_T{}^2 - Z^2 - R_1{}^2}{2R_1}$$
$$= \frac{Z_T{}^2 - (Z^2 + R_1{}^2)}{2R_1}. \tag{14-26}$$

The value of R_1, if not known, can be determined by the voltmeter-ammeter method.

This method has the disadvantage that small errors in measurements may lead to large errors in the calculated values of the resistance and reactance components, R_e and X, of the unknown impedance Z, as can be seen from an inspection of equations (14-23) and (14-26). In each of these equations the numerator is the difference between two quantities that might very well be of comparable magnitudes. In such a case a small error in either of the two quantities would lead to a large error in this difference and hence in the value of R_e. When this method is used, this fact should be kept in mind, and R_1 should be chosen or adjusted so as to avoid this possibility.

4. Determination of the Kind of Reactance Component. In the application of any of the foregoing methods only the magnitude X of the reactance component of the unknown impedance Z can be determined. Thus the methods do not provide a means for determining whether the reactance component of Z is inductive or capacitive.

In the case of a single circuit element it will usually be known whether the element is a resistance, a coil, or a condenser, so the kind of reactance will be known. Furthermore, when the unknown impedance is that of a circuit, it may be possible to determine whether the X component of the circuit impedance is inductive or capacitive from a knowledge of the circuit. Thus, if it is known that the circuit contains only resistances and inductances, then it is also known that the X component of the circuit impedance is inductive; if, on the other hand, the circuit contains only resistances and condensers, then the X component of the circuit impedance is known to be capacitive.

When a circuit contains both inductances and capacitances in addition to resistances, the X component of the circuit impedance may be either inductive or capacitive. Whether the X component is inductive or capacitive can be ascertained by connecting a reactance of known kind and magnitude in series with the circuit whose impedance is being determined. Thus a condenser may be connected in series with the circuit and a determination made of the X component of the new circuit. Since capacitive and inductive reactances have opposing effects in a series circuit, the X component of the original circuit impedance is inductive if the X component of the new circuit impedance is less than that of the original circuit or that of the added reactance; and it is capacitive if the X component of the new circuit impedance is greater than that of the original circuit and also that of the added reactance. If an inductance instead of a capacitance is connected in series with the original circuit, the original circuit reactance is capacitive if the effect of the coil is to cause the new circuit impedance to have a smaller X component than that of the original circuit or that of the added reactance, and it is inductive if the effect is to cause the X component of the new circuit impedance to be greater than that of the original circuit and also that of the added reactance. Regardless of whether an inductance or a capacitance is used, the frequency should be constant, and the test must be applied with caution, since the total reactance of the new circuit will be zero if the added reactance is equal to and of opposite kind to that of the circuit being tested, leaving the impedance of the new circuit with only a resistance component. If this resistance component is small, the current in the circuit may become large enough to cause damage to instruments or other circuit elements.

Since the reactance of a condenser is inversely proportional to the frequency of the current flowing in it and that of a coil is directly proportional to the frequency, it may be thought that the kind of X component of a circuit impedance can be readily determined by changing the frequency of the testing current and observing the effect of the change on the X component. This method is not recommended for general use, since in the case of a circuit of complex configuration the variation of the X component of the circuit impedance with change of frequency depends not only upon the frequency and the values of the R_e and X components of the circuit elements, but also upon the configuration of the circuit—that is, upon the manner in which the elements are connected to form the circuit. Such a circuit may consist of elements connected in series, in parallel, or in series parallel. In a complex circuit the impedance of the circuit and its R_e and X components may vary widely with a small change in the frequency of the testing current. To determine with certainty the kind of X component of the circuit impedance at the original testing frequency by this method, impedance determinations for many other frequencies may be required, the final conclusion being drawn from a study of the results obtained from the many tests.

Laboratory Problem No. 14-1
IMPEDANCE AND IMPEDANCE COMPONENTS

Laboratory

1. By means of a voltmeter, an ammeter, and a wattmeter, obtain data for determining the magnitudes of the resistance and reactance components of an unknown impedance at the frequency designated by the instructor.

2. By means of a voltmeter, an ammeter, and a suitable resistor, obtain data for determining the magnitudes of the resistance and reactance components of the unknown impedance at the frequency used in **1.**

3. Obtain the necessary data for determining whether the reactance component of the unknown impedance is inductive or capacitive at the frequency used in **1.**

Report

A. From the data obtained in **1,** determine the magnitudes of the resistance and reactance components of the unknown impedance.

B. From the data obtained in **2,** determine the magnitudes of the resistance and reactance components of the unknown impedance.

C. How do the values obtained in **A** and **B** compare? Discuss any discrepancies.

D. From the data obtained in **3,** determine whether the reactance component is inductive or capacitive.

E. Express the impedance of the unknown in rectangular form and also in polar form.

Laboratory Problem No. 14-2
OPPOSITION—IMPEDANCE, REACTANCE, EFFECTIVE RESISTANCE, AND OHMIC RESISTANCE

Laboratory

In all parts of this problem use an inductance coil into which a laminated-iron core can be inserted.

In order to meet the voltage and frequency requirements of parts **2** and **3**, an a-c generator driven by a d-c shunt motor can be used.

1. Use a d-c source of power for this test. Set up a circuit consisting of the coil and a suitable means for controlling the d-c current in the coil. Using a voltmeter, an ammeter, and a wattmeter, obtain data from which the voltage, current, and power of the coil can be determined for the following conditions:

> (a) Coil without an iron core.
> (b) Coil with a laminated-iron core.

2. In this test impress on the coil an a-c voltage having the magnitude and frequency designated by the instructor. Obtain data from which the voltage, current, and power of the coil can be determined for conditions (a) and (b) of **1**.

3. Repeat **2**, but with the frequency and the voltage across the coil reduced to 50 per cent of the values used in **2**. *Note:* A constant ratio of coil voltage to frequency is required in order that the maximum flux density in the core will be approximately the same regardless of the frequency used.

Report

A. From the data obtained in the laboratory, calculate the values indicated in the table below. In the table V, I, and P refer, respectively, to the voltage drop across the coil, the current in the coil, and the power supplied to the coil for the test condition indicated. Tabulate the calculated results in a copy of the table shown.

		D-C		A-C Part 2			A-C Part 3		
		$\dfrac{V}{I}$	$\dfrac{P}{I^2}$	$\dfrac{V}{I}$	$\dfrac{P}{I^2}$	$\sqrt{\left(\dfrac{V}{I}\right)^2 - \left(\dfrac{P}{I^2}\right)^2}$	$\dfrac{V}{I}$	$\dfrac{P}{I^2}$	$\sqrt{\left(\dfrac{V}{I}\right)^2 - \left(\dfrac{P}{I^2}\right)^2}$
		1	*2*	*3*	*4*	*5*	*6*	*7*	*8*
Coil without an Iron Core	*a*								
Coil with Laminated-Iron Core	*b*								

B. Compare and discuss fully the following:

(1) *1* and *2* for *a* and *b*.

(2) *2* and *4* for *a*.

(3) *4* for *a* and *b*.

(4) *4* and *7* for *b*.

(5) *5* for *a* and *b*.

(6) *5* and *8* for *b*.

(7) *1* and *3* for *a*.

(8) *3* for *a* and *b*.

(9) *3* and *6* for *b*.

CHAPTER 15
THE SERIES CIRCUIT

1. General Series Circuit. A general circuit consisting of several impedances connected in series is shown in Fig. 15-1. In such a circuit the current is the same in all of the elements, and the voltage drop across the entire circuit is equal to the vector sum of the voltage drops

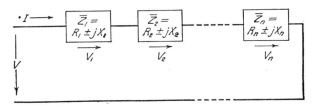

Fig. 15-1. Series circuit consisting of several impedances.

across the various impedances. Expressed mathematically,

$$\bar{V} = \bar{V}_1 + \bar{V}_2 + \cdots + \bar{V}_n. \tag{15-1}$$

According to Ohm's law,

$$\bar{V}_1 = \bar{I}\bar{Z}_1, \qquad \bar{V}_2 = \bar{I}\bar{Z}_2, \cdots, \qquad \bar{V}_n = \bar{I}\bar{Z}_n.$$

Consequently equation (15-1) can be written

$$\begin{aligned}
\bar{V} &= \bar{I}\bar{Z}_1 + \bar{I}\bar{Z}_2 + \cdots + \bar{I}\bar{Z}_n \\
&= \bar{I}(\bar{Z}_1 + \bar{Z}_2 + \cdots + \bar{Z}_n) \\
&= \bar{I}\bar{Z}, \tag{15-2}
\end{aligned}$$

where

$$\bar{Z} = \bar{Z}_1 + \bar{Z}_2 + \cdots + \bar{Z}_n, \tag{15-3}$$

$\bar{Z}$ being the circuit impedance—that is, the impedance of the entire circuit. If each of the component impedances is written in terms of its resistance and reactance, equation (15-3) becomes

$$\begin{aligned}
\bar{Z} &= (R_1 \pm jX_1) + (R_2 \pm jX_2) + \cdots + (R_n \pm jX_n) \tag{15-4} \\
&= (R_1 + R_2 + \cdots + R_n) \\
&\qquad + j(\pm X_1 \pm X_2 \pm \cdots \pm X_n) \tag{15-5} \\
&= R \pm jX, \tag{15-6}
\end{aligned}$$

where

$$R = R_1 + R_2 + \cdots + R_n, \qquad (15\text{-}7)$$

and

$$\pm jX = j(\pm X_1 \pm X_2 \pm \cdots \pm X_n). \qquad (15\text{-}8)$$

In equations (15-4), (15-5), (15-6), and (15-8) the $+$ sign is used with X when it is inductive and the $-$ sign when it is capacitive.

Equation (15-7) shows that for a series circuit the resistance component of the circuit impedance is equal to the sum of the resistance components of the impedances of the circuit elements. Likewise, in accordance with equation (15-8), the reactance component of the circuit impedance of a series circuit is equal to the algebraic sum of the reactance components of the impedances of the circuit elements. Therefore a series circuit made up of any number of impedances can be replaced at a single frequency by a simple circuit consisting of a single resistance R in series with a single reactance X.

Up to this point the quantities discussed have been treated as vector, or complex, quantities. If only the magnitudes of the circuit current and the voltage drop across the circuit are considered, then

$$V = IZ, \qquad (15\text{-}9)$$

in which

$$Z = \sqrt{R^2 + X^2}$$
$$= \sqrt{(R_1 + R_2 + \cdots + R_n)^2 + (\pm X_1 \pm X_2 \pm \cdots \pm X_n)^2}. \quad (15\text{-}10)$$

2. Resistor, Coil, and Condenser in Series. A series circuit consisting of a resistor, a coil, and a condenser provides an excellent means

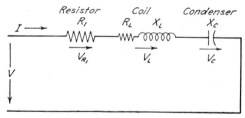

Fig. 15-2. Series circuit consisting of a resistor, a coil, and a condenser.

for a laboratory study of the series circuit. Such a circuit is represented in Fig. 15-2. Here R_1 indicates the resistance of the resistor, R_L the resistance of the coil, $X_L = 2\pi f L$, the inductive reactance of the coil, and $X_C = 1/2\pi f C$, the capacitive reactance of the condenser. In general, the resistance of a good-grade condenser is negligible when used in low-frequency circuits. However, the resistance of a coil is usually of appreciable magnitude and hence should be taken into consideration.

3. Impedance Diagrams. Assigning the correct signs to the reactance components, the impedance of the circuit of Fig. 15-2 is

$$\bar{Z} = R_1 + R_L + jX_L - jX_C = (R_1 + R_L) + j(X_L - X_C). \quad (15\text{-}11)$$

In magnitude,

$$Z = \sqrt{(R_1 + R_L)^2 + (X_L - X_C)^2}. \quad (15\text{-}12)$$

These relations can be illustrated graphically as in Fig. 15-3(a). By convention all symbols in equation (15-11) that are not associated with the operator j are horizontal components, and those which are operated on by j are vertical components. Hence, since R_1 is positive,

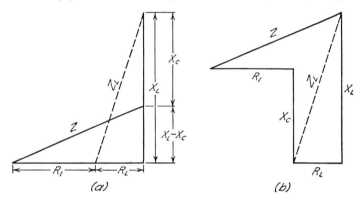

Fig. 15-3.   Impedance diagrams for the circuit of Fig. 15-2.

it is drawn horizontally to the right from the starting point. Its length must, of course, be to some selected scale, as must all other lengths on the diagram. R_L is also positive and is therefore drawn horizontally to the right from the finish end of R_1. Since X_L is operated on by $+j$, it is drawn vertically upward from the finish end of R_L. X_C is operated on by $-j$ and is thus drawn vertically downward from the finish end of X_L. A line drawn from the start of R_1 to the finish end of X_C is, in accordance with equation (15-11), the circuit impedance $\bar{Z}$. The tie between this figure and equation (15-12) is evident by inspection. In the example just covered, R_1 is arbitrarily considered to have a value greater than R_L, and X_L is considered greater than X_C.

A somewhat clearer diagram, Fig. 15-3(b), is obtained when the components of $\bar{Z}$ are considered in the order shown in the following equation:

$$\bar{Z} = R_1 - jX_C + R_L + jX_L.$$

This equation is the same as (15-11) with the terms rearranged.   Study of Figs. 15-3(a) and 15-3(b) will show that these figures are equivalent. In the figures the dotted lines represent the impedance $\bar{Z}_L$.   This fact is evident, since R_L and $+jX_L$ are the components of $\bar{Z}_L$.

Representations such as Figs. 15-3(a) and 15-3(b) are known as *impedance diagrams*.   They are useful because they give a visual picture of the manner in which impedances and their respective components are combined to give the total or equivalent circuit impedance.

4. Current-Voltage Vector Diagrams.   For the circuit of Fig. 15-2, the relationship between the total voltage drop $\bar{V}$, the circuit current $\bar{I}$, and the circuit impedance $\bar{Z}$ is

$$\bar{V} = \bar{I}\bar{Z}.$$

Substituting in this equation the value of $\bar{Z}$ from equation (15-11) gives

$$\bar{V} = \bar{I}(R_1 + R_L + jX_L - jX_C)$$
$$= \bar{I}R_1 + \bar{I}R_L + j\bar{I}X_L - j\bar{I}X_C. \qquad (15\text{-}13)$$

Since the current in a series circuit is the same in all parts of the circuit, it is only logical that the current vector be used as reference.   When this is done,

$$\bar{I} = I + j0,$$

and equation (15-13) becomes

$$\bar{V} = IR_1 + IR_L + jIX_L - jIX_C. \qquad (15\text{-}14)$$

In Fig. 15-4 the vectors representing the various components of the total voltage drop $\bar{V}$ are drawn from a common origin.   A common origin is preferable in drawing current-voltage vector diagrams because it gives a clear picture of the phase relations between

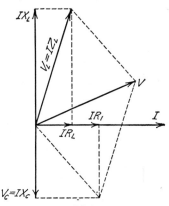

Fig. 15-4. Voltage-current vector diagram for the circuit of Fig. 15-2.

the various vectors.   The order in which the component vectors are added in determining the vector $\bar{V}$ is immaterial.

5. Resonance.   Resonance is said to exist in a series circuit containing inductance and capacitance when the voltage drop across the circuit and the circuit current are in phase; in other words, when the power factor of the circuit is unity.

Equation (15-14), which relates to the circuit in Fig. 15-2, can be written as

$$\bar{V} = I(R_1 + R_L) + jI(X_L - X_C). \qquad (15\text{-}15)$$

In the development of equation (15-14) the current vector was used as the reference. Therefore from an inspection of equation (15-15) it should be clear that to obtain resonance in the circuit—that is, for $\bar{V}$ and $\bar{I}$ to be in phase—the j term must be zero. This condition requires that the magnitudes of X_L and X_C be equal. When this condition prevails, IX_L and IX_C are equal, as shown in Fig. 15-5, which is the vector diagram for the resonant condition in the series circuit shown in Fig. 15-2. Although $IX_L = IX_C$, it does not follow that the voltage drop across the condenser is equal to the voltage drop across the coil. The drop across the coil is

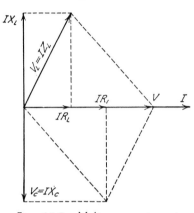

Fig. 15-5. Voltage-current vector diagram for resonant condition in the circuit of Fig. 15-2.

$$V_L = IZ_L = \sqrt{(IR_L)^2 + (IX_L)^2},$$

which obviously is greater than $IX_L = IX_C = V_C$. This point is well brought out in the vector diagram.

According to equation (15-12), when the resonant condition exists in the circuit of Fig. 15-2, the circuit impedance Z_R is

$$Z_R = \sqrt{(R_1 + R_L)^2 + (0)^2} \qquad (15\text{-}16)$$
$$= R_1 + R_L.$$

Thus at resonance the resultant impedance of the circuit is equal to its total resistance. It follows that the circuit current I_R at resonance is

$$I_R = \frac{V}{R_1 + R_L}. \qquad (15\text{-}17)$$

Consequently, when a series circuit is resonant the magnitude of the circuit current is entirely independent of the magnitudes of the inductive and capacitive reactances, being limited only by the total circuit resistance.

When resonance exists in the circuit of Fig. 15-2, the voltage drop V_{L_R} across the coil is

$$V_{L_R} = \frac{V}{R_1 + R_L} \sqrt{R_L^2 + X_L^2}, \qquad (15\text{-}18)$$

and the voltage drop V_{C_R} across the condenser is

$$V_{C_R} = \frac{V}{R_1 + R_L} X_C. \qquad (15\text{-}19)$$

Therefore, if the circuit resistance $(R_1 + R_L)$ is small compared to the reactances X_L and X_C at resonance, the voltages V_{L_R} and V_{C_R} may be several times the impressed voltage V.

To bring about the condition of resonance in a series circuit containing R, L, and C, the condition that must be attained is

$$X_L = X_C,$$

or

$$2\pi f L = \frac{1}{2\pi f C},$$

or

$$4\pi^2 f^2 LC = 1. \qquad (15\text{-}20)$$

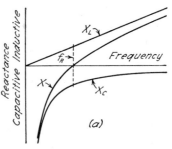

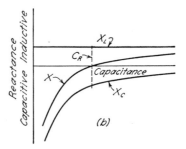

From equation (15-20) it can be seen that resonance can be produced either by varying the frequency f while holding L and C constant or by adjusting L or C or both and maintaining the frequency constant.

6. Resonance by Varying the Frequency. If the frequency is varied and L and C are kept constant, the value of frequency f_R at which resonance will occur can be determined by solving equation (15-20) for the frequency; thus

$$f_R{}^2 = \frac{1}{4\pi^2 LC},$$

and

$$f_R = \frac{1}{2\pi \sqrt{LC}}. \qquad (15\text{-}21)$$

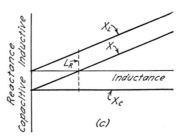

Fig. 15-6. Variation of the inductive reactance X_L, the capacitive reactance X_C, and the circuit reactance X of a series circuit containing R, L, and C (a) when the frequency is varied, (b) when the capacitance is varied, and (c) when the inductance is varied.

That there is a frequency at which $X_L = X_C$ can be seen by an inspection of Fig. 15-6(a) in which X_L and X_C are plotted as functions of frequency.

The current in the circuit of Fig. 15-2 for any condition is

$$I = \frac{V}{Z} = \frac{V}{\sqrt{(R_1 + R_L)^2 + (X_L - X_C)^2}}. \qquad (15\text{-}22)$$

If the impressed voltage V is maintained constant but the frequency is caused to vary from some value less than the resonant frequency

f_R to some value greater than f_R, the current in the circuit will change in the manner shown by the resonance curve (a) in Fig. 15-7. As indicated, the current will attain its maximum value of $V/(R_1 + R_L)$ at the resonant frequency, since at this frequency $(X_L - X_C)$ in equation (15-22) is zero and the denominator of the equation will have its minimum value.

Since the frequency at which resonance is obtained is determined by $(X_L - X_C)$, adding resistance to the circuit will not change the resonant frequency. The only effect will be to reduce the current in the circuit. The addition of such a resistance will be most effective at the resonant frequency. Thus, if the circuit resistance is doubled, the current at the resonant frequency will be $V/2(R_1 + R_L)$, or one half of its former value. The resonance curve for this condition is illustrated by curve (b) in Fig. 15-7. It will be noted that, as the frequency interval between the resonant frequency and that of the impressed voltage is increased, the effect of doubling resistance on the circuit current becomes less, as evidenced by the vertical difference between the two curves. A study of equation (15-22) will also show this to be true, for in this equation $(X_L - X_C)$ increases as the frequency of the impressed voltage is caused to depart from the resonant frequency. This fact is illustrated by the curve of X in Fig. 15-6(a), X being the circuit reactance $X_L - X_C$. Unless $(R_1 + R_L)$ is large, the current in the circuit is influenced mostly by the circuit reactance $(X_L - X_C)$ at frequencies that are considerably different from the resonant frequency. As the curves in Fig. 15-7 show, the effect of increasing the circuit resistance is to flatten the resonance curve.

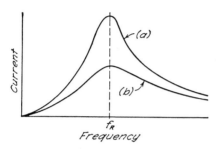

Fig. 15-7. Variation of the current in a series circuit containing R, L, and C when the impressed voltage is constant and the frequency is varied; curve (a) for small circuit resistance, and curve (b) for large circuit resistance.

For any value of current in the circuit of Fig. 15-2 the voltage drop across the coil is

$$V_L = IZ_L = \frac{V \sqrt{R_L{}^2 + X_L{}^2}}{\sqrt{(R_1 + R_L)^2 + (X_L - X_C)^2}}$$

$$= \frac{V \sqrt{R_L{}^2 + (2\pi f L)^2}}{\sqrt{(R_1 + R_L)^2 + \left(2\pi f L - \dfrac{1}{2\pi f C}\right)^2}}, \quad (15\text{-}23)$$

and the voltage drop across the condenser is

$$V_C = IX_C = \frac{VX_C}{\sqrt{(R_1 + R_L)^2 + (X_L - X_C)^2}}$$

$$= \frac{V}{2\pi f C \sqrt{(R_1 + R_L)^2 + \left(2\pi f L - \dfrac{1}{2\pi f C}\right)^2}}. \qquad (15\text{-}24)$$

It might seem that, since the circuit current is maximum at the resonant frequency, the voltages V_L and V_C would also be maximum at this frequency. This, however, is not the case if the voltage impressed on the circuit is maintained constant and the frequency is varied. Under these conditions it will be found that V_C will attain its maximum value at some frequency less than the resonant frequency f_R, and V_L will attain its maximum value at some frequency greater than f_R. The truth of this fact can be verified by differentiating equations (15-23) and (15-24) with respect to frequency, equating the derivatives to zero, and solving for the frequency in each case. Because of the presence of R_1 in the circuit the equation for the frequency at which V_L attains its maximum value is quite complex.* However, if R_1 is removed from the circuit but R_L is retained, the equation is much simplified and shows fully as well that the voltage V_L across the coil attains its maximum value at a frequency greater than the resonant frequency $f_R = 1/2\pi \sqrt{LC}$. With R_1 eliminated, V_L attains its maximum value at

$$f_{V_{L_{\max}}} = \frac{1}{2\pi \sqrt{LC}} \sqrt{\frac{1 + \sqrt{1 + \dfrac{2R_L{}^2 C}{L}}}{2}}, \qquad (15\text{-}25)$$

and V_C attains its maximum value at

$$f_{V_{C_{\max}}} = \frac{1}{2\pi \sqrt{LC}} \sqrt{1 - \frac{R_L{}^2 C}{2L}}. \qquad (15\text{-}26)$$

---

* With R_1 in the circuit, the frequency at which V_L is a maximum is

$$f_{V_{L_{\max}}} =$$

$$\frac{1}{2\pi \sqrt{LC}} \sqrt{\frac{L}{2L - R_1{}^2 C - R_1 R_L C} \left[1 + \sqrt{1 + \frac{R_L{}^2 C (2L - R_1{}^2 C - R_1 R_L C)}{L^2}}\right]},$$

and that at which V_C is a maximum is

$$f_{V_{C_{\max}}} = \frac{1}{2\pi \sqrt{LC}} \sqrt{1 - \frac{(R_1 + R_L)^2 C}{2L}}.$$

In Fig. 15-8 are shown curves typical of those of the variation of V_L and V_C as the frequency is varied while the applied voltage is maintained constant.

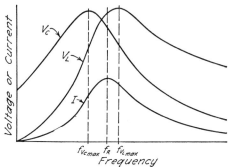

Fig. 15-8. Variation of the current I, the condenser voltage V_C, and the coil voltage V_L in a series circuit when the impressed voltage is constant and the frequency is varied.

7. Resonance by Varying Capacitance. As stated in connection with equation (15-20), resonance in a series circuit can be brought about by adjustment of L or C if the frequency of the impressed voltage is held constant. If L and the frequency of the applied voltage are constant but C is varied, the value of capacitance C_R at which resonance will be obtained can be determined by solving equation (15-20) for C. This gives

$$C_R = \frac{1}{4\pi^2 f^2 L}. \tag{15-27}$$

If the voltage impressed on the circuit is maintained constant as C is varied, the variation of the circuit current will be similar to that shown in Fig. 15-9, with maximum current flowing when the circuit is resonant. Since the impedance of the coil $Z_L = \sqrt{R_L^2 + (2\pi f L)^2}$ will not change as C is varied, the voltage across the coil will attain its maximum value when the current is maximum—that is, at resonance. Maximum voltage across the condenser, however, will occur at a value of capacitance $C_{V_{C_{\max}}}$ which is less than the value producing resonance. This fact can be shown to be true for the circuit of Fig. 15-2 by differentiating equation (15-24) with respect to C, equating the derivative to zero, and solving for C. This solution gives

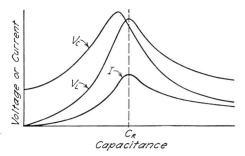

Fig. 15-9. Variation of the current I, the condenser voltage V_C, and the coil voltage V_L in a series circuit when only the capacitance is varied.

$$C_{V_{C_{\max}}} = \frac{1}{4\pi^2 f^2 L + \dfrac{(R_1 + R_L)^2}{L}}. \qquad (15\text{-}28)$$

In Fig. 15-9 the curves of V_L and V_C show typical variations of these voltages when only C is varied.

8. Resonance by Varying Inductance. If the inductance L of a series circuit is varied while C and the frequency of the impressed voltage are held constant, the inductance L_R that will produce resonance is, according to equation (15-20),

$$L_R = \frac{1}{4\pi^2 f^2 C}. \qquad (15\text{-}29)$$

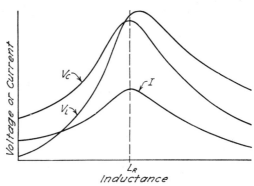

Varying L to obtain resonance results in complications, for it is hardly possible to vary an inductance without also causing its effective resistance to vary.* However, if the circuit contains other resistance, such as R_1 in Fig.

Fig. 15-10. Variation of the current I, the condenser voltage V_C, and the coil voltage V_L in a series circuit when only the inductance is varied.

15-2, making the effective resistance of the coil small compared with the resistance of the circuit, then for all practical purposes the change of coil resistance may be assumed to have negligible effect when L is varied. In this case, if the impressed voltage is kept constant, the current in the circuit will vary with L in a manner similar to that indicated in Fig. 15-10, maximum current flowing when the circuit is resonant./ Since the impedance of the condenser will not be affected by a change in L, the voltage across the condenser will also be a maximum at resonance. The voltage across the coil, however, will attain its maximum value at a value of inductance $L_{V_{L_{\max}}}$ which is greater than that at resonance. $L_{V_{L_{\max}}}$ can be determined for the circuit of Fig. 15-2 by differentiating equation (15-23) with respect

---

* The inductance can be varied without causing an appreciable change in its effective resistance if the variation in inductance is obtained by the use of two coils whose mutual inductance can be varied. For a discussion of mutual inductance see Chapter 17.

to L, setting the derivative equal to zero, and solving for L. This solution gives

$$L_{V_{L_{\max}}} = \frac{1}{2}\left[\frac{1 + \omega^2C^2(R_1{}^2 + 2R_1R_L)}{4\pi^2f^2C} + \sqrt{\left[\frac{1 + \omega^2C^2(R_1{}^2 + 2R_1R_L)}{4\pi^2f^2C}\right]^2 + \frac{4R_L{}^2}{\omega^2}}\right]. \quad (15\text{-}30)$$

Since $[1 + \omega^2C^2(R_1{}^2 + 2R_1R_L)]$ is always greater than 1, a comparison of equations (15-29) and (15-30) shows that $L_{V_{L_{\max}}} > L_R$. The curves in Fig. 15-10 show typical variations of V_L and V_C when only L is varied.

Laboratory Problem No. 15-1

SERIES A-C CIRCUITS CONTAINING RESISTANCE, INDUCTANCE, AND CAPACITANCE

Laboratory

Use the resistor, inductance coil, and condenser designated by the instructor.

1. Set up a series circuit consisting of the resistor and coil. With the a-c voltage applied to the circuit maintained constant at the value designated by the instructor, measure the following:

(a) Circuit current.

(b) Voltage applied to the circuit and the voltage across each circuit element.

(c) Power supplied to the circuit and to each circuit element.

2. Replace the coil with the condenser and make the measurements specified in **1**.

3. Connect the coil in series with the resistor and condenser and make the measurements specified in **1**.

Report

A. From the data obtained in **1** calculate the vector value of the voltage drop across each circuit element, using the circuit current as the reference vector. Draw to scale a vector diagram showing the circuit current and the voltage drops across the circuit elements. Draw all vectors from a common origin.

From the vector diagram, determine graphically the value of the voltage drop across the entire circuit and the power-factor angle of the circuit. How does the value of the circuit voltage drop compare with the measured value? How does the power-factor angle compare with that determined by calculation from data obtained in **1?** Discuss any discrepancies.

B. Repeat **A,** using the data obtained in **2.**

C. Repeat **A,** using the data obtained in **3.**

Laboratory Problem No. 15-2
RESONANCE IN A SERIES CIRCUIT—VARIABLE FREQUENCY

Laboratory

1. Set up a series circuit consisting of a resistor, an inductance coil, and a condenser.   The inductance of the coil and the capacitance of the condenser should be such that resonance will be obtained at a frequency about in the middle of the frequency range designated by the instructor.   The resistor should have sufficient resistance so that it and the resistance of the coil will limit the circuit current, the condenser voltage, and the coil voltage to permissible maximum values when the test outlined in **2** is performed.

2. With the voltage applied to the circuit maintained constant at the value designated by the instructor, vary the frequency in steps over the assigned range.   At each step obtain data for plotting the following curves:

> (a) Coil voltage V_L vs frequency.
> (b) Condenser voltage V_C vs frequency.
> (c) Current vs frequency.

In the vicinity of resonance take data at a sufficient number of frequencies to assure well-defined curves.

Report

A. On a single set of coordinate axes plot the curves for which data were obtained in **2.**

B. Why are the values of V_L and V_C different at the resonant frequency?

C. Explain why the curves of V_L and V_C do not peak at the resonant frequency.

D. Using data taken from the curves at the resonant frequency only, determine the following:

> (1) Reactance and capacitance of the condenser.
> (2) Impedance of the coil.
> (3) Reactance and inductance of the coil.

(4) Resistance of the coil.

(5) Resistance of the entire circuit.

(6) Resistance of the resistor.

E. From the curve of current determine the magnitude of the circuit current at a selected frequency midway between the resonant frequency and the maximum used. Using this current as the reference vector and using the constants of the circuit elements as determined in **D,** calculate the vector values of V_L, V_C, and the impressed voltage V for the selected frequency. Draw to scale the current-voltage vector diagram, showing all the vectors.

How do the values of V_L and V_C determined above check with the values obtained from the curves? How does the value of the impressed voltage determined above compare with the actual voltage impressed on the circuit? Discuss any discrepancies.

F. Derive the equation for the resonant frequency, $f_R = 1/2\pi \sqrt{LC}$.

Laboratory Problem No. 15-3

RESONANCE IN A SERIES CIRCUIT—VARIABLE INDUCTANCE

Laboratory

A variable inductance with a nearly constant resistance can be obtained conveniently by connecting in series two inductance coils the magnetic coupling of which can be varied. The minimum inductance of the series combination is obtained when the coils are coupled as closely as possible and the series connection is such that the magnetomotive forces produced by current in the coils are in opposite directions. The inductance can then be increased by decreasing the coupling between the coils. When further decrease in coupling causes little change in inductance, the inductance can be further increased by reversing the connections to one coil and then increasing the coupling. The maximum inductance is obtained under this condition when the coupling is again a maximum.*

1. Set up a series circuit consisting of a condenser and a variable inductance. The capacitance of the condenser should be of such a value that, at the frequency to be used, resonance will take place at a value of inductance about in the middle of the inductance range.

2. With the voltage applied to the circuit maintained constant at a value that will limit the circuit current at resonance to a value

---

* For proof of these statements see the developments of equations (17-20) and (17-23).

slightly less than the greatest permissible value, vary the inductance in steps from its minimum to its maximum value. At each step obtain data for plotting the following curves:

(a) Coil voltage V_L vs inductance.*
(b) Condenser voltage V_C vs inductance.
(c) Current vs inductance.

In the vicinity of resonance take data at a sufficient number of inductance values to assure well-defined curves.

Report

A. Make up a table containing the following items for every step of the test:

(1) Voltage applied to the circuit.
(2) Circuit current.
(3) Condenser voltage.
(4) Coil voltage.
(5) Impedance of the coil.
(6) Effective resistance of the coil.
(7) Reactance of the coil.
(8) Inductance of the coil.
(9) Capacitance of the condenser.

B. On a single set of coordinate axes, plot the following curves:

(1) Coil voltage vs inductance.
(2) Condenser voltage vs inductance.
(3) Current vs inductance.

C. Assuming that the effective resistance of the circuit remained constant for all values of inductance, calculate the value of this resistance, using the magnitude of the impressed voltage and data taken from the curve sheet.

D. At what value of inductance did resonance take place? Calculate the value of inductance at which resonance should have taken place. How do these two values check?

E. Does the curve of V_C peak at the proper value of inductance? Explain.

---

* Ii the method of varying the inductance by changing the coupling is used, the effective resistance of the coil may be assumed to remain constant for the purpose of determining what data are needed for calculating the inductance. In this case a single power measurement to determine the power dissipation in the variable inductance will be sufficient. This power measurement should be made when the circuit is at or near the condition of resonance.

F. Assuming that the effective resistance of the variable inductance does not change appreciably in the vicinity of resonance, calculate the value of inductance $L_{V_{L_{max}}}$, the inductance for which the voltage across the coil should be greatest. How does this value check with that indicated by the curve of V_L vs inductance?

Laboratory Problem No. 15-4
RESONANCE IN A SERIES CIRCUIT—VARIABLE CAPACITANCE

Laboratory

1. Set up a series circuit consisting of an inductance coil and a condenser the capacitance of which can be varied. The inductance of the coil should be such that resonance will take place in the circuit at a value of capacitance about in the middle of the range of variation of the condenser capacitance when the frequency designated by the instructor is used.

2. With the voltage applied to the circuit maintained constant at a value that will limit the circuit current at resonance to a value slightly less than the greatest permissible value, vary the capacitance in steps over its entire range of variation. At each step obtain data for plotting the following curves:

    (a) Coil voltage V_L vs capacitance.
    (b) Condenser voltage V_C vs capacitance.
    (c) Current vs capacitance.

In the vicinity of resonance take data at a sufficient number of values of capacitance to assure well-defined curves.

Report

A. Make up a table containing the following items for every step of the test:

    (1) Voltage applied to the circuit.
    (2) Circuit current.
    (3) Coil voltage.
    (4) Condenser voltage.
    (5) Reactance of the condenser.
    (6) Capacitance of the condenser.

B. On a single set of coordinate axes plot the following curves:

    (1) Coil voltage vs capacitance.
    (2) Condenser voltage vs capacitance.
    (3) Current vs capacitance.

C. Using the magnitude of the impressed voltage and data taken from the curve sheet, calculate the effective resistance of the circuit.

D. Does the curve of V_L peak at the proper value of capacitance? Explain.

E. Calculate the value of capacitance at which the voltage across the condenser should be the greatest. How does this value check with that indicated by the curve of V_c vs capacitance?

F. Explain why the curves of V_c and V_L do not intersect at the value of capacitance that causes resonance in the circuit.

CHAPTER 16

THE PARALLEL CIRCUIT

1. General Parallel Circuit. In Fig. 16-1 is shown a circuit consisting of a number of circuit elements, or impedances, connected in
parallel. In the series circuit discussed in the preceding chapter, the
current is common to all of the circuit elements, and the impressed
voltage or the voltage drop across the circuit is equal to the vector
sum of the voltage drops across the circuit elements. In a circuit
consisting of elements connected in parallel as shown in the figure, it

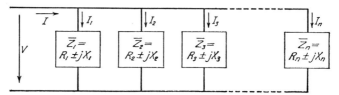

Fig. 16-1. Parallel circuit consisting of several impedances.

is the impressed voltage $\bar{V}$ that is common to all of the elements, and
the current $\bar{I}$ supplied to the circuit is equal to the vector sum of the
currents in the paralleled elements; thus

$$\bar{I} = \bar{I}_1 + \bar{I}_2 + \bar{I}_3 + \cdots + \bar{I}_n. \tag{16-1}$$

2. Admittance. If Ohm's law is applied to the circuit as a whole
and also to each branch,

$$\bar{V} = \bar{I}\bar{Z} = \bar{I}_1\bar{Z}_1 = \bar{I}_2\bar{Z}_2 = \bar{I}_3\bar{Z}_3 = \cdots = \bar{I}_n\bar{Z}_n,$$

and

$$\bar{I} = \frac{\bar{V}}{\bar{Z}}, \qquad \bar{I}_1 = \frac{\bar{V}}{\bar{Z}_1}, \qquad \bar{I}_2 = \frac{\bar{V}}{\bar{Z}_2}, \qquad \bar{I}_3 = \frac{\bar{V}}{\bar{Z}_3}, \qquad \cdots, \qquad \bar{I}_n = \frac{\bar{V}}{\bar{Z}_n}.$$

Substituting these values for the currents in equation (16-1) gives

$$\frac{\bar{V}}{\bar{Z}} = \frac{\bar{V}}{\bar{Z}_1} + \frac{\bar{V}}{\bar{Z}_2} + \frac{\bar{V}}{\bar{Z}_3} + \cdots + \frac{\bar{V}}{\bar{Z}_n},$$

and

$$\frac{1}{\bar{Z}} = \frac{1}{\bar{Z}_1} + \frac{1}{\bar{Z}_2} + \frac{1}{\bar{Z}_3} + \cdots + \frac{1}{\bar{Z}_n} \tag{16-2}$$

$$= \frac{1}{R_1 \pm jX_1} + \frac{1}{R_2 \pm jX_2} + \frac{1}{R_3 \pm jX_3} + \cdots + \frac{1}{R_n \pm jX_n}. \tag{16-3}$$

188

Rationalizing each term gives

$$\frac{1}{\bar{Z}} = \left(\frac{R_1}{Z_1^2} \mp j\frac{X_1}{Z_1^2}\right) + \left(\frac{R_2}{Z_2^2} \mp j\frac{X_2}{Z_2^2}\right) + \left(\frac{R_3}{Z_3^2} \mp j\frac{X_3}{Z_3^2}\right)$$
$$+ \cdots + \left(\frac{R_n}{Z_n^2} \mp j\frac{X_n}{Z_n^2}\right) \quad (16\text{-}4)$$

This equation may also be written in the following forms:

$$\frac{1}{\bar{Z}} = \bar{Y} = (G_1 \mp jB_1) + (G_2 \mp jB_2) + (G_3 \mp jB_3) + \cdots$$
$$+ (G_n \mp jB_n) \quad (16\text{-}5)$$
$$= \bar{Y}_1 + \bar{Y}_2 + \bar{Y}_3 + \cdots + \bar{Y}_n \quad (16\text{-}6)$$
$$= (G_1 + G_2 + G_3 + \cdots + G_n)$$
$$+ j(\mp B_1 \mp B_2 \mp B_3 \mp \cdots \mp B_n).$$

Comparing equations (16-2) and (16-6) it is seen that $\bar{Y}$, $\bar{Y}_1$, $\bar{Y}_2$, and so forth, are the reciprocals of $\bar{Z}$, $\bar{Z}_1$, $\bar{Z}_2$, and so forth, respectively. The terms $\bar{Y}$, $\bar{Y}_1$, $\bar{Y}_2$, and so forth, are called *admittances*. Admittance, like impedance, is a complex quantity. It consists of a component G called the *conductance* and a quadrature component B called the *susceptance*. From equations (16-4) and (16-5) it is seen that the conductance G is equal to the ratio of the resistance to the absolute value of the impedance squared, and the susceptance B is equal to the ratio of the reactance to the absolute value of the impedance squared. It will also be noted that these equations differ from the expression for impedance in that the sign before the quadrature component is minus instead of plus when the element is inductive and is plus instead of minus when the element is capac-

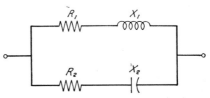

Fig. 16-2. Two-branch parallel circuit.

itive. Thus, referring to Fig. 16-2, it can be seen that

$$\bar{Z}_1 = R_1 + jX_1,$$
but
$$\bar{Y}_1 = G_1 - jB_1,$$
and
$$\bar{Z}_2 = R_2 - jX_2,$$
but
$$\bar{Y}_2 = G_2 + jB_2$$

The propriety of these equations is easily verified as follows:

$$\bar{Y}_1 = \frac{1}{\bar{Z}_1} = \frac{1}{R_1 + jX_1} = \frac{(R_1 - jX_1)}{(R_1 + jX_1)(R_1 - jX_1)} = \frac{R_1 - jX_1}{R_1^2 + X_1^2}$$
$$= \frac{R_1}{Z_1^2} - j\frac{X_1}{Z_1^2} = G_1 - jB_1.$$

$$\bar{Y}_2 = \frac{1}{\bar{Z}_2} = \frac{1}{R_2 - jX_2} = \frac{(R_2 + jX_2)}{(R_2 - jX_2)(R_2 + jX_2)} = \frac{R_2 + jX_2}{R_2{}^2 + X_2{}^2}$$

$$= \frac{R_2}{Z_2{}^2} + j\frac{X_2}{Z_2{}^2} = G_2 + jB_2.$$

To be consistent with this, it will be noted that in equation (16-3), in which the denominators are impedances, the $+$ sign is over the $-$ sign, but in equation (16-5), in which the terms enclosed within the parentheses are admittances, the $-$ sign is placed over the $+$ sign.

Admittances are rarely used in the analysis and solution of a-c circuits containing series elements only, for in such a circuit the total impedance is obtained by the simple addition of the complex quantities representing the impedances of the elements contained in the circuit. However, in a circuit containing elements connected in parallel, the use of admittances instead of impedances is advantageous, for in such a case the total admittance is the simple sum of the complex quantities representing the admittances of the elements contained in the circuit.

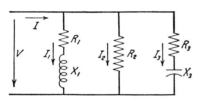

3. Admittance Diagrams. Consider the circuit shown in Fig. 16-3. The total admittance is

Fig. 16-3.   Three-branch parallel circuit.

$$\bar{Y} = \bar{Y}_1 + \bar{Y}_2 + \bar{Y}_3$$
$$= (G_1 - jB_1) + (G_2 + j0) + (G_3 + jB_3).$$

The graphical interpretation of this summation is shown in the admittance diagram in Fig. 16-4.

4. Current-Voltage Vector Diagrams. In the analysis and solution of circuits containing parallel elements only, the vector representing the voltage drop across the circuit is

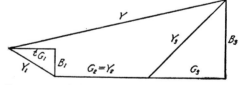

Fig. 16-4.   Admittance diagram for the circuit of Fig. 16-3.

usually taken as the reference vector, since this voltage is common to all of the parallel branches. On this basis, the complex expression for the vector representing V of Fig. 16-3 is

$$\bar{V} = V + j0$$

and $\bar{I}_1 = \dfrac{\bar{V}}{\bar{Z}_1} = \bar{V}\bar{Y}_1 = (V + j0)(G_1 - jB_1) = VG_1 - jVB_1,$

$$\bar{I}_2 = \frac{\bar{V}}{\bar{Z}_2} = \bar{V}\bar{Y}_2 = (V + j0)(G_2 + j0) = VG_2 + j0,$$

$$\bar{I}_3 = \frac{V}{\bar{Z}_3} = \bar{V}\bar{Y}_3 = (V + j0)(G_3 + jB_3) = VG_3 + jVB_3,$$

and $\bar{I} = \bar{I}_1 + \bar{I}_2 + \bar{I}_3 = V(G_1 + G_2 + G_3) + jV(B_3 - B_1).$

All of these currents are represented vectorially in Fig. 16-5.

Two very significant facts are apparent from a study of the current equations and from the vector diagram; namely, the product of the voltage and the conductance is the component of the current in phase with the voltage, and the product of the voltage and the susceptance is the component of the current in quadrature with the voltage.

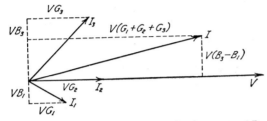

Fig. 16-5.   Voltage-current vector diagram for the circuit of Fig. 16-3.

Since power is equal to the product of the magnitudes of the voltage and the component of the current in phase with the voltage,

$$P = V \times VG = V^2 G.$$

5. Impedance of a Parallel Circuit.   Equation (16-2) shows that the reciprocal of the circuit impedance $\bar{Z}$ is equal to the sum of the reciprocals of the complex values of the impedances that are connected in parallel.   This relationship is similar to that for resistances connected in parallel.

When only two impedances are in parallel, as in Fig. 16-2, the relationship between the equivalent impedance of the circuit and the two impedances is

$$\frac{1}{\bar{Z}} = \frac{1}{\bar{Z}_1} + \frac{1}{\bar{Z}_2}.$$

Solving for $\bar{Z}$ gives

$$\bar{Z} = \frac{\bar{Z}_1\bar{Z}_2}{\bar{Z}_1 + \bar{Z}_2}. \tag{16-7}$$

Thus the single impedance that is equivalent to two impedances connected in parallel is equal to the product of the two impedances divided by their sum, the impedances being expressed in complex form.

6. Resonance.   In connection with the series circuit consisting of R, L, and C, the condition of resonance is said to exist when the circuit current is in phase with the voltage drop across the circuit or the voltage impressed on the circuit. For the sake of consistency, resonance in a parallel circuit containing L and C in parallel branches is similarly defined here. Thus resonance exists in the circuit of Fig. 16-6 when $\bar{V}$ and $\bar{I}$ are in phase, or when the power factor of the circuit is unity.

In the circuit of Fig. 16-6

$$\bar{I} = \frac{\bar{V}}{\bar{Z}} = \bar{V}\bar{Y} = \bar{V}[(G_1 + G_2) + j(B_2 - B_1)].$$

This equation shows that in order for $\bar{V}$ and $\bar{I}$ to be in phase the j term of the circuit admittance must be zero—in other words, B_1 and B_2

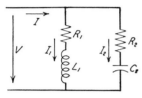

Fig. 16-6. Two-branch parallel circuit.

must be equal in magnitude. Hence the condition for resonance in the parallel circuit of Fig. 16-6 is

$$B_1 = B_2. \qquad (16\text{-}8)$$

In the series circuit consisting of R, L, and C it was shown that maximum current is obtained at resonance when the impressed voltage and R remain constant. If the voltage is maintained constant across a parallel circuit containing L and C in parallel branches, such as shown in Fig. 16-6, the line current will generally attain its minimum value near or at resonance. Because of this fact, the term *antiresonance* instead of resonance is often used in connection with the parallel circuit.

7. Resonance with L and R in Parallel with C. It is possible to construct condensers in which the energy absorbed is so small that for all practical purposes they may be assumed to have no resistance. On the other hand, it is not practicable to construct a coil without resistance of significant magnitude. In view of this fact, the circuit of Fig. 16-7 represents the condition usually found in practice.

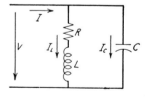

Fig. 16-7. L and R in parallel with C.

In the following it will be shown that resonance and maximum impedance in this circuit may but do not necessarily take place simultaneously, and that whether they do or do not depends upon which one of the quantities f, L, or C is varied in order to attain resonance.

It has been shown that resonance is obtained when the susceptance of a parallel circuit is zero. Thus the circuit of Fig. 16-7 is resonant when

$$B_C = B_L.$$

In this circuit

$$B_L = \frac{X_L}{R^2 + X_L{}^2},$$

and

$$B_C = \frac{X_C}{0 + X_C{}^2} = \frac{1}{X_C}.$$

Accordingly, resonance will take place when

$$\frac{1}{X_C} = \frac{X_L}{R^2 + X_L{}^2}, \tag{16-9}$$

or when

$$\omega C = \frac{\omega L}{R^2 + \omega^2 L^2},$$

or

$$2\pi f C = \frac{2\pi f L}{R^2 + (2\pi f L)^2}. \tag{16-10}$$

Hence it does not matter whether f or L or C is varied; the relation expressed in this last equation must be fulfilled in order to attain resonance.

If the frequency is varied while L, C, and R remain constant, the value of frequency f_R at which resonance will be obtained is

$$f_R = \frac{1}{2\pi \sqrt{LC}} \sqrt{1 - \frac{R^2 C}{L}}. \tag{16-11}$$

If, on the other hand, the inductance L is varied but f, C, and R are maintained constant,* then the value of inductance L_R at which resonance will be obtained is

$$L_R = \frac{\frac{1}{\omega C} \pm \sqrt{\frac{1}{\omega^2 C^2} - 4R^2}}{2\omega}. \tag{16-12}$$

But, if only the capacitance C is varied, then the value of capacitance C_R that will produce resonance is

$$C_R = \frac{L}{R^2 + \omega^2 L^2}. \tag{16-13}$$

Equations (16-11), (16-12), and (16-13) are obtained by solving equation (16-10) for f, L, and C, respectively.

---

* See footnote on page 181.

Equation (16-12) shows that there are two values of L which will cause the power factor of the circuit to be unity. When R is small, as is usually the case in practice, the impedance of the parallel resonant circuit is low when the value of the inductance is the one obtained by use of the $-$ sign in equation (16-12) and is high when the inductance is obtained by use of the $+$ sign. In the application of parallel resonant circuits it is usually desired that the resonant circuit have a high impedance. For this reason, when resonance is to be obtained by varying the inductance, it is understood that the necessary value of inductance is that determined from equation (16-12) when the $+$ sign is used before the radical.

8. Maximum Circuit Impedance with L and R in Parallel with C.
The impedance of the circuit shown in Fig. 16-7 is, by equation (16-7),

$$\bar{Z} = \frac{\bar{Z}_L \bar{Z}_C}{\bar{Z}_L + \bar{Z}_C},\qquad (16\text{-}14)$$

where $\bar{Z}_L = R + jX_L$ and $\bar{Z}_C = 0 - jX_C$. Substituting these values for $\bar{Z}_L$ and $\bar{Z}_C$ in equation (16-14) gives

$$\bar{Z} = \frac{(R + jX_L)(-jX_C)}{R + j(X_L - X_C)} = \frac{X_C(X_L - jR)}{R + j(X_L - X_C)}.$$

This equation is more readily reduced if the terms are expressed in polar coordinates. When this is done,

$$\bar{Z} = \frac{X_C \sqrt{X_L^2 + R^2}/\alpha}{\sqrt{R^2 + (X_L - X_C)^2}/\beta},$$

where $\alpha = \tan^{-1}(-R/X_L)$ and $\beta = \tan^{-1}[(X_L - X_C)/R]$. Thus

$$\bar{Z} = \frac{X_C \sqrt{X_L^2 + R^2}}{\sqrt{R^2 + (X_L - X_C)^2}}/\alpha - \beta = Z/\alpha - \beta,$$

and

$$Z = \frac{X_C \sqrt{X_L^2 + R^2}}{\sqrt{R^2 + (X_L - X_C)^2}}$$
$$= \frac{\frac{1}{2\pi fC}\sqrt{R^2 + (2\pi fL)^2}}{\sqrt{R^2 + \left(2\pi fL - \frac{1}{2\pi fC}\right)^2}}.\qquad (16\text{-}15)$$

With the resistance R constant, the condition of maximum circuit impedance can be attained by varying either the frequency f, the capacitance C, or the inductance L.

(1) *Frequency Variable.* If f is varied but L, C, and R are maintained constant, the value of frequency $f_{Z\max}$ at which the circuit impedance is a maximum can be determined by differentiating equation (16-15) with respect to f, equating the derivative to zero, and solving for f. The solution will show that

$$f_{Z\max} = \frac{1}{2\pi\sqrt{LC}}\sqrt{\sqrt{\frac{2R^2C}{L}+1}-\frac{R^2C}{L}}.\qquad(16\text{-}16)$$

A comparison of equation (16-16) with equation (16-11), the equation that gives the value of frequency at which resonance will be obtained, shows that resonance and maximum circuit impedance do not take place simultaneously in the circuit of Fig. 16-7 when the frequency is the variable.

(2) *Capacitance Variable.* If C is varied while f, L, and R are held constant, the value of capacitance $C_{Z\max}$ at which the circuit impedance is a maximum can be determined from equation (16-15) by the usual mathematical process. The result in this case is

$$C_{Z\max} = \frac{L}{R^2 + \omega^2 L^2}.\qquad(16\text{-}17)$$

The right-hand side of equation (16-17) is the same as that of equation (16-13). Hence, if C is varied while f, L, and R remain constant, maximum circuit impedance and resonance take place simultaneously in the circuit of Fig. 16-7.

(3) *Inductance Variable.* If only L in the circuit of Fig. 16-7 is varied, the value of inductance $L_{Z\max}$ that will make the circuit impedance a maximum can be shown to be

$$L_{Z\max} = \frac{\dfrac{1}{\omega C} + \sqrt{\dfrac{1}{\omega^2 C^2} + 4R^2}}{2\omega}.\qquad(16\text{-}18)$$

A comparison of this equation with equation (16-12), with only the $+$ sign before the radical in the latter being considered, will show that the two equations are not alike, the sign before the last term under the radical being different. Hence, when L is the variable, maximum circuit impedance and resonance do not take place simultaneously in the circuit of Fig. 16-7.

The circuit reactions that take place when the inductance is the variable can be brought out more clearly by a graphical method of analysis. Let V, the impressed voltage, be used as the reference vector, as shown in the diagram in Fig. 16-8. Since the impressed voltage is applied directly to the branch containing the inductance in Fig. 16-7, then

$$V = I_L Z_L,$$

as indicated in the diagram. For any selected value of inductance L_1, the resulting current $\bar{I}_{L_1}$ lags the voltage $\bar{V}$ by some angle $\theta = \tan^{-1}$ (X_{L_1}/R). Since the voltage drop across the resistance R is in phase with the current $\bar{I}_{L_1}$, it is drawn in the same direction as $\bar{I}_{L_1}$. The voltage drop across the reactance X_{L_1}, on the other hand, leads the current and hence the $\bar{I}_{L_1}R$ drop by 90° and is so drawn. Further-

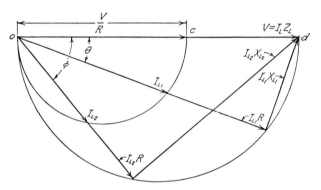

Fig. 16-8.   Voltage and current locus diagrams for the inductive branch of Fig. 16-7 when only the inductance is varied.

more, the two vectors $\bar{I}_{L_1}R$ and $j\bar{I}_{L_1}X_{L_1}$ when added must be equal to the impressed voltage $\bar{V}$. Thus $\bar{I}_{L_1}R$, $j\bar{I}_{L_1}X_{L_1}$, and $\bar{V}$ are the sides of a right triangle of which $\bar{V}$ is the hypotenuse.

Now let the inductance be increased to a new value L_2. The corresponding value of reactance X_{L_2} is increased, as is the impedance Z_{L_2}. Hence the value of the new current I_{L_2} is less than its former value, and $\bar{I}_{L_2}$ lags the voltage $\bar{V}$ by the angle $\phi = \tan^{-1}(X_{L_2}/R)$, which obviously is greater than θ. The new vectors $\bar{I}_{L_2}$, $\bar{I}_{L_2}R$, and $j\bar{I}_{L_2}X_{L_2}$ are shown in the diagram. A new triangle, which is also a right triangle and the hypotenuse of which is $\bar{V}$, has been formed. Additional triangles, representing other values of inductance, can be drawn. All such triangles will be right triangles having the common hypotenuse $od = V$. Hence the vertices at the 90° angles of the triangles must be on the arc of the semicircle, as indicated in the figure, for all triangles inscribed in a semicircle are right triangles, and, conversely, all right triangles having a common hypotenuse must be inscribed in a semicircle. Therefore the locus of the tips of the vectors representing the $I_L R$ drops is a semicircle, the diameter of which is V.

When L is zero, the $I_L X_L$ component of the impressed voltage is also zero, and

$$\bar{V} = \bar{I}_L \bar{Z}_L = \bar{I}_L(R + j0),$$
$$\bar{V} = \bar{I}_L R,$$
and
$$V = I_L R. \qquad (16\text{-}19)$$

Thus, under this condition, the voltage drop across the resistance part of the coil branch is equal to the impressed voltage and is in phase with it. Accordingly, in such a case, the tip of the $I_L R$ vector would be at d in the diagram. As the value of L is continuously increased from zero, the tip of the $I_L R$ vector moves in a clockwise direction along the arc of the semicircle, reaching and coinciding with the point o when the value of L theoretically becomes infinite and the current I_L becomes zero.

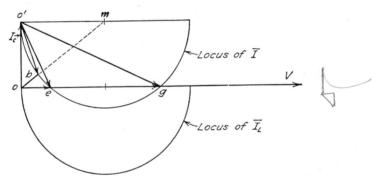

Fig. 16-9. Current locus diagram for the circuit of Fig. 16-7 when only the inductance is varied.

Since the resistance R is constant and $\bar{I}_L R$ is in phase with $\bar{I}_L$, the locus of the tip of the current vector is also a semicircle, the diameter of which is V/R. That this is the value of the diameter is readily made clear by reference to equation (16-19), which represents the condition in which the value of the inductance is zero. Under this condition the current $\bar{I}_L$ is in phase with the voltage $\bar{V} = \bar{I}_L R$; therefore the current vector is along the vector $\bar{V}$ and is equal to V/R in magnitude. In Fig. 16-8 it is shown as oc.

In Fig. 16-9 the locus of the current $\bar{I}_L$ is redrawn. The current $\bar{I}_c = j\bar{V}/X_c$ is constant in magnitude and leads the impressed voltage by 90°, as is shown in the figure.

The total current delivered to the circuit is

$$\bar{I} = \bar{I}_L + \bar{I}_c.$$

To determine the locus of the total current $\bar{I}$, it is necessary only to add the vector $\bar{I}_C$ to the locus of $\bar{I}_L$. This addition is done in a very simple manner by raising the semicircle until point o on its diameter coincides with the tip of the vector $\bar{I}_C$. Hence, since all current vectors $\bar{I}_L$ now start at the origin o', the semicircle in its new position becomes the locus of the total current $\bar{I}$. This fact is readily evident by reference to the figure.

To determine the condition for maximum circuit impedance, it is necessary to determine the condition for minimum total current. To do this, the point on the locus of $\bar{I}$ nearest to the origin o must be located. This point is at the intersection b of the arc of the semicircle and the extended radius drawn from m to o. Thus ob is the total current $\bar{I}$, and $o'b$ is the current $\bar{I}_L$ in the inductive branch when by variation of the inductance L the circuit has reached the condition of maximum impedance.

Resonance is indicated in the diagram when the current $\bar{I}$ is in phase with the voltage $\bar{V}$. It will be noted that there are two such conditions, the first of these when $\bar{I}_L$ is $o'e$, in which case $\bar{I}$ is oe, and the second when $\bar{I}_L$ is $o'g$ and $\bar{I}$ is og. Hence there are two values of inductance that will cause unity power factor. This fact is consistent with equation (16-12), which also shows that there are two values of L that will cause the power factor of the circuit to be unity. In equation (16-12) it is the value of L obtained when the $+$ sign is used before the radical that will cause the current $\bar{I}$ to be equal to oe in Fig. 16-9; and it is the value obtained when the $-$ sign is used before the radical that will cause the current $\bar{I}$ to be equal to og in the figure.

9. Parallel Resonant Circuit—Constant Line Current. When constant voltage is impressed on a series circuit containing an inductance coil and a condenser, the coil voltage and the condenser voltage do not remain constant when the frequency, inductance, or capacitance is varied, but attain peak values at or near the resonant condition. On the other hand, when a constant voltage is impressed on a circuit consisting of an inductance coil and a condenser connected in parallel, the impressed voltage, the coil voltage, and the condenser voltage are one and the same and obviously remain constant regardless of whether the frequency, the inductance, or capacitance is varied. In such a case, however, the line current does not remain constant but has its minimum value when the circuit impedance is greatest, this being near or at the resonant condition. In Fig. 16-10 curves of circuit impedance and line current are shown for a parallel circuit consisting of a coil and condenser when the impressed voltage is maintained constant but the frequency of the impressed voltage is varied. Curves very similar to these will be obtained if either the inductance or capacitance is varied.

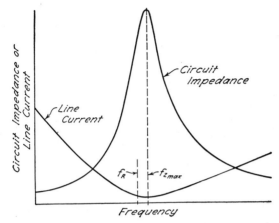

Fig. 16-10. Variation of the circuit impedance and the line current of a parallel circuit consisting of a coil and condenser, impressed voltage constant and frequency variable.

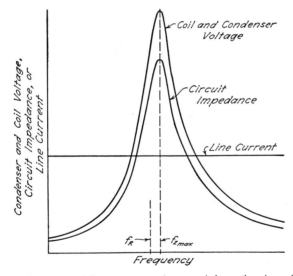

Fig. 16-11. Variation of the circuit impedance and the coil and condenser voltage of a parallel circuit consisting of a coil and condenser, line current constant and frequency variable.

The most important application of parallel resonance is in communication circuits. In these circuits the sources of alternating currents generally have high internal impedances, and the current supplied by a source of this kind is not greatly affected by the type of circuit connected to its terminals. Hence, if a parallel circuit consisting of a coil and a condenser were connected to such a source, the circuit current would remain substantially constant, but the voltage drop across the parallel branches—that is, the coil and condenser voltages—would peak at or near the resonant condition when the frequency, inductance, or capacitance is varied, the peak being reached when the circuit impedance is greatest.

Curves of coil and condenser voltage, line current, and circuit impedance for a parallel circuit consisting of a coil and condenser supplied by a constant-current generator are shown in Fig. 16-11. In this case the frequency is the independent variable. If either inductance or capacitance is made the variable, curves very similar to those shown will be obtained.

Laboratory Problem No. 16-1

PARALLEL A-C CIRCUITS CONTAINING RESISTANCE, INDUCTANCE, AND CAPACITANCE

Laboratory

Use the resistor, inductance coil, and condenser designated by the instructor.

1. Set up a parallel circuit consisting of the resistor and coil. With the a-c voltage applied to the circuit maintained constant at the value designated by the instructor, measure the following:

(a) Voltage applied to the circuit.

(b) Line current and each branch current.

(c) Power supplied to the circuit and to each branch.

2. Replace the coil by the condenser and make the measurements specified in **1.**

3. Connect the coil, condenser, and resistor in parallel and make the measurements specified in **1.**

Report

A. From the data obtained in **1** calculate the vector values of the branch currents, using the voltage drop across the circuit as the reference vector. Draw to scale a vector diagram showing this voltage and the branch currents. Draw all of the vectors from a common origin.

From the vector diagram determine graphically the value of the line current and the power-factor angle of the circuit. How does the value of the line current compare with the measured value? How does the power-factor angle compare with that determined by calculation from the data obtained in **1**? Discuss any discrepancies.

B. Repeat **A,** using the data obtained in **2.**

C. Repeat **A,** using the data obtained in **3.**

Laboratory Problem No. 16-2

RESONANCE IN A PARALLEL CIRCUIT—VARIABLE FREQUENCY

Laboratory

1. Set up a parallel circuit, one branch consisting of an inductance coil and the other consisting of a condenser. The inductance of the coil and the capacitance of the condenser should be such that resonance will take place at a value of frequency about in the middle of the frequency range designated by the instructor.

2. With the voltage applied to the circuit maintained constant at the value designated by the instructor, adjust the frequency until the condition of minimum line current is obtained. At this frequency increase the impressed voltage to as high a value as permissible without causing the voltage rating of the condenser or the voltage or current rating of the coil to be exceeded. Record the value of the line current under this condition.

By adjusting the value of the voltage applied to the circuit, maintain the line current constant at the recorded value while the frequency is varied in steps over the range that has been designated. In the vicinity of resonance the steps should be small. At each step measure the following:

      (a) Frequency.
      (b) Line current.
      (c) Impressed voltage.
      (d) Power delivered to the circuit.
      (e) Coil current.
      (f) Condenser current.

Report

A. Make up a table containing the following items for every step of the test:

      (1) Frequency.
      (2) Voltage applied to the circuit.
      (3) Line current.
      (4) Coil current.
      (5) Condenser current.
      (6) Impedance of the circuit.

(7) Apparent power of the circuit.
(8) Power delivered to the circuit.
(9) Power factor of the circuit.
(10) Resistance component of the circuit impedance.
(11) Impedance of the coil branch.
(12) Effective resistance of the coil branch.
(13) Reactance of the coil branch.
(14) Reactance of the condenser branch.
(15) Susceptance of the coil branch.
(16) Susceptance of the condenser branch.
(17) Susceptance of the circuit.

B. On a single set of coordinate axes, plot the following curves:

(1) Condenser and coil voltage vs frequency.
(2) Power factor of the circuit vs frequency.
(3) Impedance of the circuit vs frequency.
(4) Resistance component of the circuit impedance vs frequency.
(5) Susceptance of the circuit vs frequency.

C. From curves (3) and (4) of **B** determine the resonant frequency. How does this frequency check with that indicated as the resonant frequency by curve (2) of **B?** How does the resonant frequency indicated by curve (5) of **B** check with the other values obtained for the resonant frequency?

D. For a frequency near the resonant frequency calculate the capacitance of the condenser and the inductance of the coil. Using these values of L and C and the effective resistance of the coil for this same frequency, calculate the frequency at which the circuit impedance should have been a maximum and also the frequency at which resonance should have been obtained. Check these frequencies against the corresponding frequencies obtained from the curves.

Laboratory Problem No. 16-3

RESONANCE IN A PARALLEL CIRCUIT— VARIABLE INDUCTANCE

Laboratory

A variable inductance with nearly a constant resistance can be conveniently obtained by connecting in series two inductance coils the magnetic coupling of which can be varied. The minimum inductance of the series combination is obtained when the coils are coupled as closely as possible and the series connection is such that the magnetomotive forces produced by current in the coils are in opposite directions. The inductance can then be increased by decreasing the coupling between the coils. When a further decrease in coupling causes little change in the inductance, the inductance can be further increased by reversing the connections to one coil and then increasing the coupling. The maximum inductance is obtained under this condition when the coupling is again a maximum.*

1. Set up a parallel circuit, one branch consisting of the variable inductance and the other branch consisting of a condenser. The capacitance of the condenser should be such that resonance will be obtained at a value of inductance about in the middle of the inductance range when the frequency designated by the instructor is used.

2. With the a-c voltage applied to the circuit maintained constant at the value designated by the instructor, vary the inductance in several steps from the minimum value to the maximum value. At each step measure the following:

    (a) Voltage applied to the circuit.
    (b) Line current.
    (c) Power delivered to the circuit.
    (d) Coil current.
    (e) Condenser current.

In the vicinity of resonance the changes in inductance should be relatively small.

Report

A. Make up a table containing the following items for every step of the test:

    (1) Voltage applied to the circuit.
    (2) Line current.
    (3) Coil current.
    (4) Condenser current.
    (5) Power delivered to the circuit.
    (6) Apparent power of the circuit.
    (7) Power factor of the circuit.
    (8) Impedance of the coil branch.
    (9) Effective resistance of the coil branch.
    (10) Reactance of the coil branch.
    (11) Inductance of the coil branch.

---

* For proof of these statements see the developments of equations (17-20) and (17-23).

(12) Reactance of the condenser branch.
(13) Capacitance of the condenser branch.
(14) Susceptance of the coil branch.
(15) Susceptance of the condenser branch.
(16) Effective resistance of the circuit.

B. On a single set of coordinate axes, plot the following curves:

(1) Coil current vs inductance.
(2) Condenser current vs inductance.
(3) Line current vs inductance.

C. On a second sheet plot the following curves, using a single set of coordinate axes:

(1) Power factor of the circuit vs inductance.
(2) Susceptance of the coil branch vs inductance.
(3) Susceptance of the condenser branch vs inductance.
(4) Effective resistance of the circuit vs inductance.

D. Using the effective resistance of the coil branch (average value), the capacitance of the condenser branch, and the frequency used in the laboratory, calculate the value of inductance that should produce (1) resonance, and (2) maximum circuit impedance.

E. Using the effective resistance of the coil branch (average value), the capacitance of the condenser branch, and an applied voltage of the same magnitude and frequency as used in the laboratory, draw to scale the locus diagram of the line current for the condition that the inductance is the variable.

F. From the locus diagram determine the value of the inductance that should produce (1) resonance, and (2) maximum circuit impedance.

G. Make and fill in a table like that shown below.

From	Value of L for Resonance	From	Value of L for Maximum Circuit Impedance
Curve of Power Factor		Curve of Line Current	
Susceptance Curves		Calculation of Part D	
Calculation of Part D			
Locus Diagram		Locus Diagram	

H. What is the significance of the variation in the effective resistance of the circuit with inductance? Since the coil branch contains the only resistance in the circuit, does it mean that this resistance varies in the manner indicated by the curve plotted in **C?**

Laboratory Problem No. 16-4
RESONANCE IN A PARALLEL CIRCUIT—
VARIABLE CAPACITANCE

Laboratory

1. Set up a parallel circuit, one branch consisting of an inductance coil and the other of a condenser whose capacitance can be varied. The inductance of the coil should be such that resonance will be obtained at a value of capacitance that is about in the middle of the range of variation of the condenser capacitance when the frequency designated by the instructor is used.

2. With the voltage applied to the circuit maintained constant at the value designated by the instructor, vary the capacitance until the condition of minimum line current is obtained. When this condition has been obtained, increase the impressed voltage to as high a value as permissible without causing the current rating of the coil or the voltage ratings of the condenser and the coil to be exceeded. Record the value of the line current under this condition.

By adjusting the value of the voltage applied to the circuit, maintain the line current constant at the recorded value while the capacitance is varied in steps over the entire range of variation of the variable capacitance. In the vicinity of resonance the steps should be small. At each step measure the following:

(a) Line current.
(b) Impressed voltage.
(c) Power delivered to the circuit.
(d) Coil current.
(e) Condenser current.

Report

A. Make up a table containing the following items for every step of the test:

(1) Voltage applied to the circuit.
(2) Line current.
(3) Coil current.
(4) Condenser current.

(5) Impedance of the circuit.
(6) Apparent power of the circuit.
(7) Power delivered to the circuit.
(8) Power factor of the circuit.
(9) Resistance component of the circuit impedance.
(10) Reactance component of the circuit impedance.
(11) Susceptance of the circuit.
(12) Reactance of the condenser branch.
(13) Capacitance of the condenser branch.

B. On a single set of coordinate axes plot the following curves:

(1) Condenser and coil voltages vs capacitance.
(2) Power factor of the circuit vs capacitance.
(3) Susceptance of the circuit vs capacitance.

C. On a single set of coordinate axes plot the following curves:

(1) Reactance component of the circuit impedance vs capacitance. (Plot inductive reactance above the horizontal axis and capacitive reactance below.)
(2) Resistance component of the circuit impedance vs capacitance.
(3) Impedance of the circuit vs capacitance.

D. From curve (3) of **B** determine the value of capacitance needed to obtain resonance in the circuit.

E. From curve (1) of **C** determine the value of capacitance needed to obtain resonance in the circuit. How does this value compare with that obtained in **D**?

F. Does the curve of coil voltage plotted in (1) of **B** have its maximum value at the theoretically proper value of capacitance? Explain.

G. Calculate the reactance and effective resistance of the coil. Using these values and the frequency, calculate the value of capacitance at which the curve of the condenser voltage should have peaked. Does this value of capacitance check with the experimental value determined from curve (1) of **B**?

CHAPTER 17

MUTUAL INDUCTANCE

1. Mutual Induction. If two circuits are placed with respect to one another so that all or a part of the magnetic field due to current in one circuit links with the other circuit, a change of current in the first circuit will induce an emf in the second. The magnitude of the induced emf will depend upon the physical configuration of the two circuits and the rate of change of the magnetic field produced by current in the first circuit. Since the magnetic field that produces the emf in the second circuit is mutual to both circuits, the induced emf is said to be caused by mutual induction. In accordance with Lenz's law, the mutually induced emf in the second circuit at any instant will

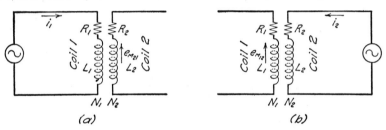

Fig. 17-1. Two inductively coupled coils (a) with current only in coil 1 and (b) with current only in coil 2.

be in such a direction that if a current were established in the second circuit by this induced voltage the resulting magnetomotive force would oppose the change in the magnetic field.

In the circuit shown in Fig. 17-1(a) the current i_1 is supplied to coil 1, which has N_1 turns. Let ϕ_1 be the flux established by this current. A certain portion of this flux links the turns of coil 2, which has N_2 turns. Let the resulting number of flux linkages with this coil be represented by $k_1 N_2 \phi_1$. The emf induced in coil 2 by a change of these flux linkages is*

$$e_{M_{21}} = -k_1 N_2 \frac{d\phi_1}{dt} \cdot 10^{-8}. \qquad (17\text{-}1)$$

---

* With the sense of the windings and the positive directions of i_1 and $e_{M_{21}}$ as shown in Fig. 17-1(a), the $-$ sign is necessary in equation (17-1) in order to express Lenz's law properly.

In the symbol $e_{M_{21}}$, the M indicates that the emf is due to mutual induction and the subscript order 21 indicates that the emf is induced in coil 2 by a flux linkage change produced by current in coil 1.

Now consider that the source of current is transferred to the terminals of coil 2 and that it supplies a current i_2 to this coil, as shown in (b) of the figure. Let ϕ_2 be the flux established by this current, a certain portion of which links the turns of coil 1. Let the resulting number of flux linkages with this coil be represented by $k_2N_1\phi_2$. The emf induced in coil 1 by a change of these flux linkages is

$$e_{M_{12}} = -k_2N_1\frac{d\phi_2}{dt} \cdot 10^{-8}. \tag{17-2}$$

The fluxes ϕ_1 and ϕ_2 produced by i_1 and i_2, respectively, are

$$\phi_1 = \frac{.4\pi N_1 i_1}{\mathfrak{R}_1} = k_1'N_1i_1, \tag{17-3}$$

and

$$\phi_2 = \frac{.4\pi N_2 i_2}{\mathfrak{R}_2} = k_2'N_2i_2, \tag{17-4}$$

$\mathfrak{R}_1$ and $\mathfrak{R}_2$ being the reluctances of the magnetic paths. From these two equations

$$\frac{d\phi_1}{dt} = k_1'N_1\frac{di_1}{dt},$$

and

$$\frac{d\phi_2}{dt} = k_2'N_2\frac{di_2}{dt}.$$

Substituting these values in equations (17-1) and (17-2) gives

$$e_{M_{21}} = -k_1k_1'N_1N_2\frac{di_1}{dt} \cdot 10^{-8} = -K_1N_1N_2\frac{di_1}{dt}, \tag{17-5}$$

and

$$e_{M_{12}} = -k_2k_2'N_1N_2\frac{di_2}{dt} \cdot 10^{-8} = -K_2N_1N_2\frac{di_2}{dt}. \tag{17-6}$$

2. Coefficient of Mutual Induction. The self-inductance L of a circuit is the constant by which the rate of change of current is multiplied in order to determine the induced emf due to self-induction. Expressed as an equation

$$\overset{\bullet}{e} = -L\frac{di}{dt}.$$

Equations (17-5) and (17-6) are of this form. Hence $K_1N_1N_2$ and $K_2N_1N_2$ are of the nature of inductances. Since these terms are the result of a mutual flux—that is, the flux established by current in one coil but linking the turns of both coils—they are called *coefficients of mutual induction,* or simply *mutual inductances.* If the symbol M is used to represent mutual inductance, equations (17-5) and (17-6) become

$$e_{M_{21}} = -K_1 N_1 N_2 \frac{di_1}{dt} = -M_{21} \frac{di_1}{dt}, \tag{17-7}$$

and

$$e_{M_{12}} = -K_2 N_1 N_2 \frac{di_2}{dt} = -M_{12} \frac{di_2}{dt}. \tag{17-8}$$

As before, the subscript 21 signifies an effect in circuit 2 resulting from a cause taking place in circuit 1, and similarly the subscript 12 signifies the effect in circuit 1 resulting from a cause taking place in circuit 2.

It can be shown* that

$$M_{21} = M_{12}, \tag{17-9}$$

and as a result the subscripts are generally omitted, the letter M alone being used.

The henry is the practical unit of mutual inductance just as it is of self-inductance. Thus, in equations (17-7) and (17-8), if M is in henrys and di/dt is in amperes per second, e_M is in volts.

3. Determination of M from Test Data. *Induced Voltage Method.* If the currents i_1 and i_2 shown in Fig. 17-1 vary sinusoidally with time, equations (17-7) and (17-8) may be written as follows, since $M_{21} = M_{12} = M$:

$$e_{M_{21}} = -M \frac{d}{dt} (I_{1\max} \sin \omega t) = -\omega M I_{1\max} \cos \omega t,$$

$$e_{M_{12}} = -M \frac{d}{dt} (I_{2\max} \sin \omega t) = -\omega M I_{2\max} \cos \omega t.$$

When expressed in terms of effective values, these two equations become

$$\bar{E}_{M_{21}} = -j\omega M \bar{I}_1,$$

and

$$\bar{E}_{M_{12}} = -j\omega M \bar{I}_2.$$

If magnitudes only are considered,

$$E_{M_{21}} = \omega M I_1, \tag{17-10}$$

* Knight, A. R., and Fett, G. H., *Introduction to Circuit Analysis,* pp. 56–58. New York: Harper & Brothers, 1943.

Lawrence, R. R., *Principles of Alternating Currents,* 2d edition, pp. 187–188. New York: McGraw-Hill Book Company, 1935.

and

$$E_{M_{12}} = \omega M I_2. \tag{17-11}$$

In equation (17-10), which was developed from a consideration of Fig. 17-1(a), $E_{M_{21}}$ is the effective value of the voltage induced in coil 2 by mutual induction when a sinusoidal current having an effective value of I_1 exists in coil 1. The current I_1 can be measured by inserting an ammeter in the circuit of coil 1. $E_{M_{21}}$ can be measured by means of a voltmeter connected to the terminals of coil 2. However, the resistance of the voltmeter used to measure $E_{M_{21}}$ must be high enough to keep the voltmeter current so small that its effect in the circuit is negligible. After I_1 and $E_{M_{21}}$ have been measured, M can be calculated, if the frequency, and hence ω, is known.

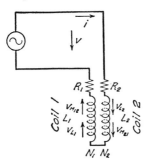

Similar considerations are applicable to equation (17-11).

Impedance Method. If the two coils are connected in series, as shown in Fig. 17-2, the mutual inductance can be calculated by determining its effect on the impedance of each coil or that of the entire circuit. Let ϕ_1 and ϕ_2 again represent the fluxes established by a current i flowing in coils 1 and 2, respectively. Since ϕ_1 and ϕ_2

Fig. 17-2. Two inductively coupled coils connected in series.

are in the same direction around the mutual magnetic path, the coils are said to be connected in *series aiding.* The portion of the voltage drop of coil 2 which is due to the part of ϕ_1 that links the turns of this coil is

$$v_{M_{21}} = -e_{M_{21}} = M_{21}\frac{di_1}{dt} = M\frac{di}{dt},$$

and the portion of the voltage drop of coil 1 which is due to the part of ϕ_2 that links the turns of this coil is

$$v_{M_{12}} = -e_{M_{12}} = M_{12}\frac{di_2}{dt} = M\frac{di}{dt}.$$

There is also a voltage drop in coil 1 due to the flux ϕ_1 linking the turn- of this coil—that is, due to the self-inductance of the coil. This volts age drop is expressed by

$$v_{L_1} = -e_{L_1} = L_1\frac{di_1}{dt} = L_1\frac{di}{dt}.$$

Similarly, there is a voltage drop in coil 2 due to its self-inductance, which is

$$v_{L_2} = -e_{L_2} = L_2 \frac{di_2}{dt} = L_2 \frac{di}{dt}.$$

If there were no mutual flux, which theoretically would be the condition if coils 1 and 2 were separated by an infinite distance, then the voltage drop across each coil would be

$$v_1 = R_1 i + L_1 \frac{di}{dt}, \tag{17-12}$$

and

$$v_2 = R_2 i + L_2 \frac{di}{dt}, \tag{17-13}$$

and that across the entire circuit would be

$$v = v_1 + v_2 = R_1 i + L_1 \frac{di}{dt} + R_2 i + L_2 \frac{di}{dt}. \tag{17-14}$$

However, because of mutual induction, the additional voltage drops $v_{M_{21}}$ and $v_{M_{12}}$ are introduced. Under this condition equations (17-12), (17-13), and (17-14) become, respectively,

$$v_{1_{aid}} = R_1 i + L_1 \frac{di}{dt} + M \frac{di}{dt}, \tag{17-15}$$

$$v_{2_{aid}} = R_2 i + L_2 \frac{di}{dt} + M \frac{di}{dt}, \tag{17-16}$$

and

$$v_{aid} = v_{1_{aid}} + v_{2_{aid}} = (R_1 + R_2)i + (L_1 + L_2 + 2M)\frac{di}{dt}. \tag{17-17}$$

The subscript *aid* is used to indicate that the coils are connected in series aiding.

When the power source supplies a current that varies sinusoidally with time, equations (17-15), (17-16), and (17-17) may be written as

$$v_{1_{aid}} = R_1 I_{max} \sin \omega t + \omega L_1 I_{max} \cos \omega t + \omega M I_{max} \cos \omega t,$$
$$v_{2_{aid}} = R_2 I_{max} \sin \omega t + \omega L_2 I_{max} \cos \omega t + \omega M I_{max} \cos \omega t,$$
and
$$v_{aid} = (R_1 + R_2) I_{max} \sin \omega t + \omega(L_1 + L_2 + 2M) I_{max} \cos \omega t.$$

When expressed in terms of effective values, these equations become

$$\bar{V}_{1_{aid}} = \bar{I}R_1 + j\bar{I}\omega(L_1 + M) = \bar{I}[R_1 + j\omega(L_1 + M)],$$
$$\bar{V}_{2_{aid}} = \bar{I}R_2 + j\bar{I}\omega(L_2 + M) = \bar{I}[R_2 + j\omega(L_2 + M)],$$

and

$$\bar{V}_{\text{aid}} = \bar{I}(R_1 + R_2) + j\bar{I}\omega(L_1 + L_2 + 2M)$$
$$= \bar{I}[(R_1 + R_2) + j\omega(L_1 + L_2 + 2M)].$$

Solving for the magnitude of the impedance in each case gives

$$Z_{1_{\text{aid}}} = \frac{V_{1_{\text{aid}}}}{I} = \sqrt{R_1{}^2 + \omega^2(L_1 + M)^2}, \qquad (17\text{-}18)$$

$$Z_{2_{\text{aid}}} = \frac{V_{2_{\text{aid}}}}{I} = \sqrt{R_2{}^2 + \omega^2(L_2 + M)^2}, \qquad (17\text{-}19)$$

and

$$Z_{\text{aid}} = \frac{V_{\text{aid}}}{I} = \sqrt{(R_1 + R_2)^2 + \omega^2(L_1 + L_2 + 2M)^2}. \quad (17\text{-}20)$$

If the coils of Fig. 17-2 are now connected in series in such a manner that ϕ_1 and ϕ_2 are in opposite directions around the mutual magnetic path—that is, connected in *series opposing*—an analysis similar to the preceding shows that there will be a minus sign before the mutual inductance terms* in equations similar to equations (17-15), (17-16), and (17-17). The resulting equations for the magnitude of the impedances are then

$$Z_{1_{\text{opp}}} = \frac{V_{1_{\text{opp}}}}{I} = \sqrt{R_1{}^2 + \omega^2(L_1 - M)^2}, \qquad (17\text{-}21)$$

$$Z_{2_{\text{opp}}} = \frac{V_{2_{\text{opp}}}}{I} = \sqrt{R_2{}^2 + \omega^2(L_2 - M)^2}, \qquad (17\text{-}22)$$

and

$$Z_{\text{opp}} = \frac{V_{\text{opp}}}{I} = \sqrt{(R_1 + R_2)^2 + \omega^2(L_1 + L_2 - 2M)^2}. \quad (17\text{-}23)$$

The value of M can be found by the use of any of the impedance relations given in equations (17-18), (17-19), (17-20), (17-21), (17-22), and (17-23). Any one of the impedances can readily be determined from a measurement of the proper voltage and the circuit current. By making a power measurement at the same time, the required resistance R_1, R_2, or $(R_1 + R_2)$ can be determined. The self-inductances L_1 and L_2 can be determined by an individual test on each coil, for

---

* A general rule to facilitate writing Kirchhoff's voltage-law equations for two inductively coupled circuits may now be stated: If the mmfs set up by currents flowing in the assumed positive current directions are in the same direction around the mutual magnetic path, the signs of the $L(di/dt)$ and $M(di/dt)$ terms are alike; if the mmfs are in opposite directions, the signs of the $L(di/dt)$ and $M(di/dt)$ terms are opposite.

when only a single coil is included in the circuit, as shown in (a) and (b) of Fig. 17-1,

$$\frac{V_1}{I_1} = Z_1 = \sqrt{R_1{}^2 + \omega^2 L_1{}^2}, \qquad (17\text{-}24)$$

and

$$\frac{V_2}{I_2} = Z_2 = \sqrt{R_2{}^2 + \omega^2 L_2{}^2}. \qquad (17\text{-}25)$$

A very important fact that should be appreciated is that the values of R_1 and R_2 differ as conditions are changed. This follows from the fact that R_1 and R_2 are effective values of resistance and depend upon local power losses, which vary with the frequency and the resultant flux linking the turns of the coils. Therefore R_1, R_2, and $(R_1 + R_2)$, as determined from power measurements made in the circuit of Fig. 17-2 when the coils are connected in series aiding, may differ from the values determined for these quantities when the series-opposing connection of the coils is used. Furthermore, the values of R_1, R_2, and $(R_1 + R_2)$ determined in either case may differ appreciably from the values determined from power measurements made in the circuits of Figs. 17-1(a) and 17-1(b). It should, accordingly, be clear that, when test data are used to determine M from any one of equations (17-18), (17-19), (17-20), (17-21), (17-22), or (17-23), the resistance value used in the equation should be determined under the same circuit condition as that prevailing when the voltage and current used in the equation are measured.

If the magnetic circuit or any portion of it contains ferrous metal, then more complications are introduced. Not only will R_1 and R_2 be affected by the power losses in the ferrous portion of the circuit, but also L_1 and L_2 may vary appreciably from instant to instant because of the variation in the permeability of the magnetic circuit as the value of the current, and hence the flux density, varies. Under this condition, values of L_1 and L_2 calculated from equations (17-24) and (17-25) are in reality apparent inductances, since these equations are theoretically correct only when the permeability of the magnetic circuit is constant. These apparent inductances, which are determined from measurements of the power and the effective values of voltage and current, may vary appreciably as the effective value of the circuit current, and hence the maximum flux density, varies. For example, if the magnetic path is entirely of ferrous metal, the apparent values of L_1 and L_2 will decrease with increasing values of current because of the decrease in the permeability of the magnetic circuit. In view of the foregoing, if values of L_1 and L_2 determined from equations (17-24) and (17-25) are to be substituted in any of equations (17-18), (17-19), (17-20), (17-21), (17-22), or (17-23), then the conditions of flux density in the magnetic circuit must be the same when data are taken for determining L_1 and L_2 as when data are taken in the circuit of Fig. 17-2 for use in any of equations (17-18) through (17-23). The value of M so determined is also an apparent value and applies only when the one particular condition of flux-density variation exists. It should be evident that the preceding statement is also true for values of M calculated from equations (17-10) and (17-11) whenever the permeability of the magnetic circuit is not constant.

4. Coefficient of Coupling. From equations (17-7), (17-8), and (17-9)

$$K_1 N_1 N_2 = K_2 N_1 N_2 = M. \qquad (17\text{-}26)$$

Inductance may be defined as the flux linkages per unit of current. Therefore, using practical units,

$$L_1 = \frac{N_1 \phi_1}{i_1} \cdot 10^{-8},$$

and

$$L_2 = \frac{N_2 \phi_2}{i_2} \cdot 10^{-8}$$

Substituting for ϕ_1 and ϕ_2 the values expressed in equations (17-3) and (17-4) gives

$$L_1 = \frac{.4\pi N_1{}^2}{\Re_1} \cdot 10^{-8}, \qquad (17\text{-}27)$$

and

$$L_2 = \frac{.4\pi N_2{}^2}{\Re_2} \cdot 10^{-8} \qquad (17\text{-}28)$$

Multiplying equation (17-27) by equation (17-28) and solving for $N_1 N_2$ gives

$$N_1 N_2 = \frac{\sqrt{\Re_1 \Re_2} \ \sqrt{L_1 L_2}}{.4\pi} \cdot 10^8.$$

Substituting this value of $N_1 N_2$ in equation (17-26) yields

$$\frac{K_1 \sqrt{\Re_1 \Re_2} \ \sqrt{L_1 L_2}}{.4\pi} \cdot 10^8 = \frac{K_2 \sqrt{\Re_1 \Re_2} \ \sqrt{L_1 L_2}}{.4\pi} \cdot 10^8 = M.$$

From equation (17-5) $K_1 = k_1 k_1' \cdot 10^{-8}$ and from equation (17-3) $k_1' = .4\pi/\Re_1$. Hence $K_1 = (k_1/\Re_1) . 4\pi \ 10^{-8}$. Similarly, $K_2 = (k_2/\Re_2)$

$.4\pi \cdot 10^{-8}$. Substituting these values for K_1 and K_2 in the preceding equation gives

$$k_1 \frac{\sqrt{\mathfrak{R}_1 \mathfrak{R}_2}}{\mathfrak{R}_1} \sqrt{L_1 L_2} = k_2 \frac{\sqrt{\mathfrak{R}_1 \mathfrak{R}_2}}{\mathfrak{R}_2} \sqrt{L_1 L_2} = M.$$

Therefore

$$k_1 \frac{\sqrt{\mathfrak{R}_1 \mathfrak{R}_2}}{\mathfrak{R}_1} = k_2 \frac{\sqrt{\mathfrak{R}_1 \mathfrak{R}_2}}{\mathfrak{R}_2} = K, \tag{17-29}$$

or

$$K = \sqrt{k_1 k_2} = \frac{M}{\sqrt{L_1 L_2}}. \tag{17-30}$$

The constant K is called the *coefficient of coupling* of the two coils. If all of the flux set up by a current in either of the coils links all of the turns of the other coil, then $k_1 = k_2 = 1$. Under this condition, the value of K would be unity, as can be seen by equation (17-30). It is, of course, impossible actually to attain this condition. In practical cases the coefficient of coupling may range from approximately 0.001 for some air-core transformers used in radio circuits to greater than 0.99 in the case of iron-core power transformers.

It should be noted that, although $M_{12} = M_{21}$, equation (17-29) shows that k_1 is not equal to k_2 unless the reluctances $\mathfrak{R}_1$ and $\mathfrak{R}_2$ are equal.

Laboratory Problem No. 17-1

MUTUAL INDUCTANCE

Laboratory

Use two coils that can be moved with respect to one another—that is, whose coupling can be varied. Designate one coil as 1 and the other as 2.

1. Obtain data from which the self-inductance of each coil can be calculated.

2. With the coils loosely coupled, introduce current into coil 1 and obtain data from which the mutual inductance can be calculated.

3. With the coils coupled as closely as possible, introduce current into coil 1 and obtain data from which the mutual inductance can be calculated.

4. Without changing the positions of the coils from those in **3**, place a laminated-iron core so that it will act as a common core for both coils. Obtain data from which the mutual inductance can be calculated.

5. Remove the iron core. Without changing the positions of the coils from those in **4,** connect the two coils in series aiding. Obtain the necessary data for determining the mutual inductance from (a) the impedance of coil 1, (b) the impedance of coil 2, and (c) the combined impedance of the coils.

6. Without changing the positions of the coils from those in **5,** connect the coils in series opposing. Obtain the necessary data for determining the mutual inductance of the coils from the combined impedance of the coils.

Report

A. Calculate the self-inductance of each coil.

B. From the results obtained in **A** and the data obtained in **2,** calculate the mutual inductance and the coefficient of coupling.

C. From the results obtained in **A** and the data obtained in **3,** calculate the mutual inductance and the coefficient of coupling.

D. From the data obtained in **4,** calculate the mutual inductance.

E. From the results obtained in **A** and the data obtained in **5,** calculate the mutual inductance in three different ways.

F. From the results obtained in **A** and the data obtained in **6,** calculate the mutual inductance.

G. Which of the values of mutual inductance calculated in **B** through **F** should have checked? Explain why.

H. Explain any difference in the values of the coefficients of coupling as determined in **B** and **C.**

CHAPTER 18
POLYPHASE CIRCUITS

1. Three-Phase Generator. In Fig. 18-1 are shown three parallel conductors so located that their ends coincide with the vertices of an equilateral triangle. Let these three conductors be assumed to rotate at a constant speed in a uniform magnetic field between the poles N and S, the axis of rotation being at the center of the triangle. As these conductors rotate, an electromotive force varying sinusoidally with time is generated in each. At the instant t_0, let the positions of the conductors be those shown in the figure. At this moment no electromotive

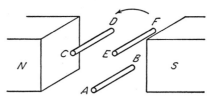

Fig. 18-1. Three equally spaced parallel conductors in a magnetic field.

force is generated in conductor AB. Therefore, in (a) of Fig. 18-2, which shows the time variation of the instantaneous values of the electromotive forces generated in the conductors, the value of e_{AB} is zero at t_0. The electromotive force generated in conductor CD will not become zero until conductor AB has moved 120° and has reached

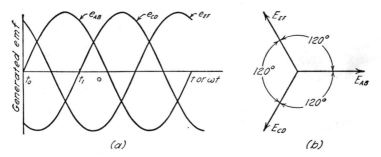

Fig. 18-2. (a) Variation with time of the voltages generated in the conductors of Fig. 18-1. (b) Vector representation of (a).

the position occupied by conductor EF in Fig. 18-1. At this same moment conductor CD will be in the position of AB shown in the figure. Thus, in (a) of Fig. 18-2, e_{CD} is zero at t_1. Accordingly, the electromotive force generated in conductor CD lags that generated in

217

conductor AB by 120°. By the same logic, it should be evident that the electromotive force generated in conductor EF lags that generated in conductor CD by 120° and lags that generated in conductor AB by 240°, as indicated in (a) of the figure. The vector representation of these generated electromotive forces is shown in (b) of the figure.

By replacing each of the conductors AB, CD, and EF by a winding consisting of a number of conductors connected in series and by placing the windings in the proper locations, the simplified generator shown in Fig. 18-3 is obtained.

With the armature core and windings rotating in the direction indicated by the arrow, the algebraic sum of the electromotive forces

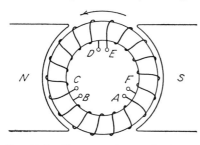

generated in the conductors of winding AB is zero at the instant when this winding is in the position shown in the figure. Let this instant correspond to t_0 in (a) of Fig. 18-2. Then the curve of e_{AB} can also be used to represent the instantaneous values of the electromotive force generated in winding

Fig. 18-3. Elements of a simple three-phase generator.

AB. Obviously, the algebraic sum of the electromotive forces generated in the conductors of winding CD will not become zero until the moment when this winding reaches the position occupied by winding AB in Fig. 18-3. At this moment winding AB will have advanced 120° ahead of the position it occupied at time t_0. Therefore the electromotive force generated in the winding CD lags that generated in winding AB by 120°. Similarly the electromotive force generated in winding EF lags that in winding CD by 120° and that in winding AB by 240°. Hence the curves designated as e_{CD} and e_{EF} in (a) of Fig. 18-2 apply to the electromotive forces generated in the windings CD and EF of Fig. 18-3 as well as to the electromotive forces generated in the conductors CD and EF in Fig. 18-1. The vector diagram shown in (b) of Fig. 18-2 also applies to the generator in Fig. 18-3.

Generators of the type discussed above, having three windings and generating equal electromotive forces per winding which differ in phase by 120°, are called *three-phase generators*.

Two methods are used for interconnecting the separate windings. In one of these the three windings are connected in series, and then the two free ends are joined. This connection is shown schematically in (a) of Fig. 18-4. This scheme of connections is called the *delta* connection. In the second method one terminal of each winding is connected to one terminal of each of the others, leaving three free terminals, as indicated in (b) of the figure. This connection is called the *star* or *wye* connection. Great care must be exercised when the interconnections are made. In the delta connection, the windings must be so connected that the vector sum of the generated voltages in the windings or phases is zero, as indicated in (c) of the figure. In the wye connection, the interconnections must be such that the voltages

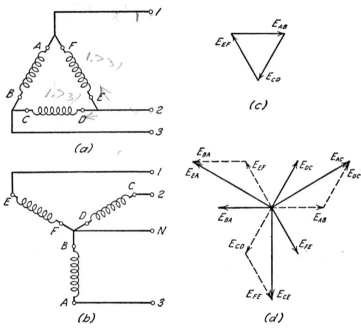

Fig. 18-4. Windings of Fig. 18-3 (a) connected in delta and (b) connected in wye. Vector diagrams of the generated voltages (c) for the connections in (a), and (d) for the connections in (b).

between the terminals C, E, and A are equal and the vectors representing these voltages are 120° apart, as shown in (d) of the figure.

When the armature windings are connected in delta, connections are brought out to three terminals, as indicated in (a) of the figure by 1, 2, and 3. When the armature windings are connected in wye, connections are brought out to four terminals, as indicated by 1, 2, 3, and N in (b) of the figure. In this case terminals 1, 2, and 3 are referred to as the *line terminals*, and terminal N is referred to as the *neutral terminal*.

2. Two-Phase Generator. On the armature core shown in Fig. 18-5 are four like windings. When the armature is rotating in the direction indicated, the algebraic sum of the electromotive forces generated in the conductors of winding AB is zero at the moment when this winding is in the position shown. If this moment is designated as time t_0, the time variation of the instantaneous value of electromotive force generated in this winding in one revolution of the armature is that indicated by e_{AB} in (a) of Fig. 18-6.

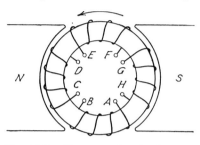

Fig. 18-5. Elements of a simple two-phase or four-phase generator.

At time t_1 winding AB will have been advanced 90° in the direction of rotation. At this moment winding CD will have been advanced to the position in which winding AB is shown in Fig. 18-5. Therefore, at time t_1 the algebraic sum of the electromotive forces generated in the conductors of winding CD is zero. Curve e_{CD}, which represents the time variation of the instantaneous value of the electromotive force generated in winding CD accordingly lags that of e_{AB} by 90°, as shown in (a) of Fig. 18-6.

By the same logic it should be evident that the electromotive force generated in winding EF lags by 90° that generated in winding CD, and the electromotive force generated in winding GH lags that

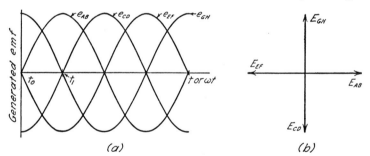

Fig. 18-6.   (a) Variation with time of the voltages generated in the windings of Fig. 18-5.
(b) Vector representation of (a).

generated in winding EF by 90°. The curves representing the time variation of the instantaneous values of these electromotive forces are shown in (a) of Fig. 18-6. The vectors representing the effective values E_{AB}, E_{CD}, E_{EF}, and E_{GH} are shown in (b) of the figure.

If terminal B of winding AB is connected to terminal F of winding EF, the voltage appearing between the free terminals A and E is

$$\bar{E}_{AE} = \bar{E}_{AB} + \bar{E}_{FE}.$$

This vector sum is shown in (b) of Fig. 18-7.

If terminal D of winding CD is connected to terminal H of winding GH, the voltage appearing between the free terminals C and G is

$$\bar{E}_{CG} = \bar{E}_{CD} + \bar{E}_{HG}.$$

This vector sum is also shown in (b) of the figure.

The generator may now be considered to consist of only two windings, in which are generated equal electromotive forces differing

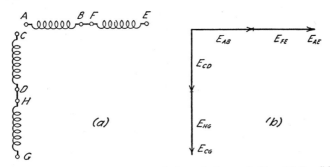

Fig. 18-7. (a) Two-phase connection of the windings of Fig. 18-5. (b) Vector diagram of the generated voltages for the connection of (a).

in phase by 90°. Such a machine is called a *two-phase generator*. It is sometimes referred to as a *quarter-phase generator*. In general, in such a machine connections are brought out from the free terminals A, E, C, and G, as shown schematically in (a) of the figure.

3. Two-Phase Balanced Systems. Two-phase loads may be either of the four-wire type or of the three-wire type, as illustrated in (a) and (b), respectively, of Fig. 18-8.

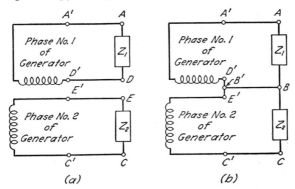

Fig. 18-8. Two-phase loads: (a) Four wire and (b) three wire.

In a balanced two-phase system the two load impedances are identical, and the phase voltages are equal in magnitude and differ in phase by 90°.

It should be evident that the four-wire system shown in (a) of the figure is in reality two single-phase circuits and can be treated as such in circuit problems involving this type of load connection.

In the three-wire balanced system, a definite relationship exists between the magnitudes of the current in each phase, or branch, of the load and the magnitude of the current in the common, or middle, line. Furthermore, a similar relationship exists between the magnitude of the voltage across each branch and that between the two outside lines.

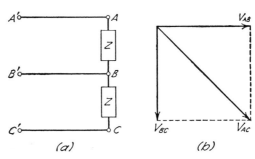

Fig. 18-9. (a) Balanced two-phase three-wire load. (b) Voltage vector diagram for (a)

A balanced two-phase three-wire system is shown in (a) of Fig. 18-9 In (b) of the figure the vectors representing the phase voltages are drawn, $\bar{V}_{AB}$ having been chosen as the reference vector. Since the system is balanced, the voltages $\bar{V}_{AB}$ and $\bar{V}_{BC}$ are of the same magnitude. Let V represent this magnitude; then

$$\bar{V}_{AB} = V(1 + j0),$$

and

$$\bar{V}_{BC} = V(0 - j1).$$

By Ohm's law,

$$\bar{I}_{AB} = \frac{\bar{V}_{AB}}{\bar{Z}} = \frac{V(1 + j0)}{Z\underline{/\theta}}, \tag{18-1}$$

and

$$\bar{I}_{CB} = \frac{\bar{V}_{CB}}{\bar{Z}} = \frac{-\bar{V}_{BC}}{\bar{Z}} = \frac{V(0 + j1)}{Z\underline{/\theta}}. \tag{18-2}$$

Application of Kirchhoff's law of currents to point B of the circuit gives

$$\bar{I}_{BB'} = \bar{I}_{AB} + \bar{I}_{CB}. \tag{18-3}$$

Substituting the values of $\bar{I}_{AB}$ and $\bar{I}_{CB}$ from equations (18-1) and (18-2) in equation (18-3) gives

$$\bar{I}_{BB'} = \frac{V(1+j0)}{Z\underline{/\theta}} + \frac{V(0+j1)}{Z\underline{/\theta}} = \frac{V(1+j1)}{Z\underline{/\theta}} = \frac{\sqrt{2}V(.707+j.707)}{Z\underline{/\theta}}$$

$$= \frac{\sqrt{2}V\underline{/45°}}{Z\underline{/\theta}} = \frac{\sqrt{2}V}{Z}\underline{/45° - \theta}. \quad (18\text{-}4)$$

But in equations (18-1) and (18-2) V/Z is the magnitude of the currents in the phases or branches of the load. If I_ϕ represents this magnitude, then from equation (18-4) the magnitude of $I_{BB'}$ is

$$I_{BB'} = \sqrt{2}I_\phi.$$

Therefore, in a balanced two-phase three-wire system, the magnitude of the current in the common line is equal to the magnitude of the phase currents multiplied by $\sqrt{2}$. It should be noted that the angle of the impedance, $\theta = \text{arc tan } (X/R)$, does not in any manner affect the relationship. Hence the above development is general. The R and X components of $\bar{Z}$ may have any values; they must, however, be the same in both branches.

The voltage between terminals A and C of the load is

$$\bar{V}_{AC} = \bar{V}_{AB} + \bar{V}_{BC}.$$

This vector sum is shown in (b) of Fig. 18-9. From this diagram, when magnitudes only are considered,

$$V_{AC} = \sqrt{2}\,V_{AB} = \sqrt{2}\,B_{BC} = \sqrt{2}V_\phi, \quad (18\text{-}6)$$

V_ϕ being the magnitude of the phase voltages. Therefore, in a balanced two-phase three-wire system, the voltage between the two outside lines is equal to the magnitude of the phase voltage multiplied by $\sqrt{2}$.

4. Three-Phase Balanced Systems. Three-phase loads are connected either in delta or wye as shown in (a) and (b), respectively,

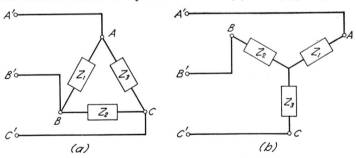

Fig. 18-10. Three-phase loads: (a) Delta connected and (b) wye connected.

in Fig. 18-10. The load is said to be balanced when the branch impedances $\bar{Z}_1$, $\bar{Z}_2$, and $\bar{Z}_3$ are identical. The system is said to be balanced when the load is balanced and when the voltages applied to the load are equal in magnitude and differ in phase by 120°.

5. Balanced Delta System. In a balanced three-phase system in which the load is connected in delta a definite relationship exists between the magnitude I_ϕ of the current in each branch of the load and the magnitude I_L of the current in each line to the load. Let $\bar{Z} = Z/\theta$ represent the impedance of each branch of such a system, and let V_L represent the magnitudes of the voltages between any and all pairs of lines. The circuit representing such a balanced system is shown in

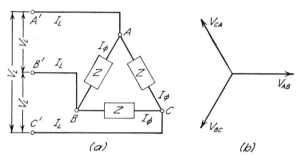

Fig. 18-11. (a) Balanced delta-connected load. (b) Voltage vector diagram for (a).

(a) of Fig. 18-11. In (b) of the figure the voltages between the lines are shown, $\bar{V}_{AB}$ having been chosen as the reference vector. Hence

$$\bar{V}_{AB} = V_L (\cos 0 + j \sin 0) = V_L(1 + j0), \qquad (18\text{-}7)$$
$$\bar{V}_{BC} = V_L (\cos 240° + j \sin 240°) = V_L(-.5 - j.866), \qquad (18\text{-}8)$$

and

$$\bar{V}_{CA} = V_L (\cos 120° + j \sin 120°) = V_L(-.5 + j.866). \qquad (18\text{-}9)$$

The currents in the branches can now be determined.

$$\bar{I}_{AB} = \frac{\bar{V}_{AB}}{\bar{Z}} = \frac{V_L(1 + j0)}{\bar{Z}} = \frac{V_L/0°}{Z/\theta}, \qquad (18\text{-}10)$$

$$\bar{I}_{AC} = \frac{\bar{V}_{AC}}{\bar{Z}} = \frac{-\bar{V}_{CA}}{\bar{Z}} = \frac{V_L(.5 - j.866)}{\bar{Z}} = \frac{V_L/-60°}{Z/\theta}, \qquad (18\text{-}11)$$

and

$$\bar{I}_{BC} = \frac{\bar{V}_{BC}}{\bar{Z}} = \frac{V_L(-.5 - j.866)}{\bar{Z}} = \frac{V_L/-120°}{Z/\theta}. \qquad (18\text{-}12)$$

Referring to (a) of the figure, it can be seen that

$$\bar{I}_{A'A} = \bar{I}_{AB} + \bar{I}_{AC}.$$

Substituting for $\bar{I}_{AB}$ and $\bar{I}_{AC}$ the values from equations (18-10) and

(18-11) gives

$$\bar{I}_{A'A} = \frac{V_L(1 + j0 + .5 - j.866)}{\bar{Z}} = \frac{\sqrt{3} \, V_L(.866 - j.5)}{\bar{Z}}$$

$$= \frac{\sqrt{3} \, V_L \underline{/-30°}}{Z\underline{/\theta}} = \frac{\sqrt{3} \, V_L \underline{/-(30° + \theta)}}{Z}. \quad (18\text{-}13)$$

Similarly

$$\bar{I}_{B'B} = \bar{I}_{BC} + \bar{I}_{BA} = \bar{I}_{BC} - \bar{I}_{AB}.$$

Substituting for $\bar{I}_{BC}$ and $\bar{I}_{AB}$ the values from equations (18-12) and (18-10) gives

$$\bar{I}_{B'B} = \frac{V_L(-.5 - j.866 - 1 - j0)}{\bar{Z}} = \frac{\sqrt{3} \, V_L(-.866 - j.5)}{\bar{Z}}$$

$$= \frac{\sqrt{3} \, V_L \underline{/-150°}}{Z\underline{/\theta}} = \frac{\sqrt{3} \, V_L \underline{/-(150° + \theta)}}{Z}. \quad (18\text{-}14).$$

Also

$$\bar{I}_{C'C} = \bar{I}_{CA} + \bar{I}_{CB} = -\bar{I}_{AC} - \bar{I}_{BC}.$$

Substituting for $\bar{I}_{AC}$ and $\bar{I}_{BC}$ the values from equations (18-11) and (18-12) gives

$$\bar{I}_{C'C} = \frac{V_L(-.5 + j.866 + .5 + j.866)}{\bar{Z}} = \frac{\sqrt{3} \, V_L \, (0 + j1)}{\bar{Z}}$$

$$= \frac{\sqrt{3} \, V_L \underline{/90°}}{Z\underline{/\theta}} = \frac{\sqrt{3} \, V_L \underline{/90°} - \theta}{\bar{Z}}. \quad (18\text{-}15)$$

In equations (18-10), (18-11), (18-12), (18-13), (18-14), and (18-15) V_L/Z is the magnitude I_ϕ of the current in each branch as it would be measured by ammeters placed in the various branches. From an inspection of equations (18-13), (18-14), and (18-15) it will be noted that the magnitudes of the currents in the lines to the circuit are equal, and hence

$$I_{A'A} = I_{B'B} = I_{C'C} = \frac{\sqrt{3} \, V_L}{Z} = \sqrt{3} \, I_\phi.$$

Therefore in a balanced three-phase system with a delta-connected load the line currents are equal, the magnitude I_L being the magnitude I_ϕ of the branch currents multiplied by the $\sqrt{3}$, or

$$I_L = \sqrt{3} \, I_\phi. \quad (18\text{-}16)$$

It should be noted that the angle of the impedance, $\theta = \text{arc tan} \, (X/R)$, does not in any way affect this relationship.   Hence the above development is general. The R and X components may have any values; they must, however, be the same in all branches.

6. Balanced Wye System. In a balanced three-phase system in which the load is connected in wye, a definite relationship exists between the magnitude V_ϕ of the voltage across each leg of the load and the magnitude V_L of the voltage between the lines to the load. The circuit of such a balanced system is shown in (a) of Fig. 18-12. In (b) of the figure the voltages between the lines, or line voltages, are shown in their proper phase relationship, $\bar{V}_{AB}$ having been chosen as

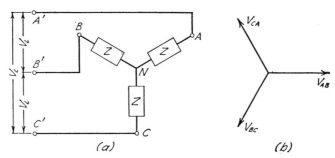

(a) (b)

Fig. 18-12. (a) Balanced wye-connected load. (b) Voltage vector diagram for (a)

the reference vector. This diagram is the same as that shown in (b) of Fig. 18-11. Therefore the complex expressions for $\bar{V}_{AB}$, $\bar{V}_{BC}$, and $\bar{V}_{CA}$ are equations (18-7), (18-8), and (18-9).

From (a) of Fig. 18-12 it is seen that

$$\bar{V}_{AB} = \bar{I}_{AN}\bar{Z} + \bar{I}_{NB}\bar{Z}, \tag{18-17}$$
$$\bar{V}_{BC} = \bar{I}_{BN}\bar{Z} + \bar{I}_{NC}\bar{Z}, \tag{18-18}$$

and

$$\bar{V}_{CA} = \bar{I}_{CN}\bar{Z} + \bar{I}_{NA}\bar{Z}. \tag{18-19}$$

By Kirchhoff's law of currents

$$\bar{I}_{NB} = \bar{I}_{AN} + \bar{I}_{CN}.$$

Substituting this value for $\bar{I}_{NB}$ in equation (18-17) gives

$$\bar{V}_{AB} = \bar{I}_{AN}\bar{Z} + (\bar{I}_{AN} + \bar{I}_{CN})\bar{Z} = (2\bar{I}_{AN} + \bar{I}_{CN})\bar{Z}. \tag{18-20}$$

Subtracting equation (18-19) from equation (18-20) gives

$$\bar{V}_{AB} - \bar{V}_{CA} = (2\bar{I}_{AN} + \bar{I}_{CN})\bar{Z} - (\bar{I}_{CN} + \bar{I}_{NA})\bar{Z} = 3\bar{I}_{AN}\bar{Z}.$$

Substituting for $\bar{V}_{AB}$ and $\bar{V}_{CA}$ the values shown in equations (18-7) and (18-9) gives

$$\bar{V}_{AB} - \bar{V}_{CA} = V_L[(1+j0) - (-.5+j.866)] = V_L(1.5 - j.866) = 3\bar{I}_{AN}\bar{Z}.$$

Therefore

$$\bar{I}_{AN}\bar{Z} = \bar{V}_{AN} = \frac{V_L}{\sqrt{3}}(.866 - j.5) = \frac{V_L}{\sqrt{3}} \underline{/-30^\circ}, \quad (18\text{-}21)$$

and

$$V_{AN} = \frac{V_L}{\sqrt{3}}. \quad (18\text{-}22)$$

Referring to (a) of Fig. 18-12, it can be seen that

$$\bar{V}_{AB} = \bar{V}_{AN} + \bar{V}_{NB} = \bar{V}_{AN} - \bar{V}_{BN},$$

and

$$\bar{V}_{BN} = \bar{V}_{AN} - \bar{V}_{AB}.$$

Substituting for $\bar{V}_{AB}$ and $\bar{V}_{AN}$ the values shown in equations (18-7) and (18-21) gives

$$\bar{V}_{BN} = \frac{V_L}{\sqrt{3}}(.866 - j.5) - V_L(1 + j0)$$

$$= \frac{V_L}{\sqrt{3}}(-.866 - j.5) = \frac{V_L}{\sqrt{3}} \underline{/-150^\circ}, \quad (18\text{-}23)$$

or

$$V_{BN} = \frac{V_L}{\sqrt{3}}. \quad (18\text{-}24)$$

Again referring to (a) of Fig. 18-12, it is seen that

$$\bar{V}_{BC} = \bar{V}_{BN} + \bar{V}_{NC} = \bar{V}_{BN} - \bar{V}_{CN},$$

and

$$\bar{V}_{CN} = \bar{V}_{BN} - \bar{V}_{BC}.$$

Substituting for $\bar{V}_{BC}$ and $\bar{V}_{BN}$ the values shown in equations (18-8) and (18-23) gives

$$\bar{V}_{CN} = \frac{V_L}{\sqrt{3}}(-.866 - j.5) - V_L(-.5 - j.866)$$

$$= \frac{V_L}{\sqrt{3}}(0 + j1) = \frac{V_L}{\sqrt{3}} \underline{/90^\circ},$$

and

$$V_{CN} = \frac{V_L}{\sqrt{3}}. \quad (18\text{-}25)$$

From equations (18-22), (18-24), and (18-25) it is seen that the voltages across the branches of the wye-connected load are equal, the magnitude

V_ϕ being equal to the magnitude V_L of the line voltages divided by $\sqrt{3}$, or

$$V_\phi = \frac{V_L}{\sqrt{3}},$$

and

$$V_L = \sqrt{3}\, V_\phi. \tag{18-26}$$

7. Two-Phase Unbalanced Three-Wire Load. In Fig. 18-13 is shown a two-phase three-wire system in which the load connected to phase AB is a pure resistance and that connected to phase BC is a

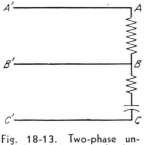 resistance and condenser connected in series. A', B', and C' indicate the source terminals.

From the figure it is evident that

$$\bar{I}_{A'A} = \bar{I}_{AB},$$

and $\qquad \bar{I}_{C'C} = \bar{I}_{CB}.$

Applying Kirchhoff's current law at junction point B gives

Fig. 18-13. Two-phase un-balanced three-wire load.

$$\bar{I}_{AB} + \bar{I}_{B'B} + \bar{I}_{CB} = 0. \tag{18-27}$$

The voltage drop $\bar{V}_{AC}$ is equal to the vector sum of the drops $\bar{V}_{AB}$ and $\bar{V}_{BC}$. Expressed mathematically,

$$\bar{V}_{AC} = \bar{V}_{AB} + \bar{V}_{BC},$$

or, since $\bar{V}_{CA} = -\bar{V}_{AC}$,

$$\bar{V}_{AB} + \bar{V}_{BC} + \bar{V}_{CA} = 0. \tag{18-28}$$

Equations (18-27) and (18-28) provide the basis for either a mathematical analysis of the circuit in Fig. 18-13 or the construction of the vector diagram representing the circuit conditions. The vector diagram for this circuit is shown in Fig. 18-14. The only data necessary for constructing the vector diagram are the magnitudes of the currents I_{AB}, $I_{B'B}$, and I_{CB} and the magnitudes of the voltages V_{AB}, V_{BC}, and V_{CA}, these quantities being readily determined by ammeters and voltmeters. The vector $\bar{V}_{AB}$ is taken as reference, and it is assumed that $\bar{V}_{BC}$ lags $\bar{V}_{AB}$. Thus $\bar{V}_{BC}$ is drawn downward from the origin of the reference vector. Although a two-phase system is under consideration, it should not be assumed that $\bar{V}_{BC}$ lags $\bar{V}_{AB}$ by 90°. This condition can exist only when the phase voltages V_{AB} and V_{BC} are equal and V_{AC} is equal to $\sqrt{2}$ times the phase voltage. In most cases this will not be true because of the impedance drops in the source. Equation (18-28), however, must be satisfied regardless of magnitudes or phase relations. To satisfy this equation, $\bar{V}_{AB} + \bar{V}_{BC} + \bar{V}_{CA}$ must form a closed triangle. The location of one side, $\bar{V}_{AB}$, of the triangle has already been established, this vector having been chosen as the reference. The triangle is completed by drawing an arc having a radius equal to V_{BC} with the tip of vector $\bar{V}_{AB}$ as the center, and by drawing a second arc having a radius equal to V_{CA} with the origin O as the center. Since it has been assumed that $\bar{V}_{BC}$ lags $\bar{V}_{AB}$, the intersection of the arcs below vector $\bar{V}_{AB}$ locates the third vertex of the desired triangle. The construction is shown in Fig. 18-14(a), the sides of the

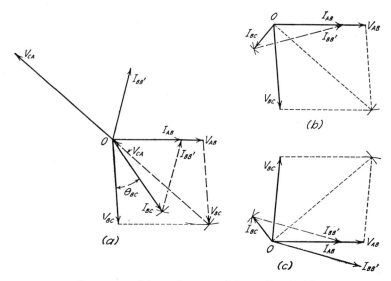

Fig. 18-14. Vector diagrams relating to Fig. 18-13.

triangle being the voltage vectors $\bar{V}_{AB}$, $\bar{V}_{BC}$, and $\bar{V}_{CA}$. The vectors $\bar{V}_{BC}$ and $\bar{V}_{CA}$ are also shown drawn from the common origin for the sake of clarity.

Since the load connected to phase AB consists of a pure resistance, $\bar{I}_{AB}$ is in phase with $\bar{V}_{AB}$. All that is known about the phase relation of $\bar{I}_{BC}$ and $\bar{V}_{BC}$ is that $\bar{I}_{BC}$ leads $\bar{V}_{BC}$ by some angle θ_{BC}. As yet the exact value of θ_{BC} is unknown. Also, only the magnitude of $I_{BB'}$ is known. However, the positions of the current vectors $\bar{I}_{BC}$ and $\bar{I}_{BB'}$ can be determined by use of the relation expressed in equation (18-27). This equation can be written as

$$\bar{I}_{BC} + \bar{I}_{BB'} = \bar{I}_{AB}. \tag{18-29}$$

Since $\bar{I}_{BC}$ must lead $\bar{V}_{BC}$, vector $\bar{I}_{BC}$ should lie somewhere in the quadrant between vectors $\bar{V}_{BC}$ and $\bar{V}_{AB}$. To determine the proper position of the vectors $\bar{I}_{BC}$ and $\bar{I}_{BB'}$, an arc of radius I_{BC} is drawn from the origin O. A second arc, of radius $I_{BB'}$, is drawn with the tip of the vector $\bar{I}_{AB}$ as the center. The intersection of these two arcs below the horizontal axis locates the tip of vector $\bar{I}_{BC}$. This vector may now be drawn by joining the origin with the point of intersection of the arcs. The arcs and the vector $\bar{I}_{BC}$ are shown in Fig. 18-14(a). The current triangle can be closed by drawing a line from the tip of the vector $\bar{I}_{BC}$ to the tip of the vector $\bar{I}_{AB}$. This line is vector $\bar{I}_{BB'}$, as should be evident from inspection of equation (18-29), for vector $\bar{I}_{BB'}$ added to vector $\bar{I}_{BC}$ must be equal to vector $\bar{I}_{AB}$. This construction also satisfies equation (18-27), since a closed triangle is formed. Vector $\bar{I}_{BB'}$ is also shown translated to the origin of the diagram.

The measured magnitudes I_{BC} and $I_{BB'}$ may be such that the intersection of the arcs, and hence the tip of vector $\bar{I}_{BC}$, falls in the quadrant to the left of $\bar{V}_{BC}$ instead of to the right as expected. An example of this possibility is shown in (b) of Fig. 18-14. When this happens, it is evidence that voltage $\bar{V}_{BC}$ actually leads $\bar{V}_{AB}$ instead of lags as originally assumed. To obtain the proper vector diagram, the voltage triangle must be inverted so that $\bar{V}_{BC}$ will lead $\bar{V}_{AB}$. The current triangle must also be inverted to locate properly the current vectors $\bar{I}_{BC}$ and $\bar{I}_{BB'}$. The conversion is shown in (c) of Fig. 18-14.

If in (c) the current arcs had been extended, a second intersection would have occurred in the third quadrant. Thus a second position of $\bar{I}_{BC}$, the same as shown in (b), would have been obtained. Obviously this would have been an impossible solution, since the angle between $\bar{I}_{BC}$ and $\bar{V}_{BC}$ cannot be greater than 90°. Hence it was possible to construct the correct vector diagram knowing the phase angle of only load AB. However, when neither of the phase loads is a pure resistance nor a pure reactance, it is possible for the two intersections of the current arcs to occur in the same quadrant. In such a case it is necessary to know the phase angle of each of the two loads in order to construct the correct vector diagram.

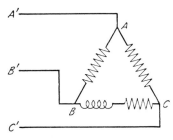

8. Three-Phase Unbalanced Delta Load. Fig. 18-15 shows an unbalanced three-phase delta-connected load.

Fig. 18-15. Unbalanced delta-connected load.

Phases AB and CA are loaded by resistors and phase BC by a coil having resistance as shown.

Application of Kirchhoff's current law at points A, B, and C gives

$$\bar{I}_{A'A} = \bar{I}_{AB} + \bar{I}_{AC}, \qquad (18\text{-}30)$$

$$\bar{I}_{B'B} = \bar{I}_{BA} + \bar{I}_{BC}, \qquad (18\text{-}31)$$

and

$$\bar{I}_{C'C} = \bar{I}_{CB} + \bar{I}_{CA}. \qquad (18\text{-}32)$$

Adding equations (18-30), (18-31), and (18-32) and arranging terms yields

$$\bar{I}_{A'A} + \bar{I}_{B'B} + \bar{I}_{C'C} = \bar{I}_{AB} + \bar{I}_{BA} + \bar{I}_{BC} + \bar{I}_{CB} + \bar{I}_{CA} + \bar{I}_{AC}. \qquad (18\text{-}33)$$

Since $\bar{I}_{AB} = -\bar{I}_{BA}$, $\bar{I}_{BC} = -\bar{I}_{CB}$, and $\bar{I}_{CA} = -\bar{I}_{AC}$, equation (18-33) becomes

$$\bar{I}_{A'A} + \bar{I}_{B'B} + \bar{I}_{C'C} = 0. \qquad (18\text{-}34)$$

In accordance with Kirchhoff's voltage law the voltage equation for loop $ABCA$ is

$$\bar{V}_{AB} + \bar{V}_{BC} + \bar{V}_{CA} = 0. \qquad (18\text{-}35)$$

Equations (18-30), (18-31), (18-32), (18-34), and (18-35) are the fundamental relations necessary for an analysis of the circuit shown. In this particular circuit only the magnitudes of the line currents and phase currents—namely, $I_{A'A}$, $I_{B'B}$, $I_{C'C}$, I_{AB}, I_{BC}, and I_{CA}—and the magnitudes of the line voltages—V_{AB}, V_{BC}, and V_{CA}—are necessary for constructing the vector diagram. All of these quantities are determined readily by ammeters and voltmeters.

In the case of a delta-connected load such as that under consideration, the determination of the proper locations of the various vectors is simplified by starting with the current relation expressed in equation (18-34). To satisfy this equation graphically, vectors $\bar{I}_{A'A}$, $\bar{I}_{B'B}$, and $\bar{I}_{C'C}$ when placed end to end must form a closed triangle, as shown in (a) of Fig. 18-16. Unless the sequence of the rotating vectors is known, the order in which the vectors are connected to each other to form the triangle must be an arbitrary choice. Making such a choice is, in fact, assuming a certain sequence. Whether or not this assumption is the correct one will be determined in the development of the rest of the vector diagram. In constructing the current triangle, $\bar{I}_{A'A}$ is taken as reference and $\bar{I}_{B'B}$ is assumed to lead $\bar{I}_{A'A}$.

As is evident from an inspection of Fig. 18-15 and as stated in equations (18-30) and (18-31), the current in phase AB is a component of the current in line $A'A$ and also of the current in line $B'B$. The vector $\bar{I}_{AB}$ must therefore be so placed in the diagram that it is common to the two vectors, $\bar{I}_{A'A}$ and $\bar{I}_{B'B}$. Accordingly, one end must coincide with the vertex of the latter two vectors. With the vertex formed by

$\bar{I}_{A'A}$ and $\bar{I}_{B'B}$ in Fig. 18-16(a) as a center, an arc of radius equal to I_{AB} is drawn. The other end of vector $\bar{I}_{AB}$ is at some point on this arc. Likewise, since current $\bar{I}_{BC}$ is common to $\bar{I}_{B'B}$ and $\bar{I}_{CC'}$, and current $\bar{I}_{CA}$ is common to $\bar{I}_{C'C}$ and $\bar{I}_{AA'}$, an arc of radius I_{BC} is drawn from the vertex formed by vectors $\bar{I}_{B'B}$ and $\bar{I}_{C'C}$, and another arc of radius I_{CA} is drawn from the vertex formed by vectors $\bar{I}_{C'C}$ and $\bar{I}_{A'A}$. If the data

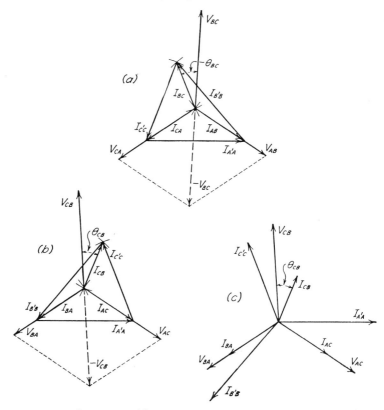

Fig. 18-16.   Vector diagrams relating to Fig. 18-15.

available are accurate, the three arcs will have a common point of intersection. Lines drawn from this point of intersection to each of the vertices of the triangle are the vectors representing the currents in the branches of the delta. The proper designation of these vectors is determined by equations (18-30), (18-31), and (18-32), for these equations must be satisfied. It will be noted that this is the case in the figure.

Since phase AB contains pure resistance, $\bar{V}_{AB}$ is drawn in phase with $\bar{I}_{AB}$, as shown in the figure. Likewise, $\bar{V}_{CA}$ is drawn in phase with

$\bar{I}_{CA}$. The exact phase relation between $\bar{V}_{BC}$ and $\bar{I}_{BC}$ is not yet known. Equation (18-35), however, must be satisfied. Rearrangement of this equation shows that $\bar{V}_{AB} + \bar{V}_{CA} = -\bar{V}_{BC} = \bar{V}_{CB}$. Therefore $\bar{V}_{AB}$ is added to $\bar{V}_{CA}$, giving $-\bar{V}_{BC}$. $\bar{V}_{BC}$ is then determined by reversing $-\bar{V}_{BC}$. The magnitude of $\bar{V}_{BC}$ scaled from the diagram should, of course, check with the value measured in the laboratory.

It will be noted that, on the basis of the conventional counterclockwise rotation of vectors, $\bar{I}_{BC}$ leads $\bar{V}_{BC}$. This condition is impossible, since the load on phase BC is inductive. This fact indicates that the assumption made in drawing the line-current triangle that $\bar{I}_{B'B}$ leads $\bar{I}_{A'A}$ is wrong and that $\bar{I}_{B'B}$ actually lags $\bar{I}_{A'A}$.

Had the original assumption of the sequence been opposite to that made, the resulting construction of the vector diagram would have been that shown in (b) of the figure. It is seen that in accordance with the conventional direction of vector rotation—that is, counterclockwise—$\bar{I}_{CB}$ lags $\bar{V}_{CB}$, as it must.

In (c) of the figure the vectors of (b) are drawn from a common origin. This drawing gives a clearer picture of the phase relations.

9. Three-Phase Unbalanced Wye Load Without Neutral Connection. An unbalanced three-phase three-wire wye-connected load is shown in Fig. 18-17. Phase AN consists of a resistor, phase BN a coil having appreciable resistance, and phase CN a capacitance of negligible resistance.

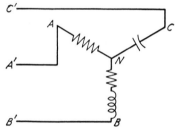

Fig. 18-17. Unbalanced three-wire wye-connected load.

Inspection of the figure shows that

$$\bar{I}_{A'A} = \bar{I}_{AN},$$
$$\bar{I}_{B'B} = \bar{I}_{BN},$$

and

$$\bar{I}_{C'C} = \bar{I}_{CN}.$$

Application of Kirchhoff's current law at junction point N gives

$$\bar{I}_{AN} + \bar{I}_{BN} + \bar{I}_{CN} = 0. \tag{18-36}$$

From the figure it is evident that

$$\bar{V}_{AB} = \bar{V}_{AN} + \bar{V}_{NB}, \tag{18-37}$$
$$\bar{V}_{BC} = \bar{V}_{BN} + \bar{V}_{NC}, \tag{18-38}$$

and

$$\bar{V}_{CA} = \bar{V}_{CN} + \bar{V}_{NA}. \tag{18-39}$$

Adding equations (18-37), (18-38), and (18-39) yields

$$\bar{V}_{AB} + \bar{V}_{BC} + \bar{V}_{CA} = \bar{V}_{AN} + \bar{V}_{NA} + \bar{V}_{BN} + \bar{V}_{NB} + \bar{V}_{CN} + \bar{V}_{NC}. \tag{18-40}$$

Since $\bar{V}_{AN} = -\bar{V}_{NA}$, $\bar{V}_{BN} = -\bar{V}_{NB}$, and $\bar{V}_{CN} = -\bar{V}_{NC}$, equation (18-40) becomes

$$\bar{V}_{AB} + \bar{V}_{BC} + \bar{V}_{CA} = 0. \tag{18-41}$$

The only test data necessary for constructing the vector diagram representing conditions in the circuit under consideration are the measured values of I_{AN}, I_{BN}, I_{CN}, V_{AB}, V_{BC}, V_{CA}, V_{AN}, V_{BN}, and V_{CN}. The vector diagram for the circuit of Fig. 18-17 is shown in Fig. 18-18.

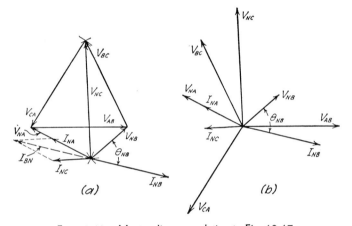

Fig. 18-18.   Vector diagrams relating to Fig. 18-17.

$\bar{V}_{AB}$ is taken as the reference vector. The line-voltage triangle is constructed in accordance with equation (18-41). Unless the sequence of the rotating vectors is known, the order in which the vectors are connected to each other must be an arbitrary choice. Making such a choice, of course, assumes a certain sequence. Whether or not this assumption is correct will be determined in the development of the rest of the vector diagram. In this case $\bar{V}_{BC}$ is assumed to lead $\bar{V}_{AB}$. Vectors $\bar{V}_{AB}$, $\bar{V}_{BC}$, and $\bar{V}_{CA}$ cannot be assumed to differ in phase by 120° unless $V_{AB} = V_{BC} = V_{CA}$. Because of impedance drops in the source, this condition rarely exists. In any case, equation (18-41) must be satisfied.

In determining the positions of $\bar{V}_{NA}$, $\bar{V}_{NB}$, and $\bar{V}_{NC}$ the conditions expressed in equations (18-37), (18-38), and (18-39) must be fulfilled. It is evident from Fig. 18-17 that the voltage $\bar{V}_{AN}$ across phase AN is a component of the voltage $\bar{V}_{AB}$ and also a component of the voltage $\bar{V}_{AC}$. Therefore, with the vertex formed by $\bar{V}_{AB}$ and $\bar{V}_{CA}$ in Fig.

18-18(a) as a center, an arc of radius equal to V_{AN} is drawn. Similarly, since $\bar{V}_{BN}$ is a component of both $\bar{V}_{BA}$ and $\bar{V}_{BC}$, an arc is drawn with the vertex formed by $\bar{V}_{AB}$ and $\bar{V}_{BC}$ as a center and having a radius equal to V_{BN}. Also, since $\bar{V}_{CN}$ is a component of $\bar{V}_{CA}$ and $\bar{V}_{CB}$, an arc is drawn with the vertex formed by $\bar{V}_{BC}$ and $\bar{V}_{CA}$ as a center and having a radius equal to V_{CN}. If the data available are accurate, the three arcs that have been drawn will have a common point of intersection. Lines drawn from this point of intersection to each of the vertices of the triangle are the vectors representing the voltages across the branches of the wye. The proper designation of these vectors is determined by equations (18-37), (18-38), and (18-39). It will be noted that this is the case in (a) of the figure. It should be observed that the position of the electrical neutral, which is determined by the intersection of $\bar{V}_{NA}$, $\bar{V}_{NB}$, and $\bar{V}_{NC}$, is not within the line-voltage triangle.

$\bar{I}_{NA}$ is drawn in phase with $\bar{V}_{NA}$, since the load on phase AN is a resistor. Since phase CN consists of a condenser with negligible resistance, $\bar{I}_{NC}$ is drawn 90° ahead of $\bar{V}_{NC}$. $\bar{I}_{NB}$ is constructed so that it is equal and opposite to the sum of $\bar{I}_{NA}$ and $\bar{I}_{NC}$, for from equation (18-36)

$$\bar{I}_{NB} = -(\bar{I}_{NA} + \bar{I}_{NC}).$$

The manner in which this construction is carried out is indicated in the figure. The magnitude of $\bar{I}_{NB}$ should, of course, check with the measured value. It will be noted that $\bar{I}_{NB}$ lags $\bar{V}_{NB}$ by the angle θ_{NB}. Inasmuch as this represents the condition that is known to exist in phase BN, the original assumption of $\bar{V}_{BC}$ leading $\bar{V}_{AB}$ is correct. If it had been assumed that $\bar{V}_{BC}$ lags $\bar{V}_{AB}$, then in the development of the rest of the vector diagram the vector $\bar{I}_{NB}$ would have led $\bar{V}_{NB}$ by an angle θ_{NB}. This solution, of course, would be impossible, and would indicate that the sequence of the rotating vectors had been incorrectly assumed. Thus Fig. 18-18(a) represents conditions in the circuit of Fig. 18-17. In (b) of the figure the vectors of (a) are drawn from a common origin.

10. Three-Phase Unbalanced Wye Load with Neutral Connection. Fig. 18-19 shows the circuit of Fig. 18-17 with the neutral connection added. Voltage equations (18-37), (18-38), (18-39), and (18-41), which were written for the circuit of Fig. 18-17, also apply to the circuit of Fig. 18-19. A new current equation, however, must be written for junction point N. In accordance with Kirchhoff's current law

$$\bar{I}_{AN} + \bar{I}_{BN} + \bar{I}_{CN} + \bar{I}_{N'N} = 0. \qquad (18\text{-}42)$$

If measured values of I_{AN}, I_{BN}, I_{CN}, $I_{N'N}$, V_{AB}, V_{BC}, V_{CA}, V_{AN}, V_{BN}, V_{CN}, and the power in branch BN are available, the vector diagram for the circuit of Fig. 18-19 can be constructed from the relations expressed in equations (18-37), (18-38), (18-39), (18-41), and (18-42). The completed vector diagram is shown in Fig. 18-20(a).

Inasmuch as the voltage equations for Fig. 18-19 are the same as those for Fig. 18-17, the voltage vectors in (a) of Fig. 18-20 are located in the same manner as described in the construction of Fig. 18-18(a).

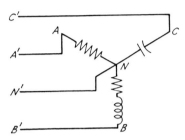

Fig. 18-19. Unbalanced wye-connected load with neutral connection.

In Fig. 18-20(a) the electrical neutral formed by the intersection of $\bar{V}_{NA}$, $\bar{V}_{NB}$, and $\bar{V}_{NC}$ lies in the center portion of the line-voltage triangle. This is as would be expected, since the neutral connection to the power source definitely establishes the voltages to neutral. If there were no impedance drops in the various phases of the source, the voltages to neutral would always be equal in magnitude and would differ in phase by 120°. In such a case the line-voltage

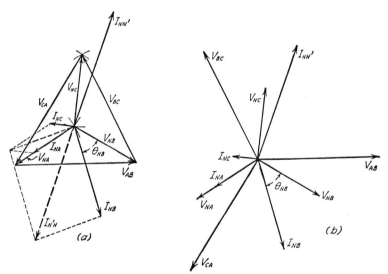

Fig. 18-20. Vector diagrams relating to Fig. 18-19.

triangle would be equilateral, and the electrical neutral would be at the center of the triangle.

In (a) of Fig. 18-20, $\bar{I}_{NA}$ is drawn in phase with $\bar{V}_{NA}$, since the load on phase AN is a resistor. Since the load on phase CN is a condenser of negligible resistance, $\bar{I}_{NC}$ leads $\bar{V}_{NC}$ by 90°, as shown. The phase angle θ_{NB} between $\bar{I}_{NB}$ and $\bar{V}_{NB}$ is determined from observed data, and then $\bar{I}_{NB}$ is drawn as indicated in the figure. The phase relation of $\bar{I}_{N'N}$ to any other vector can now be determined since equation (18-42) must be satisfied. To do this $\bar{I}_{N'N}$ must equal $\bar{I}_{NA} + \bar{I}_{NB} + \bar{I}_{NC}$. Thus $\bar{I}_{NA}$ and $\bar{I}_{NC}$ are added, and then to this sum is added $\bar{I}_{NB}$. The magnitude of the vector $\bar{I}_{N'N}$ resulting from this addition should check the measured value of the neutral current. If a reasonably close check is not obtained, it is an indication that the wrong sequence was assumed originally. In such an event, the correct vector diagram can be constructed using the correct sequence. Fig. 18-20(b) is the common origin vector diagram for the vectors of (a).

11. Data Necessary for Constructing Vector Diagrams for Unbalanced Polyphase Loads. From the foregoing it should be evident that vector diagrams for three-wire and four-wire unbalanced polyphase loads can always be constructed from measurements made of all voltages and currents provided that the phase angles of at least two of the phase loads are known in the case of three-wire loads and the phase angle of each of the phase loads is known in the case of four-wire loads. The magnitude of a phase angle can be determined from measurements of the voltage, current, and power of the phase load. In addition to the magnitude of the phase angle, it must be known whether the angle is one of lead or lag. Generally, this will be known from the character of the phase load.

Laboratory Problem No. 18-1
BALANCED POLYPHASE CIRCUITS

Laboratory

1. Connect a resistance load to a two-phase three-wire source. Balance the load, using the current value designated by the instructor. When the load is balanced, measure the following:

> (a) Each line current.
> (b) Each line-to-line voltage.

2. Set up a delta-connected resistance load. Connect this load to a three-phase source. Balance the load, using the current value designated by the instructor. When the load is balanced, measure the following:

> (a) Each phase (branch) current.
> (b) Each line current.
> (c) Each line voltage.
> (d) Power of each phase.

3. Reconnect the balanced load of **2** in wye.   Connect this load to the three-phase source and measure the following:

> (a) Each line current.
> (b) Each line voltage.
> (c) Each phase (branch) voltage.
> (d) Power of each phase.

Report

A. Using the data obtained in **1,** calculate the following:

> (1) Ratio of the current in the common line to the current in either of the other two lines.
> (2) Ratio of the voltage between the common line and either of the other lines to the voltage between the other two lines.

How do the above calculated ratios compare with those which theoretically exist in a balanced two-phase three-wire system?   Discuss any discrepancies.

B. Using the data obtained in **2,** calculate the ratio of the line current to the phase current.   How does the calculated ratio compare with that which theoretically exists in a balanced three-phase system when the load is delta connected?   Discuss any discrepancy.

C. Using the data obtained in **3,** calculate the ratio of the line voltage to the phase voltage.   How does the calulated ratio compare with that which theoretically exists in a balanced three-phase system when the load is wye connected?   Discuss any discrepancy.

D. Determine by two different methods the total power delivered to the load in **2.**

E. Determine by two different methods the total power delivered to the load in **3.**

Laboratory Problem No. 18-2
UNBALANCED THREE-PHASE CIRCUITS

Laboratory

As a source of power use a three-phase generator that has a neutral connection available.   In all of the tests outlined below, maintain the magnitude and frequency of the voltage between the generator line terminals constant at the values designated by the instructor.

1. Set up the circuit shown in Fig. 18-21.   For Z_1, Z_2, and Z_3 use the impedances designated by the instructor.   Connect the load to the generator and measure the following:

(a) Each phase (branch) current.

(b) Each line current.

(c) Each line voltage.

(d) Power of each phase load whose power factor is not known.

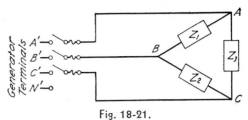

Fig. 18-21.

2. Set up the circuit shown in Fig. 18-22, using the same impedances as were used in **1.** With the switch in the neutral line open, measure the following:

(a) Each line current.

(b) Each phase (branch) voltage.

(c) Each line voltage.

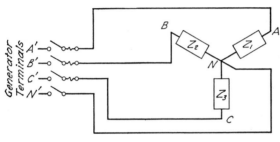

Fig. 18-22.

3. Close the switch in the neutral line and make measurements as in **2** above, but in addition measure the current in the neutral line.

Report

Note: Each of the vector diagrams indicated below must be drawn on a separate sheet and must be to scale. State the scale used in each case.

Each polygon vector diagram sheet must contain a schematic diagram of the circuit to which the vector diagram refers.

Each polygon vector diagram sheet must contain, clearly symbolized, the data from which the diagram was plotted.

Each vector must be identified by double subscripts.

A. Draw the polygon and common-origin current-voltage vector diagrams representing the circuit conditions which existed in **1.**

B. Draw the polygon and common origin current-voltage vector diagrams representing the circuit conditions which existed in **2.**

C. Draw the polygon and common origin current-voltage vector diagrams representing the circuit conditions which existed in **3.**

Laboratory Problem No. 18-3
PHASE-SEQUENCE INDICATORS

Laboratory

1. Set up the circuit shown in Fig. 18-23(a). Use two similar lamps (or similar groups of lamps), each having a resistance approximately equal in magnitude to the reactance of the inductance coil. Connect the three-phase source terminals designated by the instructor as A', B', and C' to the terminals of the disconnect switch as shown in the figure.

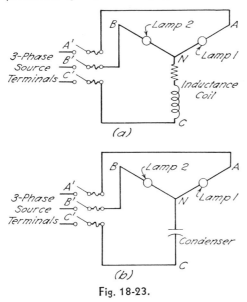

(a)

(b)

Fig. 18-23.

Close the disconnect switch and make a record of which lamp (or lamp group) is the brighter.

Interchange the connections of lines B and C to the disconnect switch so that B is connected to C' and C to B' when the switch is closed. Make a record of which lamp (or lamp group) is the brighter under this condition.

2. Set up the circuit shown in (b) of Fig. 18-23. Use a condenser having a reactance approximately equal in magnitude to the resistance of each lamp (or lamp group).

Repeat the test procedure of **1.**

Report

A. Assuming that the resistance of lamp 1, the resistance of lamp 2, and the reactance of the coil in Fig. 18-23(a) are all equal, solve the circuit to determine which phase sequence makes lamp 2 brighter than lamp 1. Neglect the resistance of the coil.

B. Using the results obtained in **A** and the data taken in **1,** determine the phase sequence of the source used in the laboratory. Explain how this determination was made.

C. If a phase-sequence indicator were made by use of the circuit shown in Fig. 18-23(a), what directions should be supplied with the indicator in order that the phase sequence of a three-phase system could be determined by observing the difference in brilliancy of the lamps?

D. What would be the answer to **C** if the circuit shown in (b) of Fig. 18-23 were used?

CHAPTER 19
MEASUREMENT OF POLYPHASE POWER

1. The $n - 1$ Wattmeter Method. A load that is supplied power through n lines may be considered to receive the power from $n - 1$ generators. A load supplied by four lines is shown in (a) of Fig. 19-1, the $n-1$, or three, equivalent generators that may be considered to supply the power being shown in (b) of the figure. The power delivered to the load in (a) is determined by the magnitudes and phase relations of the voltages between the lines regardless of the nature of the source of these voltages. It is necessary only that generators Nos. 1, 2, and 3 produce at their respective output terminals voltages equal to $\bar{V}_{A'D'}$, $\bar{V}_{B'D'}$, and $\bar{V}_{C'D'}$ of the circuit in (a). When the generators fulfill these requirements, they are equivalent to whatever may be the actual source of the power. Therefore the circuit shown in (b) may be considered the equivalent of that shown in (a).

In (c) of the figure wattmeters having negligible losses are shown connected in such a manner that each one of the wattmeters measures the output power of one of the equivalent generators. Since the power supplied to the load must come from the equivalent generators, the algebraic sum of the wattmeter power indications is the power delivered to the load. Therefore, circuits (a) and (b) being equivalent, the total power supplied to the load in (a) can be determined by connecting wattmeters in this circuit in a manner similar to that shown in (c).

The term "algebraic sum of the wattmeter power indications" is used above because it is possible under certain conditions for the power delivered by one or more of the equivalent generators to be negative. Such a condition exists when the current in the line from an equivalent generator leads or lags the terminal voltage of that generator by an angle greater than 90°. For example, the power delivered by equivalent generator No. 1 is $I_{A'A} V_{A'D'} \cos \theta$, θ being the phase angle between $\bar{I}_{A'A}$ and $\bar{V}_{A'D'}$. When this angle is greater than 90°, $\cos \theta$ is negative, the power is negative, and the deflection of the pointer of wattmeter W_1 is backward. In this case, the connections to the current coil of W_1 must be reversed to obtain an up-scale pointer deflection, and the power indication must be assigned a negative sign.

242

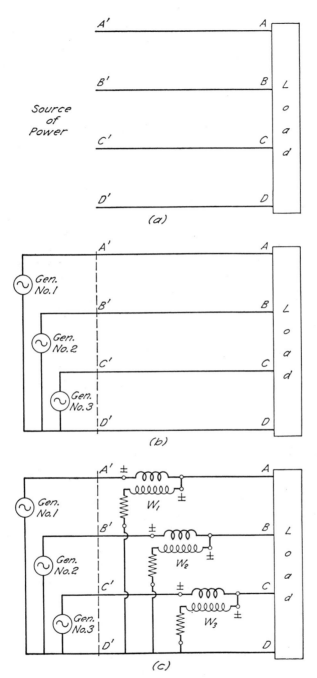

Fig. 19-1. (a) A load supplied by n lines. (b) Voltages between lines in (a) replaced by equivalent voltages from $n-1$ generators. (c) $n-1$ wattmeters connected to measure the power supplied by $n-1$ generators.

In the equivalent circuit (b), the number of equivalent generators is one less than the number of lines; accordingly, in (c) the number of wattmeters required is one less than the number of lines. This leads to the general conclusion that the power delivered to a load fed by n lines can be measured with $n - 1$ wattmeters by (1) inserting a wattmeter current coil in each of $n - 1$ lines with the $\pm$ terminal of each coil toward the source and (2) connecting the $\pm$ or equivalent terminal of the potential circuit of each wattmeter to the load side of its associated current coil and the unmarked terminal of each potential circuit to the line not containing a wattmeter. When a wattmeter current coil does not have a polarity mark, it may be connected so that it produces an up-scale pointer deflection, and a test can be made to determine whether a $+$ or $-$ sign should be given the power indication. Various ways of determining the proper sign for a wattmeter power indication are discussed in a later section.

In applying the $n - 1$ wattmeter method it will be necessary in many cases to correct the wattmeter power indications for power losses in the wattmeters if the actual power delivered to the load is to be determined. Owing to the advantages of a potential-circuit correction over a current-coil correction, the potential circuits should generally be connected on the load side of the current coils. As will be shown later, a wattmeter power indication that must be assigned a negative sign is not corrected in the usual manner.

2. Wattmeter Indications for a Balanced Three-Phase Three-Wire Load. In the preceding discussion it is shown that, in using the $n - 1$ wattmeter method, conditions may be such that all of the wattmeter power indications cannot be taken as positive, but that one or more may have to be given negative signs. As an illustration of the latter possibility, an analysis is made of a balanced three-phase three-wire load. This type of load is studied because many interesting and useful conclusions can be drawn from the analysis. The analysis is made from the standpoint of the power

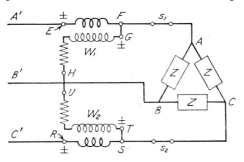

Fig. 19-2.   Two wattmeters connected according to the $n - 1$ wattmeter method.

supplied and with the intent of showing under what conditions in a load of this type the minus sign should be assigned to either one or the other of the wattmeter power indications.

In Fig. 19-2 are shown two wattmeters connected according to the $n - 1$ method. A balanced delta load is shown in the figure, but a balanced wye load could just as well be used for the analysis and would give the same results in regard to the wattmeter indications and their signs. This follows from the fact that for every delta load there is an equivalent wye load and for every wye load there is an equivalent delta load.

Referring to Fig. 19-2, let W_1 be the power indication of wattmeter W_1, and W_2 be the power indication of wattmeter W_2. If the effect of the power loss and inductance of the potential circuit of each watt-

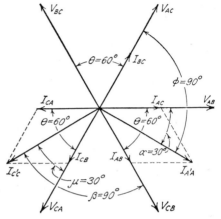

Fig. 19-3. Vector diagram for the load of Fig. 19-2 when balanced and the power factor is .5 lagging.

meter is neglected, a review of the development of equation (11-13) will show that

$$W_1 = I_{A'A}V_{AB} \cos \alpha, \quad (19\text{-}1)$$

and

$$W_2 = I_{C'C}V_{CB} \cos \beta. \quad (19\text{-}2)$$

In these equations α is the angle between the current $\bar{I}_{A'A}$ and the voltage $\bar{V}_{AB}$, and β is the angle between the current $\bar{I}_{C'C}$ and the voltage $\bar{V}_{CB}$.

Fig. 19-3 is the vector diagram for the balanced delta load of Fig. 19-2 when the power factor is .5 lagging— that is, when the phase currents lag the phase voltages by $\theta = 60°$. It will be noted that the angle β is $90°$; therefore W_2 will indicate zero power.

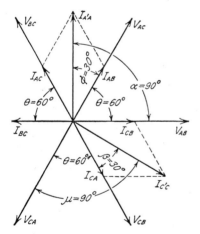

Fig. 19-4. Vector diagram for the load of Fig. 19-2 when balanced and the power factor is .5 leading.

Fig. 19-4 is the vector diagram for the balanced delta load when the power factor is .5 leading, or the phase currents lead the phase voltages by $\theta = 60°$. In this case it will be noted that the angle α is $90°$; therefore W_1 will indicate zero power.

If the power-factor angle θ in Fig. 19-3 is changed to one that is less than 60° lagging (power factor greater than .5), the effect will be to rotate the phase-current vectors $\bar{I}_{AB}$, $\bar{I}_{BC}$, and $\bar{I}_{CA}$ in a counterclockwise direction through an angle of $(60° - \theta)$ from the positions shown. The vectors $\bar{I}_{A'A}$ and $\bar{I}_{C'C}$ will as a result also be rotated through the same angle and in the same direction. The voltage vectors $\bar{V}_{AB}$, $\bar{V}_{BC}$, and $\bar{V}_{CA}$, being fixed by the source, will not be affected by the change in the power factor of the load if it is assumed that the source has negligible impedance. The angle α will now be less than 30°, being $30° - (60° - \theta)$, or $(\theta - 30°)$, and the angle β will be less than 90°, being $90° - (60° - \theta)$, or $(30° + \theta)$. Hence

$$W_1 = I_{A'A}V_{AB} \cos (\theta - 30°), \qquad (19\text{-}3)$$

and

$$W_2 = I_{C'C}V_{CB} \cos (30° + \theta). \qquad (19\text{-}4)$$

Therefore W_1 and W_2 will both be assigned positive signs for all lagging-power-factor angles less than 60°.

If the power-factor angle θ in Fig. 19-4 is changed to one that is less than 60° leading, the effect will be to rotate all current vectors in a clockwise direction through an angle of $(60° - \theta)$ from the positions shown. The angle α will now be less than 90°, being $90° - (60° - \theta)$, or $(30° + \theta)$, and the angle β will be less than 30°, being $30° - (60° - \theta)$, or $(\theta - 30°)$. Thus

$$W_1 = I_{A'A}V_{AB} \cos (30° + \theta), \qquad (19\text{-}5)$$

and

$$W_2 = I_{C'C}V_{CB} \cos (\theta - 30°). \qquad (19\text{-}6)$$

W_1 and W_2, accordingly, will both be assigned positive signs for all leading-power-factor angles less than 60°.

Whenever the power factor of the load is unity—that is, $\theta = 0°$—equations (19-3), (19-4), (19-5), and (19-6) show that the indications W_1 and W_2 will be equal and positive.

For a power-factor angle θ greater than 60° lagging (power factor less than .5), all of the current vectors of Fig. 19-3 must be rotated in a clockwise direction by an angle of $(\theta - 60°)$ from the positions shown, this angle being the angle by which the power-factor angle exceeds 60°. In this case the angle α will be greater than 30°, being $30° + (\theta - 60°)$, or $(\theta - 30°)$, and the angle β will be greater than 90°, being $90° + (\theta - 60°)$, or $(\theta + 30°)$. Hence

$$W_1 = I_{A'A}V_{AB} \cos (\theta - 30°), \qquad (19\text{-}7)$$

and

$$W_2 = I_{C'C}V_{CB} \cos (\theta + 30°). \qquad (19\text{-}8)$$

W_1 will, accordingly, be assigned a positive sign and W_2 a negative sign whenever θ exceeds 60° lagging. The latter follows since cos $(\theta + 30°)$ in this instance will be negative, since it will be the cosine of an angle greater than 90°.

For a power-factor angle θ greater than 60° leading, all of the current vectors of Fig. 19-4 must be rotated in a counterclockwise direction through an angle of $(\theta - 60°)$ from the positions shown. In this case the angle α will be greater than 90°, being 90° $+ (\theta - 60°)$, or $(\theta + 30°)$, and β will be greater than 30°, being 30° $+ (\theta - 60°)$, or $(\theta - 30°)$. Thus

$$W_1 = I_{A'A}V_{AB} \cos (\theta + 30°), \tag{19-9}$$

and

$$W_2 = I_{C'C}V_{CB} \cos (\theta - 30°). \tag{19-10}$$

Therefore W_1 will be assigned a negative sign and W_2 a positive sign whenever the power-factor angle θ is more than 60° leading.

The foregoing conclusions based on the vector diagrams of Figs. 19-3 and 19-4 are for the phase sequence ACB used in these figures. A similar analysis for an ABC phase sequence will show that, regardless of the phase sequence, the following general conclusions may be drawn in regard to the power indications of the two wattmeters used to measure the power delivered to a balanced three-phase three-wire load:

1. When the power factor of the balanced load is unity (power-factor angle is 0°), the power indications of the two wattmeters are equal.

2. When the power factor of the balanced load is .5 leading or lagging (power-factor angle is 60° leading or lagging), the power indication of one of the wattmeters is zero.

3. When the power factor of the balanced load is greater than .5 leading or lagging (power-factor angle is less than 60° leading or lagging), the power indications of the two wattmeters are assigned positive signs.

4. When the power factor of the balanced load is less than .5 leading or lagging (power-factor angle is greater than 60° leading or lagging), the power indication of one of the wattmeters must be assigned a negative sign.

It should be remembered that in determining the magnitudes of the power indications given in the preceding discussion the potential circuits of the wattmeters were assumed to have negligible power losses.

3. Determination of the Sign of a Wattmeter Indication. Since the power indicated by one or more of the $n - 1$ wattmeters used to measure the power supplied to a load by n lines may need to be assigned a negative sign, it is necessary that there be methods for determining when and to which wattmeter power indication the negative sign must be applied.

(1) Terminal-Identification Method. In order to use this method when the current coil of a wattmeter does not have a polarity mark it is necessary to first introduce the wattmeter into a single-phase circuit in which the direction of energy transfer is known. In connecting the instrument into the circuit the precaution must be taken to connect the $\pm$ or equivalent terminal of the potential circuit of the wattmeter to the line into which the current coil is to be introduced as shown

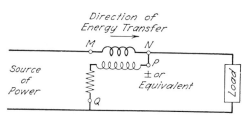

in Fig. 19-5. The connections to the current coil are then made so that the deflection of the instrument pointer is up scale. Identification symbols are now arbitrarily assigned to the current-coil terminals and potential-circuit terminals of the wattmeter, as illustrated in the figure. In

Fig. 19-5. Test circuit for determining the relation between the direction of energy transfer and the wattmeter current-coil connection which causes an up-scale deflection.

this case the terminals of the current coil have been assigned the identification letters M and N, and the potential-coil circuit the letters P and Q.

The direction of the energy transfer in the circuit is from left to right, obviously being from the source to the load. Accordingly, it has now been definitely established that whenever this wattmeter is connected into a circuit and the connection between the current coil and potential-coil circuit of the instrument is that shown in the figure—namely, terminal M of the current coil toward the source and terminal N connected to terminal P of the potential-coil circuit— the transfer of the energy in the circuit is in the direction M to N when the pointer deflection is up scale.

As an example of the application of this method, let the wattmeter shown in Fig. 19-5 be transferred to one pair of the lines shown in (a) of Fig. 19-6. In making the connections care has been taken to maintain the relative connections shown in Fig. 19-5—namely, terminal N connected to terminal P, and terminal M toward the source. It is not yet known whether the transfer of the energy in this pair of lines is from left to right or vice versa. Let it be assumed that the pointer deflection is backward instead of up scale. This condition at once indicates that the direction in which the energy is being transferred is from right to left, for from the preliminary test made with the known circuit conditions of Fig. 19-5, it has been definitely established, that whenever the pointer deflection is up scale with the wattmeter connected as shown in Fig. 19-6(a) the transfer of energy is in the

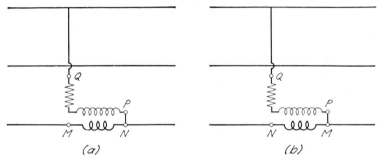

(a)   (b)

Fig. 19-6. Wattmeter connections for illustrating the terminal-identification method for determining the direction of energy transfer.

direction from terminal M to terminal N of the current coil. Thus, if the load is on the right, a negative sign must be assigned the watt-meter power indication which is determined from an up-scale pointer deflection produced by reversing the connections to the current coil as shown in (b) of the figure.

A standard method of marking the terminals of wattmeters has been adopted by instrument manufacturers, and, when wattmeters of comparatively recent manufacture are used, it is usually not necessary to make a preliminary test, as discussed above, in order to determine in which direction energy is being transferred. The standard method of identifying the terminals is to mark one of the current-coil terminals and one of the

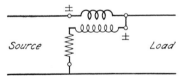

Fig. 19-7. Proper connection of a wattmeter having standard polarity markings.

terminals of the potential-coil circuit with a $\pm$ sign. When the wattmeter is placed in the circuit, the coils are connected as shown in Fig. 19-7. Note the position of the $\pm$ terminal of the current coil with respect to the $\pm$ terminal of the potential circuit of the instrument. When the coils are connected in this manner, the transfer of energy is in the direction from the $\pm$ terminal of the current coil toward the unmarked terminal whenever the pointer deflection is up scale.

It should now be clear that, with the direction of energy transfer determinable from the manner in which the connections to the wattmeter are made, the proper signs to be applied to the power indications of the wattmeters used to measure the power supplied to a load by n lines can readily be determined.

(*2*) *Symmetrical-Interchange Method.* To illustrate a second method for determining the proper sign to be applied to a wattmeter power indication, a three-wire three-phase load is assumed. Such a load with the supply lines is shown in Fig. 19-8. This second method is known as the *symmetrical-interchange method.* It is a convenient one to use when the wattmeters do not have the ± polarity markings, since it avoids the necessity of making a separate test to determine the

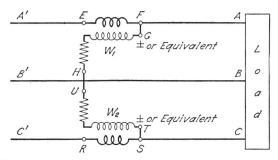

Fig. 19-8.   Wattmeters connected for measuring the power supplied to a three-wire load.

relation between the direction of energy transfer and the wattmeter connections.

The two wattmeters W_1 and W_2 needed to measure the power are connected in the circuit as shown, the current-coil connections being such as to result in an up-scale deflection of the pointers of both instruments. Identification letters are arbitrarily assigned to the terminals of the current coils and to the terminals of the potential-coil circuits as indicated in the figure. Let W_2 be momentarily taken out of the circuit, and let it be replaced by W_1. It is important in making this replacement that the relative connection between the current coil and potential-coil circuit of W_1 be maintained—that is, that terminals F and G are connected together and terminal E is toward the source side of the circuit. The position of W_1 after this change has been made is shown in (a) of Fig. 19-9. If the pointer of W_1 now deflects up scale, the energy transfer between lines $C'C$ and $B'B$ must be in the same direction as that between $A'A$ and $B'B$. This conclusion should be obvious, since in the former and latter positions of W_1 the deflections of the pointer were up scale. Hence the signs to be applied to the power indications of W_1 and W_2 in Fig. 19-8 are the same and positive, for obviously the net energy transfer is from the source to the load.

If, on the other hand, the deflection of the pointer of W_1 had been backward when in the position shown in (a) of Fig. 19-9, the energy transfer between lines $C'C$ and $B'B$ must be in a direction opposite to that in which it is transferred between lines $A'A$ and $B'B$. Accordingly, in such a case the sign of the power indication of either W_1 or W_2 in Fig. 19-8 must be negative. It should be evident that the negative sign should be applied to the smaller of the two.

The possibility always exists that an error may be made when W_1 is transferred from its original position to that shown in (a) of

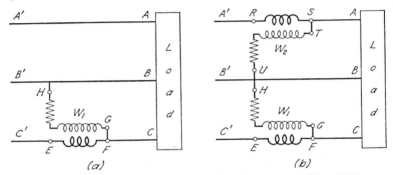

Fig. 19-9. (a) Wattmeter W_2 of Fig. 19-8 replaced by wattmeter W_1. (b)Wattmeters W_1 and W_2 of Fig. 19-8 symmetrically interchanged.

Fig. 19-9. A check can be obtained if W_2 is placed in the position formerly occupied by W_1, care being taken to maintain the relative connection between the current coil and the potential-coil circuit of W_2 the same as that in its original position shown in Fig. 19-8— namely, terminal S connected to terminal T, and terminal R toward the source side of the circuit. The positions of W_1 and W_2 after their positions have been interchanged are shown in (b) of Fig. 19-9. The wattmeters have, in a sense, been symmetrically interchanged. The effect of the interchange of positions on the pointer deflections must be the same in both wattmeters. That is, if the pointer of W_1 deflects up scale in its new position, the pointer of W_2 will also deflect up scale when it is in its new position; or, if in the new position the pointer of W_1 deflects backward, then the deflection of the pointer of W_2 will also be backward when this wattmeter is in its new position. If the effect on the direction of pointer deflection is not the same for both wattmeters when their positions are interchanged, it is evidence that an error was made in the connections when the transfer was made, and the test must be repeated. The success of the method depends upon maintaining the relative connection between the current coil and the potential-coil circuit of each wattmeter. A precaution that will help to avoid reversing the connections to the potential circuits of the wattmeters is to avoid disturbing the potential-circuit connection to the line which does not contain a wattmeter, line $B'B$ of the circuit used in this discussion. It will be noted that terminals H and U are connected to line $B'B$ in both Fig. 19-8 and (b) of Fig. 19-9. In a sense the process of interchanging the wattmeters is that of swinging W_1 from line $A'A$ to line $C'C$, with line $B'B$ being used as a hinge, and similarly swinging W_2 from line $C'C$ to line $A'A$, also with line $B'B$ being used as a hinge.

This method of symmetrically interchanging wattmeters is a positive test for determining the proper signs to be applied to the wattmeter power indications. It is applicable to any system in which more than one wattmeter is needed to measure the power. Whether or not the load is balanced does not matter.

(3) *Transfer-of-Potential-Leads Method for Balanced Three-Phase Loads.* When the load is three-phase and balanced, another method can be used to determine the sign to be assigned to a wattmeter power indication. This method is indicated in (a) and (b) of Fig. 19-10. The wattmeters are connected in (a) of the figure in the usual manner for determining the power supplied to the load, the connections to the current coils being made so that the pointer deflections are up scale on both wattmeters. Terminal H of W_1 is then disconnected from line $B'B$ and connected to line $C'C$; terminal U of W_2 is now disconnected from line $B'B$ and connected to line $A'A$. The connections to the wattmeters after these changes have been made are shown in (b) of Fig. 19-10. If, after these changes have been made, the pointer deflections of W_1 and W_2 continue to be up scale, positive signs are applied to both of the wattmeter power indications obtained when these instruments were in the positions shown in (a) of the figure. If the pointer deflections of both wattmeters are backward, then a negative sign must be applied to the smaller of the original power indications. The effect of making the changes must be the same in both wattmeters; otherwise the test is void.

Proof that this method is a test when the load is three-phase and balanced can readily be developed from the vector diagram shown in Fig. 19-3. When wattmeter W_1 is connected as shown in (a) of Fig. 19-10, the power indicated by W_1 is

$$W_1 = I_{A'A}V_{AB} \cos \alpha,$$

and when connected as shown in (b)

$$W_1 = I_{A'A} V_{AC} \cos \phi.$$

From Fig. 19-3, the vector diagram of a balanced three-phase load of lagging power factor, it can be seen that when the power-factor angle θ is less than 60° (power factor greater than .5), all current vectors will be shifted in a counterclockwise direction, and angles α and ϕ will both be less than 90°. The pointer of wattmeter W_1 will accord-

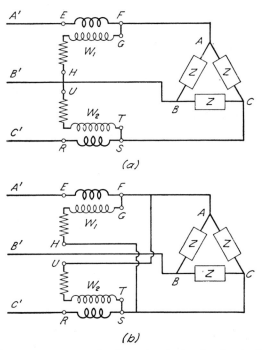

Fig. 19-10. Wattmeter connections for illustrating the transfer-of-potential leads method for determining the sign of a wattmeter indication.

ingly deflect in the same direction whether connected as shown in (a) or (b) of Fig. 19-10.

For the connections shown in (a), the power indicated by W_2 is

$$W_2 = I_{C'C} V_{CB} \cos \beta,$$

and for the connections shown in (b)

$$W_2 = I_{C'C} V_{CA} \cos \mu.$$

Again with reference to Fig. 19-3, when the power-factor angle is less than 60° lagging, angles β and μ will both be less than 90°, and the pointer of W_2 will deflect in the same direction whether connected as shown in (a) or as shown in (b) of Fig. 19-10.

It can now be definitely stated that if the power factor of a balanced three-phase load is greater than .5 lagging (power-factor angle less than 60° lagging) the directions of the pointer deflections of both W_1 and W_2 will not change when the connections of these wattmeters are changed from those shown in (a) to those shown in (b).

In the case when the power-factor angle θ is changed from one less than 60° to one greater than 60° lagging (power factor less than .5 lagging), the effect is to rotate all current vectors in Fig. 19-3 in a clockwise direction. In such a case angle α remains less than 90° and angle ϕ becomes greater than 90°, so that when the connections to W_1 are changed from those shown in (a) to those shown in (b) of Fig. 19-10 the direction of the pointer deflection will be reversed. Also, in this same case, angle β becomes greater than 90° and angle μ remains less than 90°, so that when the connections of W_2 are changed from those shown in (a) to those shown in (b) the direction of the pointer deflection of this wattmeter will also be reversed.

In view of the above, it can now further be definitely stated that if the power factor is less than .5 lagging (power-factor angle θ greater than 60° lagging) the directions of the deflections of the pointers of both W_1 and W_2 will be reversed when the connections to these wattmeters are changed from those shown in (a) to those shown in (b).

A similar analysis of the vector diagram shown in Fig. 19-4 for a balanced three-phase load of leading power factor will show that the following conclusions may be drawn:

In the case of a balanced three-phase load, the power factor of the load is greater than .5 and the power indications of W_1 and W_2 are assigned positive signs when connected as shown in (a) in Fig. 19-10 if the pointer deflections continue in the same direction when the connections are changed to those shown in (b) of the figure. The power factor of the load is less than .5, and the smaller of the power indications of W_1 and W_2 is assigned a negative sign when connected as shown in (a) of the figure if the directions of the pointer deflections reverse when the connections are changed to those shown in (b) of the figure.

It should be noted that these conclusions are based on an analysis of a balanced three-phase load. Therefore this method can be relied upon only when applied to this type of load.

4. Correction of a Negative Wattmeter Indication for Potential-Circuit Loss. The method of correcting a positive wattmeter power indication for the power loss in the potential circuit is discussed in

Chapter 11. It is now necessary to consider the method of making such a correction when a wattmeter power indication must be assigned a negative sign.

An inspection of Fig. 19-2 shows that the magnitude of the current in the current coil of W_1 is

$$|\bar{I}_{AB} + \bar{I}_{AC} + \bar{I}_{GH}|,$$

the vertical lines being used to indicate that only the magnitude of the resultant vector sum is under consideration. Now referring to Fig. 19-11, which is the vector diagram that applies to the circuit of Fig. 19-2 for the case when the power indication of W_1 should be assigned a nega- tive sign (α greater than 90°), it can be seen that the actual power indication of W_1 is

$$W_1 = |\bar{I}_{AB} + \bar{I}_{AC} + \bar{I}_{GH}| V_{AB} \cos \alpha. \quad (19\text{-}11)$$

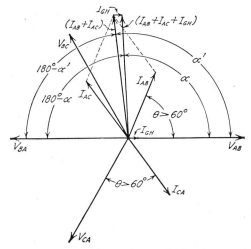

From Figs. 19-2 and 19-11 it is evident that the part of the power indication of wattmeter W_1 which represents true power deliv- ered to the load is

$$P_1 = |\bar{I}_{AB} + \bar{I}_{AC}| V_{AB} \cos \alpha'. \quad (19\text{-}12)$$

Fig. 19-11. Vector diagram for the circuit and wattmeter W_1 of Fig. 19-2, load power factor lead- ing and less than .5.

Since the potential circuit is very nearly a pure resistance circuit, the power loss in the potential circuit, which is also a part of the power indication of wattmeter W_1, is $I_{GH}V_{AB}$. Therefore equation (19-11) may be written as

$$W_1 = |\bar{I}_{AB} + \bar{I}_{AC}| V_{AB} \cos \alpha' + I_{GH}V_{AB}. \quad (19\text{-}13)$$

Since α' is greater than 90°, $|\bar{I}_{AB} + \bar{I}_{AC}| V_{AB} \cos \alpha'$ is a negative quantity. $I_{GH}V_{AB}$ is a positive quantity. Hence equation (19-13) becomes

$$W_1 = -|\bar{I}_{AB} + \bar{I}_{AC}| V_{AB} \cos (180° - \alpha') + I_{GH}V_{AB}. \quad (19\text{-}14)$$

Equation (19-14) shows that W_1, instead of indicating the arith- metical sum of the power to the load and the power supplied to the potential circuit of the wattmeter, indicates the arithmetical differ- ence. Consequently the power indication of W_1 is less than the true power by the amount of power supplied to the potential circuit; and to determine the true power, the loss in the potential circuit must be added to the wattmeter power indication rather than subtracted from it, as is the usual procedure.   Thus, if the test to determine the sign to be assigned to the power indication of W_1 shows that it should be negative, then the true power P_1 represented by the power indication of W_1 is

$$P_1 = -\left(W_1 + \frac{V_{AB}{}^2}{R_{p_1}}\right) = -W_1 - \frac{V_{AB}{}^2}{R_{p_1}}, \qquad (19\text{-}15)$$

where W_1 is the magnitude of the actual power indication and R_{p_1} is the resistance of the potential circuit of wattmeter W_1.   The power loss in the potential circuit is given in equation (19-15) by $V_{AB}{}^2/R_{p_1}$ rather than $I_{GH}V_{AB}$, since in practice I_{GH} is not measured, whereas the value of R_{p_1} is supplied by the instrument manufacturer.

When it is necessary to assign a negative sign to the power indication of wattmeter W_1 of Fig. 19-2, the power indication of W_2 in the figure will accordingly be positive.   In accordance with the method for correcting a positive wattmeter power indication for the power loss in the potential circuit, the true power P_2 represented by the power indication of W_2 is

$$P_2 = W_2 - \frac{V_{CB}{}^2}{R_{p_2}}, \qquad (19\text{-}16)$$

W_2 being the magnitude of the actual power indication of wattmeter W_2 and R_{p_2} being the resistance of its potential circuit.

A physical conception of equations (19-15) and (19-16) can be obtained.   Consider that both wattmeters W_1 and W_2 in Fig. 19-2, in addition to their usual scales, have scales calibrated for a short distance backward, as indicated in (b) and (a), respectively, of Fig. 19-12. Also consider that these wattmeters indicate directly in watts and are so connected in the circuit that when the load is connected the pointer deflections are up scale in a clockwise direction.   As before, assume that tests show that the power indication of W_1 should be given a negative sign.   Let the power indicated on the scale of wattmeter W_2 be $OA = W_2$ and that of wattmeter W_1 be $OC = W_1$, as shown in Fig. 19-12.

Since wattmeter W_2 reads up scale in a clockwise direction when energy is transferred from left to right in Fig. 19-2, opening switch s_2 will result in a power indication of $OB = V_{CB}{}^2/R_{p_2}$ on the scale of W_2 in Fig. 19-12(a).   This result is due to the fact that energy is still being transferred from the source when s_2 is open because of the wattmeter potential-circuit loss.   Therefore, with switch s_2 closed, the part of the power indicated on the scale of W_2 which actually represents power delivered to the load is $BA = P_2$, as indicated in Fig. 19-12(a). Hence it follows from the figure that

$$P_2 = W_2 - \frac{V_{CB}{}^2}{R_{p_2}},$$

which is the same as equation (19-16).

Inasmuch as wattmeter W_1 is connected to read up scale in a clockwise direction when energy is transferred from right to left in Fig. 19-2, opening switch s_1 will result in a deflection backward in a counterclockwise direction from O. The power indication will be $OD = V_{AB}{}^2/R_{p_1}$, as shown in (b) of Fig. 19-12. This follows since

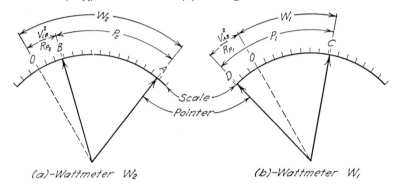

(a)-Wattmeter W_2 (b)-Wattmeter W_1

Fig. 19-12.   Pictorial representation (a) of equation (19-16) and (b) of equation (19-15).

with s_1 open energy is transferred to the potential circuit of W_1 in the direction from left to right, which is opposite to the direction of energy transfer that produces an up-scale deflection. Therefore, when s_1 is closed, the true power causes the deflection to change from point D to point C on the scale, and hence the true power represented by the power indication of W_1 is $DC = P_1$, as shown in Fig. 19-12(b). Accordingly

$$P_1 = -\left(W_1 + \frac{V_{AB}{}^2}{R_{p_1}}\right) = -W_1 - \frac{V_{AB}{}^2}{R_{p_1}}.$$

which is the same as equation (19-15).

5. General Rule for Correcting the $n - 1$ Wattmeter Indications for Potential-Circuit Losses.   Under the conditions assumed in the preceding section, the power delivered to the load is

$$P_1 + P_2 = -W_1 - \frac{V_{AB}{}^2}{R_{p_1}} + W_2 - \frac{V_{CB}{}^2}{R_{p_2}}$$

$$= (W_2 - W_1) - \left(\frac{V_{AB}{}^2}{R_{p_1}} + \frac{V_{CB}{}^2}{R_{p_2}}\right). \qquad (19\text{-}17)$$

Had tests indicated that both wattmeter power indications should be assigned positive signs, then

$$P_1 = W_1 - \frac{V_{AB}^2}{R_{p_1}},$$ (19-18)

$$P_2 = W_2 - \frac{V_{CB}^2}{R_{p_2}},$$ (19-19)

and

$$P_1 + P_2 = (W_1 + W_2) - \left(\frac{V_{AB}^2}{R_{p_1}} + \frac{V_{CB}^2}{R_{p_2}}\right).$$ (19-20)

It will be noted that in both equation (19-17) and equation (19-20) the power loss in the potential circuits is subtracted from the algebraic sum of the wattmeter power indications. This fact suggests the following rule, which avoids confusion in the determination of whether the loss in the potential circuit should be subtracted or added to the power indication of a particular wattmeter.

To Determine the Power Delivered to a Load over n Lines: Take the algebraic sum of the power indications of the n − 1 wattmeters and from this subtract the sum of the potential-circuit losses of all the wattmeters.

6. Determination of the Power Factor of a Balanced Three-Phase Load. It is often desirable to be able to determine the power factor of a balanced three-phase load from measurements obtained by use of only the three-phase supply lines rather than measurements made in the separate phases or branches of the load. This is particularly true in the case of three-phase machines in which the introduction of instruments into the phases is not convenient. The following discussion presents two methods for determining the magnitude of the power factor, the nature of the load in most cases being sufficient to indicate whether it is leading or lagging.

(1) Volt-Ampere, Power Method. Since the delta load of Fig. 19-2 is balanced and is supplied from a balanced three-phase source, all of the phase voltages are equal in magnitude, the phase currents are all equal in magnitude, and the power factors of the three phases or branches of the load are the same. If V_ϕ is the voltage across each phase, I_ϕ is the current in each phase, and $\cos \theta$ is the power factor of each phase, then the power per phase is

$$P_\phi = V_\phi I_\phi \cos \theta,$$ (19-21)

and the power delivered to the entire load is

$$P = 3P_\phi = 3V_\phi I_\phi \cos \theta.$$ (19-22)

In the case of a balanced delta-connected load the line current

$I_L = \sqrt{3}I_\phi$, or $I_\phi = I_L/\sqrt{3}$.   Also, in such a case the phase voltage V_ϕ is equal to the voltage V_L between lines.   Using these relations in equation (19-22) gives

$$P = 3V_L \frac{I_L}{\sqrt{3}} \cos \theta = \sqrt{3}\, V_L I_L \cos \theta. \qquad (19\text{-}23)$$

Now consider the balanced wye load of Fig. 19-13.   Again let the subscript ϕ denote phase quantities and L denote line quantities.   In the case of a balanced wye-connected load all of the phase voltages are equal and have a value $V_\phi = V_L/\sqrt{3}$. Also, in this case the phase currents are equal and have a value $I_\phi = I_L$, and the power factors of the three phases or branches of the load are equal.   Thus the power supplied to each phase of the wye load is

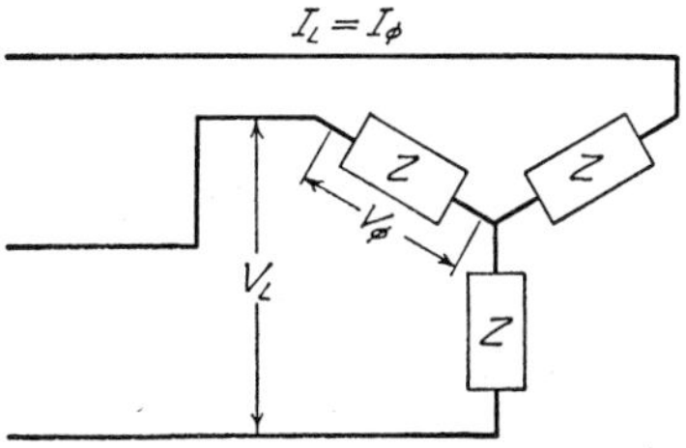

Fig. 19-13.   Balanced wye-connected load.

$$P_\phi = V_\phi I_\phi \cos \theta, \qquad (19\text{-}24)$$

and the power supplied to the entire load is

$$P = 3P_\phi = 3V_\phi I_\phi \cos \theta = 3\,\frac{V_L}{\sqrt{3}}\, I_L \cos \theta = \sqrt{3}\, V_L I_L \cos \theta. \quad (19\text{-}25)$$

Inspection of equations (19-23) and (19-25) shows that these equations are identical.   This is as would be expected, since for any wye-connected load there is an equivalent delta-connected load and vice versa.

Solving either equation (19-23) or (19-25) for power factor gives

$$\cos \theta = \frac{P}{\sqrt{3}\, V_L I_L}. \qquad (19\text{-}26)$$

Therefore the power factor of a balanced three-phase load can be determined by equation (19-26), which requires data that can be obtained by making measurements that involve only the three-phase supply lines.   It should be noted that $\cos \theta$ is the power factor of the phase loads whether they are connected in wye or delta.

(2) *Watt-Ratio Curve.*   A second method for determining the power factor of a balanced three-phase load from line measurements makes use of the watt-ratio curve, the equation for which is developed in the discussion that follows.

Inspection of equations (19-3) and (19-7) shows that for all lagging-power-factor angles in the case of a balanced load, the power indication of wattmeter W_1 is

$$W_1 = I_{A'A}V_{AB} \cos (\theta - 30°), \qquad (19\text{-}27)$$

and equations (19-5) and (19-9) show that for all leading-power-factor angles

$$W_1 = I_{A'A}V_{AB} \cos (\theta + 30°). \qquad (19\text{-}28)$$

Likewise from equations (19-4) and (19-8), for all lagging-power-factor angles

$$W_2 = I_{C'C}V_{CB} \cos (\theta + 30°), \qquad (19\text{-}29)$$

and from equations (19-6) and (19-10), for all leading-power-factor angles

$$W_2 = I_{C'C}V_{CB} \cos (\theta - 30°). \qquad (19\text{-}30)$$

It should be remembered that in the development of equations (19-3) through (19-10), the power-factor angle θ is always taken as a positive angle, the statement being made in each case as to whether it is an angle of lead or lag. Thus equations (19-27), (19-28), (19-29), and (19-30) show that W_2 gives a smaller power indication than W_1 in the case of lagging-power-factor angles and W_1 gives a smaller power indication than W_2 for leading-power-factor angles. These statements are true for the phase sequence ACB used in the vector diagrams of Figs. 19-3 and 19-4. Investigation will show that for an ABC phase sequence equations (19-27) and (19-29) apply for leading-power-factor angles and equations (19-28) and (19-30) for lagging-power-factor angles. Regardless of the phase sequence or whether θ is an angle of lead or lag, the expression containing the term $\cos (\theta + 30°)$ indicates the wattmeter having the smaller power indication. Since in magnitude all the line currents are equal and all the line voltages are equal, the ratio a of the smaller wattmeter power indication to the larger wattmeter power indication* is

$$a = \frac{\text{Smaller Wattmeter Power Indication}}{\text{Larger Wattmeter Power Indication}} \qquad (19\text{-}31)$$

$$= \frac{\cos (\theta + 30°)}{\cos (\theta - 30°)} = \frac{\cos \theta \cos 30° - \sin \theta \sin 30°}{\cos \theta \cos 30° + \sin \theta \sin 30°}$$

$$= \frac{\dfrac{\sqrt{3}}{2} \cos \theta - \dfrac{1}{2} \sin \theta}{\dfrac{\sqrt{3}}{2} \cos \theta + \dfrac{1}{2} \sin \theta}. \qquad (19\text{-}32)$$

---

*The algebraic sign of a is determined by the sign of the smaller wattmeter power indication.

Dividing the numerator and denominator of equation (19-32) by $(\cos \theta)/2$ gives

$$a = \frac{\sqrt{3} - \tan \theta}{\sqrt{3} + \tan \theta},$$

or

$$(1 + a) \tan \theta = \sqrt{3} (1 - a),$$

or

$$\tan \theta = \frac{\sqrt{3} (1 - a)}{(1 + a)}. \qquad (19\text{-}33)$$

Squaring both sides of equation (19-33) gives

$$\tan^2 \theta = \frac{3(1 - a)^2}{(1 + a)^2}. \qquad (19\text{-}34)$$

However,

$$\tan^2 \theta = \frac{\sin^2 \theta}{\cos^2 \theta} = \frac{1 - \cos^2 \theta}{\cos^2 \theta} = \frac{1}{\cos^2 \theta} - 1.$$

Hence equation (19-34) becomes

$$\frac{1}{\cos^2 \theta} = 1 + 3 \frac{(1 - a)^2}{(1 + a)^2},$$

or

$$\cos \theta = \frac{1}{\sqrt{1 + 3 \left(\dfrac{1 - a}{1 + a} \right)^2}}. \qquad (19\text{-}35)$$

Equation (19-35) is the equation of the watt-ratio curve. A watt-ratio curve plotted from data calculated by substituting various values for a in equation (19-35) is shown in Fig. 19-14. That a can have negative values follows from the fact that the power indication of one of the wattmeters must be assigned a negative sign whenever the power factor of the load is less than .5, a fact that has already been proved.

Since a is always the ratio of the smaller wattmeter power indication to the larger wattmeter power indication, it should be evident from the foregoing that the watt-ratio curve will give the power factor of either a leading or lagging three-phase balanced load regardless of the phase sequence. To make use of this curve, the only data necessary are the corrected power indications of the two wattmeters. That the corrected indications must be used to determine the ratio a should be apparent, since the equations used in the development of equation (19-35) are based on negligible potential-circuit losses.

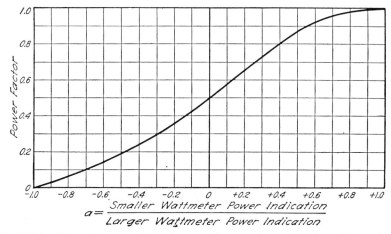

Fig. 19-14. Watt-ratio curve; relation between the power factor of a balanced three-phase system and the ratio of the two wattmeter power indications.

Laboratory Problem No. 19-1

MEASUREMENT OF THE POWER SUPPLIED TO BALANCED THREE-PHASE LOADS

Laboratory

1. Set up a delta-connected resistance load. Connect the load to a three-phase source and make the adjustments needed to obtain a balanced load having the current value designated by the instructor. When the load is balanced, measure the following:

(a) Power supplied to each phase (branch) of the load.

(b) Total power supplied to the load.   Use the $n - 1$ wattmeter method.

2. In the remaining parts of this problem use a three-phase induction motor as a balanced three-phase load.

(a) Set up the circuits necessary for operating the induction motor under loads varying from no load to its rated load.

Connect wattmeters so that the power supplied to the induction motor can be measured by the $n - 1$ wattmeter method.   Be certain to connect the $\pm$ terminal (or equivalent) of the potential circuit of each wattmeter to the load side of its current coil.

(b) Start the motor.   Note the direction of the pointer deflection of each wattmeter.   Reverse the connections to the terminals of the current coil of any wattmeter whose pointer deflection is backward. Record the power indication of each wattmeter.   Also record the motor line voltage and line current.

(c) By means of the following methods, determine the algebraic sign that must be assigned to each of the wattmeter power indications of (b):

    (1) The terminal-identification method.
    (2) The symmetrical-interchange method.
    (3) The transfer-of-potential-leads method.

On the data sheet, illustrate the above methods by means of circuit diagrams. On each circuit diagram, record the direction of the pointer deflection of each wattmeter. State the effects of the circuit changes made in each test on the directions of these deflections. Explain the meaning of the effects in terms of the algebraic sign that should be assigned to the power indication of each wattmeter.

3. Increase the load on the induction motor in steps until the load is equal to the rated load of the motor. At each step measure the following:

    (a) The line current of the motor.
    (b) The line voltage of the motor.
    (c) The total power supplied to the motor.

Report

A. From the data obtained in **1**(a) and also from the data obtained in **1**(b), determine the total power supplied to the load. Discuss any discrepancy in the results.

B. How does the part of the load power measured by one of the wattmeters used in **1**(b) compare with that measured by the other? For a balanced three-phase system, how should these values compare theoretically?

C. Calculate data for and draw a watt-ratio curve.

D. From the data obtained in **2** and **3,** make a table including in separate columns the following items for every step of the test on the induction motor:

    (1) Line voltage.
    (2) Line current.
    (3) Portion of the motor power, with proper algebraic sign, as measured by one of the wattmeters.
    (4) Portion of the motor power, with proper algebraic sign, as measured by the second wattmeter.
    (5) Total power supplied to the motor.
    (6) Total volt-amperes of the motor.
    (7) Power factor of the motor from items (5) and (6).

(8) Algebraic ratio of (3) to (4) or (4) to (3), whichever **gives** the smaller value.

(9) Power factor of the motor from item (8) and the watt-ratio curve plotted in **C**.

E. How do the power factors determined in (7) and (9) of **D** compare? Discuss any discrepancies.

Laboratory Problem No. 19-2
MEASUREMENT OF THE POWER SUPPLIED TO A LOAD BY n LINES

Laboratory

As a source of power use a three-phase generator which has a neutral connection available. Maintain the magnitude and frequency of the voltage between the generator line terminals constant at the values designated by the instructor.

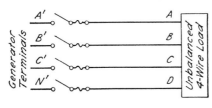

Fig. 19-15.

Set up the circuit shown in Fig. 19-15, using the load designated by the instructor. By means of the $n-1$ wattmeter method, measure the total power supplied to the load when the common connection of the potential circuits is made to:

(a) Line $A'A$.
(b) Line $B'B$.
(c) Line $C'C$.
(d) Line $N'D$.

Report

A. Using each of the four sets of data obtained in the laboratory, determine the total power supplied to the load. Discuss any discrepancies.

B. The rate at which energy is being transferred over the three wires shown in Fig. 19-16 is measured by two wattmeters connected as shown. The pointer deflections in terms of the instrument scales (instruments not connected in circuit simultaneously) are as follows:

V_1	V_2	I_1	I_2	W_1	W_2
220	220	5.1	8.2	2248	861

The following data on the wattmeters are available:

Wattmeter W_1

Rating 10/20 amp   150/300 volts   750/1500/3000 watts
Scale   3000 watts
Resistance of the 10-amp current coil = .04 ohm
Resistance of the 20-amp current coil = .01 ohm
Resistance of the 150-volt potential circuit = 2420 ohms
Resistance of the 300-volt potential circuit = 4840 ohms

Wattmeter W_2

Rating 10 amp   150/300 volts   1500/3000 watts
Scale   1500 watts
Resistance of the 10-amp current coil = .05 ohm
Resistance of the 150-volt potential circuit = 3025 ohms
Resistance of the 300-volt potential circuit = 6050 ohms

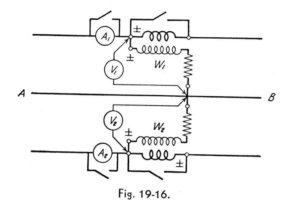

Fig. 19-16.

If the 10-amp and 300-volt terminals of both W_1 and W_2 are connected in the circuit, determine:

(1) Whether the load is connected to the circuit at side A or at side B. Explain how this determination was made.
(2) The actual power delivered to the load.

CHAPTER 20

MEASUREMENT OF REACTIVE VOLT-AMPERES BY MEANS OF WATTMETERS

1. Reactive Volt-Amperes. The *reactive volt-amperes* of a circuit in which the voltage and current vary sinusoidally with time are equal to the product of the effective value of the voltage, the effective value of the current, and the sine of the phase angle. The symbol for reactive volt-amperes is Q, and the unit is the *var*, a term derived from the first letters of the words "volt-amperes reactive." In equation form,

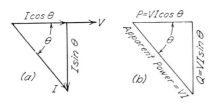

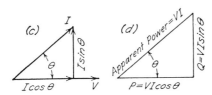

Fig. 20-1. (a) Vector diagram for a single-phase inductive load. (b) Power triangle for the load of (a). (c) Vector diagram for a single-phase capacitive load. (d) Power triangle for the load of (c).

$$Q = VI \sin \theta \text{ vars.} \quad (20\text{-}1)$$

For obvious reasons $\sin \theta$ is called the *reactive factor*.

In (a) and (c) of Fig. 20-1 are shown current-voltage vector diagrams for lagging and for leading current conditions, respectively. The circuit current in each case is resolved into two components, $I \cos \theta$ and $I \sin \theta$. The component $I \cos \theta$ is commonly referred to as the *in-phase component, power component, active component,* or *energy component* of the current. Similarly, $I \sin \theta$ is known as the *out-of-phase component, quadrature component, reactive component,* or *wattless component* of the current. If the circuit current and each of its two components in Figs. 20-1(a) and 20-1(c) are multiplied by the circuit voltage V, the power triangles shown in (b) and (d) of the figure are obtained. The product VI is known as the *apparent power* or the *volt-amperes* of the circuit. As indicated in the figure, the apparent power may be represented as the hypotenuse of a right triangle, one of whose legs is the real power $P = VI \cos \theta$ and the other the reactive volt-amperes $Q = VI \sin \theta$.   In equation form,

$$VI = \sqrt{P^2 + Q^2}. \tag{20-2}$$

This relation is very useful when problems involving power and reactive volt-amperes are being considered.

The power $VI \cos \theta$ is the average rate at which electrical energy is converted to some other form in a circuit, and hence energy must be continuously supplied at this average rate to the circuit by a source. Reactive volt-amperes, on the other hand, require no average energy input to a circuit by a source, as will become evident from the following discussion.

Reactive volt-amperes are said to be lagging reactive volt-amperes when they result from a lagging current and leading reactive volt-amperes when they result from a leading current.   The function of lagging reactive volt-amperes is to supply the energy required to establish magnetic fields and to return this energy to the source when the magnetic fields collapse.   In connection with condensers, the function of leading reactive volt-amperes is to supply the energy for charging the condensers and to return this energy to the source when the condensers discharge.   Hence, reactive volt-amperes, as such, require no average energy input to the circuit.   However, for the same power delivered, an increase in the reactive volt-amperes necessitates an increase in the volt-amperes supplied by the source.   Therefore, since the volt-amperes that a given source can supply is limited, the reactive volt-amperes of a circuit indirectly determine the power that the source can supply, the available power being reduced as the required reactive volt-amperes increase.   It should also be apparent that for a given power delivered to a load an increase in the reactive volt-amperes increases the loss in the transmission circuit between the source and load.   As a result of these effects, it is now common in commercial practice to penalize customers having loads of low lagging power factor—that is, high reactive factor.

In order to distinguish between leading and lagging reactive volt-amperes some authorities assign a positive sign to leading reactive volt-amperes while others assign a positive sign to lagging reactive volt-amperes.   In general, in classical circuit theory the positive sign is given to leading reactive volt-amperes.   In commercial practice the positive sign is given to lagging reactive volt-amperes because of the preponderance of such loads.   Since no general agreement exists, descriptive terms such as "lagging" and "leading" or "inductive" and "capacitive" will be used in this chapter.

The total number of reactive volt-amperes of a system is equal to the algebraic sum of the reactive volt-amperes of the individual loads.   In the case of a balanced three-phase system, the total number of reactive volt-amperes is

$$Q = 3Q_\phi = 3V_\phi I_\phi \sin \theta = \sqrt{3}\, V_L I_L \sin \theta, \qquad (20\text{-}3)$$

where the angle θ and the subscript ϕ refer to phase quantities and the subscript L refers to line quantities.   Equation (20-3) is applicable to both delta-connected and wye-connected loads and will give the total number of lagging or leading reactive volt-amperes of the balanced system, depending on whether the load is inductive or capacitive.

2. Measurement of the Reactive Volt-Amperes of a Single-Phase Load.   It has been shown that the indication of a wattmeter is equal to the product of the effective value of the voltage drop across the potential circuit, the effective value of the current in the current coil,

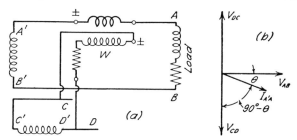

Fig. 20-2.   (a) Wattmeter connected for measuring the reactive volt-amperes of an inductive load supplied by one phase of a balanced two-phase source.   (b) Vector diagram of (a).

and the cosine of the angle between the vectors representing these quantities, the positive directions of the voltage and current being taken in the direction from the $\pm$ terminals (or their equivalents) to the unmarked terminals of the respective coils.   It should be remembered that this statement is based on the assumption that the effect of the inductance of the potential circuit of the wattmeter is negligible. The term *wattmeter indication* as used above means the actual scale indication multiplied by the scale-multiplying factor that may be necessary because of multiple current and voltage ranges.   Whenever the term *wattmeter indication* is used in the rest of this chapter it will have the same meaning.

On the basis of the foregoing it will now be shown that a wattmeter can be used to measure reactive volt-amperes.   In (a) of Fig. 20-2 is shown a wattmeter connected so that it will measure the reactive volt-amperes of an inductive load connected to one phase of a balanced two-phase source.   The vector diagram for the circuit of (a) based upon the assumption that the voltage drop across the wattmeter current coil is negligible is shown in (b) of the figure.   Under this condition the indication of the wattmeter is

$$W_Q = V_{CD}I_{A'A} \cos (90° - θ).$$

Since $V_{CD} = V_{AB}$, owing to the source being balanced, and since $I_{A'A} = I_{AB}$,

$$W_Q = V_{AB}I_{AB} \cos (90° - θ),$$

or

$$W_Q = V_{AB}I_{AB} \sin θ, \tag{20-4}$$

which is the reactive volt-amperes of the load.

When the load is capacitive, the angle between $\bar{V}_{CD}$ and $\bar{I}_{A'A}$ will be $(90° + θ)$, and with the wattmeter connected as shown in (a) the pointer deflection will be backward.   However, an up-scale deflection of the pointer can be obtained and thus the reactive volt-amperes of the capacitive load can be measured by reversing the connections to the potential circuit of the wattmeter.

If the phase sequence is opposite to that shown in Fig. 20-2(b), so that $\bar{V}_{CD}$ leads $\bar{V}_{AB}$, an up-scale pointer deflection will be obtained when the wattmeter is connected as shown in (a) and the load is capacitive, and a backward deflection will be obtained when the load is inductive.   The reactive volt-amperes of an inductive load can be measured by reversing the connections to the potential circuit.

A general statement can now be made concerning the use of a wattmeter to measure reactive volt-amperes.   Regardless of the kind of load, inductive or capacitive, the current coil of the wattmeter is inserted in the usual manner in a line to the load.   The voltage applied to the potential circuit should be equal to but must be in quadrature with that which would be used on the potential circuit when measuring power, and it must lag this voltage when the load is inductive and must lead when the load is capacitive.

In the foregoing, the quadrature voltage to be used in connection with the wattmeter for measuring the reactive volt-amperes of a single-phase load was obtained by using a two-phase power source. Quadrature voltages for use in connection with single-phase loads connected to three-phase power sources can be obtained when the source is wye-connected and has the neutral available, and also when the source is delta-connected and has a centertap connection in the phase to be loaded.   In (a), (c), and (e) of Fig. 20-3 wattmeters are shown connected for measuring the reactive volt-amperes of single-

phase inductive loads connected to balanced three-phase sources of
ABC phase sequence.   In (a) the potential circuit of the wattmeter
would have been connected to terminals A' and B' of the source if
power were to have been measured.   To measure the reactive volt-
amperes, the necessary lagging voltage in quadrature with $\bar{V}_{A'B'}$ is

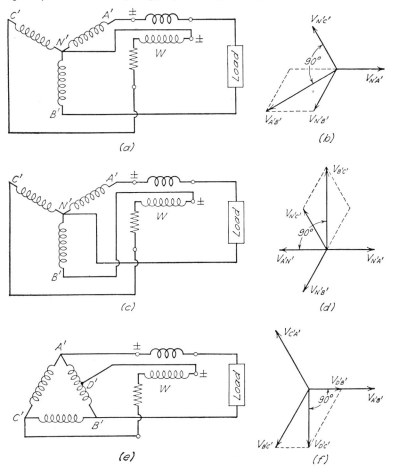

Fig. 20-3.   (a), (c), (e) Methods of connecting a wattmeter for measuring the reactive
volt-amperes of a single-phase inductive load supplied by a balanced three-phase source
of ABC phase sequence.   (b), (d), (f) Corresponding vector diagrams.

obtained by connecting the potential circuit of the wattmeter to
terminals N' and C' of the source as shown.   As is evident from (b)
of the figure, $V_{N'C'} = V_{A'B'}/\sqrt{3}$; therefore the wattmeter indication
must be multiplied by $\sqrt{3}$ in order to determine the correct reactive
volt-amperes.   In the connection shown in (c), the potential circuit

would have been connected to source terminals A' and N' if power were to have been measured. The lagging voltage in quadrature with $\bar{V}_{A'N'}$ is $\bar{V}_{B'C'}$, so the potential circuit is connected as shown to terminals B' and C' of the source. As indicated by the vector diagram in (d) of the figure, $V_{B'C'} = \sqrt{3} V_{A'N'}$; consequently, the wattmeter indication must be divided by $\sqrt{3}$ in order to determine the reactive volt-amperes. In (e) of the figure, the necessary lagging quadrature voltage for the potential circuit of the wattmeter is obtained by connecting its terminals to C' and D' as shown, D' being the center-tap of the loaded phase. In this case the wattmeter indication must be multiplied by $2/\sqrt{3}$, since $V_{D'C'} = (\sqrt{3}/2) V_{A'B'}$, $\bar{V}_{A'B'}$ being the voltage which would have been applied to the potential circuit had the wattmeter been connected for measuring power.

In any connection of a wattmeter for measuring reactive volt-amperes, a study of the circuit is necessary in order to determine whether or not an error is present in the wattmeter indication due to current taken by the potential circuit of the wattmeter or due to the potential drop across the current coil. In none of the circuits so far discussed does the current in the potential circuit also flow in the current coil. However, in each of the cases the quadrature voltage applied to the potential circuit of the wattmeter is a source voltage, and hence the reactive volt-amperes obtained in each instance include those of the current coil of the wattmeter in addition to the load reactive volt-amperes. In order to correct for this error it is necessary to calculate the reactive volt-amperes of the current coil. If the subscript cc is used with symbols representing quantities relative to the current coil, the reactive volt-amperes of the current coil are

$$Q_{cc} = V_{cc}I_{cc}\sin\theta_{cc} = I_{cc}Z_{cc}I_{cc}\frac{X_{cc}}{Z_{cc}},$$

or

$$Q_{cc} = I_{cc}^2 X_{cc}. \tag{20-5}$$

The value of X_{cc} can be determined if the frequency and the inductance of the current coil are known. The inductance of the current coil is generally given on the certificate fastened to the lid of the wattmeter. Since the current coil of a wattmeter is inductive, Q_{cc} of equation (20-5) represents lagging reactive volt-amperes. Therefore, to obtain the reactive volt-amperes of the load whenever Q_{cc} is appreciable, Q_{cc} is subtracted from the reactive volt-amperes obtained after the proper multiplying factors have been applied to the wattmeter indication in the case of an inductive load and added when the load is capacitive.

In commercial practice the reactive volt-amperes of single-phase loads are seldom measured directly because the necessary quadrature voltage is not usually available. Although phase-shifting circuits that will produce the required quadrature voltage can be designed, they are rarely used. Instead the reactive volt-amperes are calculated by means of equation (20-2), with measured values of the load voltage, current, and power being used.

3. The $n - 1$ Wattmeter Method for Measuring Reactive Volt-Amperes. It is shown in Chapter 19 that a source which supplies power to a load over n lines may be replaced by $n-1$ equivalent generators. Refer to Fig. 19-1. Since the equivalent generators replace the true source, they not only supply the power to the load but also supply the reactive volt-amperes. If separate wattmeters having negligible current-coil impedances and potential-circuit currents are connected so as to measure the reactive volt-amperes delivered by the separate equivalent generators, the algebraic sum of the wattmeter indications is the number of reactive volt-amperes supplied to the load. Thus, $n-1$ wattmeters are sufficient to measure the reactive volt-amperes supplied to a load over n lines.

If the potential circuit of each wattmeter in (c) of Fig. 19-1 is connected to a voltage equal in magnitude but lagging by 90° the voltage to which it is connected in the figure, each wattmeter will be connected for measuring the reactive volt-amperes delivered by its equivalent generator. A wattmeter will have an up-scale pointer deflection when its associated generator is delivering lagging reactive volt-amperes and a backward deflection when the equivalent generator associated with it is delivering leading reactive volt-amperes. The wattmeters showing backward deflections are made to give up-scale deflections by reversing the connections to either their potential circuits or current coils. The reactive volt-amperes measured by these wattmeters must then be given a sign opposite to that assigned to the indications of the wattmeters that originally gave up-scale deflections. The value of the total reactive volt-amperes delivered by the source to the load is then obtained by taking the algebraic sum of the wattmeter indications.

When the quadrature voltage applied to the potential circuit of any one of the wattmeters is not of the correct magnitude, a multiplying factor equal to the ratio of the correct magnitude to that used must be applied to the wattmeter indication. Other corrections may need to be made because of the voltage drop across the current coil or current in the potential circuit.

In the circuits usually found in practice various means are employed to secure the necessary quadrature voltages. In any case, the general procedure of the $n-1$ wattmeter method for determining the reactive volt-amperes delivered over n lines is the same and may be summarized as follows:

1. Insert the current coils of $n-1$ wattmeters in $n-1$ lines so that the $\pm$ terminal of each current coil is toward the source.

2. Connect the potential circuit of each wattmeter to a voltage that lags by 90° the voltage to which it would be connected in the $n-1$ wattmeter method for measuring power.

3. For convenience, assign a $+$ sign to the indication of each wattmeter whose pointer deflection is up scale and assign $-$ signs to those which must be made to deflect up scale by reversing either the current-coil or potential-circuit connections.

4. If the magnitude of the quadrature voltage impressed on the potential circuit of any wattmeter is k times the magnitude of the voltage which would be used in the $n-1$ wattmeter method for measuring power, multiply the wattmeter indication by $1/k$.

5. Take the algebraic sum of the wattmeter indications after they have been corrected, when necessary, as discussed in 4. If this algebraic sum results in a positive quantity, the reactive volt-amperes are lagging; if it results in a negative quantity, they are leading. The algebraic sum will be the reactive volt-amperes delivered to the load if it is not necessary to make the correction discussed in 6.

6. Inspect the circuit connections to see if a correction of the algebraic sum of 5 is necessary because of the effects of potential-circuit currents or current-coil voltage drops. Make the necessary correction.

4. Measurement of the Reactive Volt-Amperes of a Three-Phase Three-Wire Load. *General Conditions.* In Fig. 20-4(a) two wattmeters are shown connected according to the $n-1$ wattmeter method for measuring the reactive volt-amperes of a three-wire inductive load supplied by a balanced three-phase source having an ABC phase sequence. In this case the needed quadrature voltages are secured by means of two similar auto-transformers T_1 and T_2. Taps are brought out from each of the transformer windings so that $\bar{V}_{14} = (2/\sqrt{3})\bar{V}_{A'B'}$, $\bar{V}_{34} = (1/\sqrt{3})\bar{V}_{A'B'}$, $\bar{V}_{47} = (2/\sqrt{3})\bar{V}_{B'C'}$, and $\bar{V}_{45} = (1/\sqrt{3})\bar{V}_{B'C'}$. The vector diagram showing the voltages of the balanced three-phase source and the various voltages of the auto-transformers is shown in (b) of the figure.

The voltage impressed on the potential circuit of wattmeter W_1 is $\bar{V}_{37}$, and that impressed on the potential circuit of wattmeter W_2 is $\bar{V}_{15}$.

$$\bar{V}_{37} = \bar{V}_{34} + \bar{V}_{47} = \frac{1}{\sqrt{3}} \bar{V}_{A'B'} + \frac{2}{\sqrt{3}} \bar{V}_{B'C'}. \qquad (20\text{-}6)$$

$$\bar{V}_{15} = \bar{V}_{14} + \bar{V}_{45} = \frac{2}{\sqrt{3}} \bar{V}_{A'B'} + \frac{1}{\sqrt{3}} \bar{V}_{B'C'}. \qquad (20\text{-}7)$$

Since the line voltages are balanced, $V_{B'C'} = V_{A'B'}$; and a vector equal to the vector $\bar{V}_{B'C'}$ can be obtained by rotating vector $\bar{V}_{A'B'}$ in a clockwise direction through 120°, and a vector equal to the vector $\bar{V}_{A'B'}$ can be obtained by rotating vector $\bar{V}_{B'C'}$ in a counterclockwise

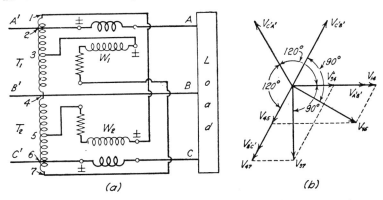

Fig. 20-4. (a) Two wattmeters connected for measuring the reactive volt-amperes of a three-wire inductive load supplied by a balanced three-phase source of ABC phase sequence. (b) Voltage vector diagram of (a).

direction through the same angle. Thus

$$\bar{V}_{B'C'} = \bar{V}_{A'B'} \, cjs(-120°) = \bar{V}_{A'B'} \left(-.5 - j\frac{\sqrt{3}}{2} \right), \qquad (20\text{-}8)$$

and

$$\bar{V}_{A'B'} = \bar{V}_{B'C'} \, cjs(120°) = \bar{V}_{B'C'} \left(-.5 + j\frac{\sqrt{3}}{2} \right). \qquad (20\text{-}9)$$

From equations (20-6) and (20-8)

$$\bar{V}_{37} = \frac{1}{\sqrt{3}} \bar{V}_{A'B'} + \frac{2}{\sqrt{3}} \left[\bar{V}_{A'B'} \left(-.5 - j\frac{\sqrt{3}}{2} \right) \right]$$

$$= -j\bar{V}_{A'B'}.$$

Thus $\bar{V}_{37}$ lags $\bar{V}_{A'B'}$ by 90°. From equations (20-7) and (20-9)

$$\bar{V}_{15} = \frac{2}{\sqrt{3}} \left[\bar{V}_{B'C'} \left(-.5 + j\frac{\sqrt{3}}{2} \right) \right] + \frac{1}{\sqrt{3}} \bar{V}_{B'C'}$$

$$= j\bar{V}_{B'C'} = -j\bar{V}_{C'B'}.$$

Hence $\bar{V}_{15}$ lags $\bar{V}_{C'B'}$ by 90°. These relations are indicated in the vector diagram and show that with a balanced three-phase source of

ABC phase sequence the voltages impressed on the potential circuits of the wattmeters are equal to and lag by 90° the voltages that would be impressed on the potential circuits if they were connected according to the $n-1$ wattmeter method for measuring power.   Therefore the wattmeters connected as shown can be used to measure the reactive volt-amperes of an inductive load supplied by a balanced three-phase source of ABC phase sequence.   It should be noted that, although it is necessary that the three-phase source be balanced in order to obtain quadrature voltages of the proper magnitude, the load need not be balanced.

An analysis similar to the foregoing will show that if the phase sequence of the balanced three-phase source is changed to ACB the wattmeters connected as in Fig. 20-4(a) can be used to measure the reactive volt-amperes of a capacitive load.   Furthermore, if the connections of the potential circuit wattmeter W_1 are reversed and those of wattmeter W_2 are also reversed, the two wattmeters can be used to measure the reactive volt-amperes supplied by a balanced three-phase source to a capacitive load if the phase sequence is ABC or to an inductive load if the phase sequence is ACB.

Regardless of which of the above-mentioned conditions prevails, the algebraic sum of the two wattmeter indications gives the total reactive volt-amperes supplied to the circuit at the right of the auto-transformers and hence includes the reactive volt-amperes of the two wattmeter current coils in addition to that of the load.   Since the current coils are inductive, the total lagging reactive volt-amperes supplied to them is equal to the sum of the reactive volt-amperes of the separate coils, each of which may be calculated by equation (20-5). Expressed in equation form,

$$Q_{cc_t} = I^2_{cc_1}X_{cc_1} + I^2_{cc_2}X_{cc_2}, \qquad (20\text{-}10)$$

where the subscripts cc_1 and cc_2 refer, respectively, to the current coils of W_1 and W_2.   In order to obtain the total reactive volt-amperes of the load, Q_{cc_t} is subtracted from the algebraic sum of the wattmeter indications when this sum represents lagging reactive volt-amperes and is added when this sum represents leading reactive volt-amperes.

Balanced Loads.   Owing to the large number of balanced three-phase three-wire loads found in practice, it is worth while to investigate both the magnitude and the sign to be assigned the indications of the two wattmeters used to measure the reactive volt-amperes of such a load under various conditions of power factor.   In Fig. 20-5 is shown the vector diagram for the load in Fig. 20-4(a) when the load is balanced and inductive, it being assumed that the voltage drops across the wattmeter current coils are negligible.   It can be seen from

Fig. 20-5 that the indications of wattmeters W_1 and W_2 in Fig. 20-4(a) for the assumed conditions are

$$W_{Q_1} = V_{37}I_{A'A} \cos (60° - \theta), \qquad (20\text{-}11)$$

and

$$W_{Q_2} = V_{15}I_{C'C} \cos (120° - \theta), \qquad (20\text{-}12)$$

where θ is the magnitude of the power-factor angle of the load. V_{37} and V_{15} are equal in magnitude to the line voltages, and $I_{A'A}$ and $I_{C'C}$ are line currents. If the magnitude of the line voltages is represented by V_L and the magnitude of the line currents by I_L, equations (20-11) and (20-12) may be written as

$$W_{Q_1} = V_L I_L \cos (60° - \theta), \qquad (20\text{-}13)$$

and

$$W_{Q_2} = V_L I_L \cos (120° - \theta). \qquad (20\text{-}14)\text{.}$$

It should be kept in mind that equations (20-13) and (20-14) apply to the wattmeters when a balanced three-phase source of ABC phase sequence supplies a balanced inductive load and the voltage drops across the wattmeter current coils are negligible.

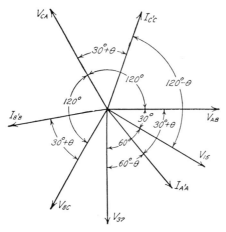

In a preceding part of this discussion it is pointed out that the wattmeters connected as in Fig. 20-4(a) can also be used to measure the reactive volt-amperes of a capacitive load if the phase sequence is ACB. It is further pointed out that when the potential-circuit connections of the wattmeters are the reverse of those shown in the figure the two wattmeters can be used

Fig. 20-5. Vector diagram for the load in Fig. 20-4(a) when balanced and inductive.

to measure the reactive volt-amperes supplied to a capacitive load if the phase sequence is ABC or to an inductive load if the phase sequence is ACB. If vector diagrams for these three conditions are drawn, balanced loads and negligible voltage drops across the current coils being assumed, it will be found in each case that one of the two wattmeter indications will be $V_L I_L \cos (60° - \theta)$ and the other will be $V_L I_L \cos (120° - \theta)$, θ being the magnitude of the power-factor angle regardless of whether the load is wye-connected or delta-connected.

A study of the terms $V_L I_L \cos (60° - \theta)$ and $V_L I_L \cos (120° - \theta)$ shows that the following conclusions may be drawn:

1. When the power factor of the balanced load is unity (power-factor angle is 0°), the magnitudes of the wattmeter indications are equal but are assigned opposite signs.

2. When the power factor of the balanced load is .866 leading or lagging (power-factor angle is 30° leading or lagging), one of the wattmeter indications is zero.

3. When the power factor of the balanced load is greater than .866 leading or lagging (power-factor angle is less than 30° leading or lagging), the wattmeter indications are assigned opposite signs.

4. When the power factor of the balanced load is less than .866 leading or lagging (power-factor angle is greater than 30° leading or lagging), both wattmeter indications are assigned the same sign.

5. Measurement of the Reactive Volt-Amperes of a Three-Phase Four-Wire Load. The three wattmeters shown in Fig. 20-6(a) are connected for measuring the reactive volt-amperes of a four-wire inductive load supplied by a balanced three-phase source having an ABC phase sequence. In the figure $N'N$ is the neutral line.

In Fig. 20-6(b) is shown the voltage vector diagram for the load. In drawing this diagram it has been assumed that the voltage drops across the current coils of the wattmeters are negligible. The voltages applied to potential circuits of wattmeters W_1, W_2, and W_3 are $\bar{V}_{BC}$, $\bar{V}_{CA}$, and $\bar{V}_{AB}$, respectively. As shown in the vector diagram, these voltages lag by 90° the voltages $\bar{V}_{AN}$, $\bar{V}_{BN}$, and $\bar{V}_{CN}$, the voltages that would be impressed on the potential circuits of W_1, W_2, and W_3, respectively, if the power to the load were to be measured. Therefore the phase of each of the voltages impressed on the potential circuits of the wattmeters as shown connected in the figure is correct for measuring the lagging reactive volt-amperes supplied to the load. However, the magnitude of each of the voltages $\bar{V}_{BC}$, $\bar{V}_{CA}$, and $\bar{V}_{AB}$ is $\sqrt{3}$ times the magnitude of each of the voltages $\bar{V}_{AN}$, $\bar{V}_{BN}$, and $\bar{V}_{CN}$, and therefore a correction factor of $1/\sqrt{3}$ must be applied to each of the wattmeter indications.

The current coils of the wattmeters may be inserted in any three of the four lines. If the current coil of one of the wattmeters is placed in the neutral line, there will not be a common voltage correction factor for each of the wattmeter indications. In such a case the factor which must be applied to the indication of the wattmeter whose current coil is inserted in the neutral line will be different from that which must be applied to the indications of the other two wattmeters. Obviously this is a disadvantage in using the neutral line.

Although the current in the potential circuit of any one wattmeter in Fig. 20-6(a) flows through the current coils of the other two watt-meters, the error introduced by neglecting the effect of this current is negligible. This is true because the impedances of the potential circuits are nearly pure resistances, and hence a negligible number of reactive volt-amperes is supplied to them by the source.

If the potential circuits of the wattmeters shown in Fig. 20-6(a) are connected on the source side of the current coils, corrections for

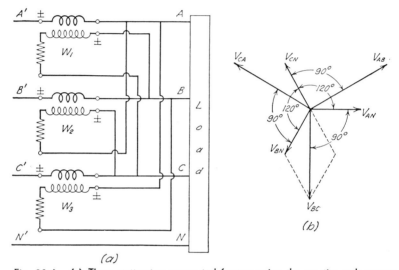

Fig. 20-6. (a) Three wattmeters connected for measuring the reactive volt-amperes of a four-wire inductive load supplied by a balanced three-phase source of *ABC* phase sequence. (b) Voltage vector diagram of (a).

the lagging reactive volt-amperes of the current coils must be made in order to determine the reactive volt-amperes supplied to the load. However, the need for such a correction depends upon the magnitude of the correction as compared with the total reactive volt-amperes. Since this type of correction is not required when the potential cir-cuits are connected on the load side of the current coils, as in Fig. 20-6(a), this connection is usually preferred.

6. Electric Fields in Wattmeters Connected for Measuring Reac-tive Volt-Amperes. It is possible for an electric field of appreciable magnitude to be set up in a wattmeter when a difference of potential exists between the potential coil and the current coil. The effect of the electric field is to produce a force between the two coils that may be sufficient to influence the pointer deflection, causing an error in the indication. From an inspection of Figs. 20-2, 20-3, 20-4, and 20-6 it will be seen that any of the wattmeters shown may be so affected.

When wattmeters are connected as shown in Figs. 20-2, 20-3, and 20-4, tests can be made to see if the electric-field effect is appreciable by disconnecting the load and noting whether or not a pointer deflection occurs in any of the wattmeters. A sizable deflection in any case is an indication that the electric field may appreciably affect the pointer indication at all points on the scale regardless of the fact that the magnitude of the effect on the pointer deflection will vary at different points because of the change in relative positions of the potential and current coils. Wattmeters connected as shown in the circuit of Fig. 20-6 can be similarly tested if the potential circuits are moved to the source side of the current coils.

Whenever it is found that the effect of the electric field in a wattmeter is appreciable, a simple first attempt to remedy the situation is to replace the wattmeter by another wattmeter of different design and to repeat the test. If such a substitution is not possible or fails to correct the difficulty, the connections should be studied to see if it is possible to make any changes, such as reversing the connections to both the potential circuit and the current coil, which will result in putting the potential coil and current coil at more nearly the same potential. When neither of the foregoing methods prove successful in eliminating the effect of the electric field, current and potential transformers can be used to isolate electrically the current coil and potential coil of the affected wattmeter from the circuit. To assure that the potential coil and current coil will be at the same potential, the $\pm$ terminal (or equivalent) of the potential circuit and one end of the current coil should be connected together.

Laboratory Problem No. 20-1

MEASUREMENT OF THE REACTIVE VOLT-AMPERES OF A SINGLE-PHASE LOAD

Laboratory

In order to obtain good results, a well-regulated source of power should be used.

If the wattmeter to be used to measure reactive volt-amperes in **1** and **3** does not have a current-coil polarity mark, connect the wattmeter in a single-phase circuit in which the direction of energy transfer is known and determine which terminal should be assigned the $\pm$ sign.

1. By means of a wattmeter, measure the reactive volt-amperes supplied to the single-phase load designated by the instructor. This measurement must be made in such a manner that it will be known whether the measured reactive volt-amperes are inductive or capacitive. Make certain to obtain all the data that are needed for making such corrections of the wattmeter indication as may be necessary in determining the actual reactive volt-amperes of the load.

On the data-sheet circuit diagram, be certain to indicate the $\pm$ terminals (or their equivalents) of the wattmeter current coil and potential circuit.

2. Measure the voltage, current, and power of the load used in **1.**

3. Connect the resistor designated by the instructor in parallel with the load used above and repeat **1** and **2.**

Report

A. How many reactive volt-amperes were supplied to the load in **1?** Show and explain completely any corrections of the wattmeter indication that may have been necessary.

B. From the data obtained in **2,** calculate the reactive volt-amperes of the load. How does this value compare with the measured value of **A?** Discuss any discrepancy.

C. Were the reactive volt-amperes of the load used in **1** inductive or capacitive? Explain how this determination was made.

D. Letter or number a diagram of the circuit used in **1** so that double-subscript notation can be used with the voltages and currents. Using double-subscript notation, draw to scale a voltage-current vector diagram for the circuit. Use the vector representing the voltage drop across the load as the reference. Be certain to include the voltage applied to the wattmeter potential circuit.

E. Compare the values of the load reactive volt-amperes and power measured in **1** and **2** with the values measured in **3.** Which values should check? Why? Which should not check? Why?

Laboratory Problem No. 20-2
MEASUREMENT OF THE REACTIVE VOLT-AMPERES OF A THREE-PHASE THREE-WIRE LOAD

Laboratory

Use two properly tapped auto-transformers (the unit being known as a Reactive-Component Compensator, a Reactiformer, or a Quadraphaser) in order to obtain the necessary quadrature voltages for the potential circuits of the wattmeters to be used to measure reactive volt-amperes.

If any of the wattmeters to be used does not have a current-coil polarity mark, connect the wattmeter in a single-phase circuit in which the direction of energy transfer is known and determine which terminal should be assigned the $\pm$ sign.

1. Arbitrarily label the terminals of the auto-transformers with numbers or letters for the purpose of identification, or label them in accordance with directions given by the instructor.

Properly connect the line terminals of the auto-transformers to a three-phase source and measure the voltages between each terminal and every one of the other terminals of the auto-transformers.

On the data sheet draw a schematic diagram similar to that shown in Fig. 20-7. On the diagram label the line terminals, using the same identification marks as were used on the auto-transformers. From the voltage measurements made above, determine which terminals on the auto-transformers correspond to the unmarked terminals of the schematic diagram. Properly label these unmarked terminals.

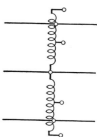

Fig. 20-7.

2. Using the auto-transformers and two wattmeters, measure the reactive volt-amperes supplied to the three-phase three-wire load designated by the instructor. This measurement must be made in such a manner that it will be known whether the measured reactive volt-amperes are inductive or capacitive. Make certain to obtain all the data that are needed for making such corrections of the wattmeter indications as may be necessary in determining the actual reactive volt-amperes of the load.

On the data-sheet circuit diagram, be certain to indicate the ± terminals (or their equivalents) of the wattmeter current coils and potential circuits.

Report

A. How many reactive volt-amperes were supplied to the load in 2? Show and explain completely any corrections of the wattmeter indications that may have been necessary.

B. Were the reactive volt-amperes of the load inductive or capacitive? Explain how this determination was made.

C. Draw to scale a voltage vector diagram showing the voltages of the source, the voltages applied to the potential circuits of the wattmeters, and the components of these voltages. Use double subscripts consistent with the identification marks assigned in **1** to the auto-transformer terminals.

D. A three-wire capacitive load is connected to the line terminals of a wye-connected alternator with an available neutral connection.

Draw a circuit diagram showing wattmeters connected so that they can be used to measure the reactive volt-amperes of the load when the phase sequence is ABC. No auxiliary equipment is to be used for securing quadrature voltages.

Explain why the connections shown in the diagram are satisfactory. Include a discussion of any corrections of the wattmeter indications that may be necessary in order to determine the actual reactive volt-amperes of the load.

Laboratory Problem No. 20-3
MEASUREMENT OF THE REACTIVE VOLT-AMPERES OF A THREE-PHASE FOUR-WIRE LOAD

Laboratory

To supply power to the four-wire load designated by the instructor, use a wye-connected source with an available neutral connection.

If any of the wattmeters to be used to measure reactive volt-amperes does not have a current-coil polarity mark, connect the wattmeter in a single-phase circuit in which the direction of energy transfer is known and determine which terminal should be assigned the $\pm$ mark.

1. Measure all of the line-to-line voltages and all of the line-to-neutral voltages.

2. Using wattmeters, measure the reactive volt-amperes supplied to the load. This measurement must be made in such a manner that it will be known whether the measured reactive volt-amperes are inductive or capacitive. Be certain to obtain all the data needed for making such corrections of the wattmeter indications as may be necessary in determining the actual reactive volt-amperes of the load.

On the data-sheet circuit diagram be certain to indicate the $\pm$ terminals (or their equivalents) of the wattmeter current coils and potential circuits.

Report

A. How many reactive volt-amperes were supplied to the load used in the laboratory? Show and explain completely any corrections of the wattmeter indications that may have been necessary.

B. Were the reactive volt-amperes of the load inductive or capacitive? Explain how this determination was made.

C. Draw to scale a voltage vector diagram showing all of the source voltages and the voltages applied to the potential circuits of the wattmeters.

CHAPTER 21
OSCILLOGRAPHS

1. Common Types. An oscillograph is an instrument which is usually used to show wave forms of voltages and currents graphically on a screen. The ordinates of the graph are proportional to the instantaneous values of the voltages or currents, and the abscissas are proportional to time. If desired, these wave forms can be recorded photographically.

There are two types of oscillographs in general use, the electromagnetic oscillograph and the cathode-ray oscillograph. The electromagnetic type is normally used in circuits of relatively low frequency and where the power required by the oscillograph is not important. The cathode-ray type is well adapted for use in high-frequency circuits, its usable range extending into the radio frequencies. This type is also very useful in low-power or low-current circuits, since the input impedance of the oscillograph is very high, usually a megohm or more.

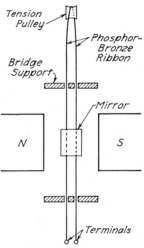

Fig. 21-1. Schematic diagram showing the essential parts of the type of permanent-magnet, D'Arsonval galvanometer used in electromagnetic oscillographs.

2. Electromagnetic Oscillograph. *The Galvanometer.* The principal part of the electromagnetic oscillograph is a permanent-magnet, D'Arsonval type galvanometer. The moving part of the galvanometer is a small phosphor-bronze ribbon loop which is tightly stretched, forming two parallel conductors between the poles of a permanent magnet as shown schematically in Fig. 21-1. In this type of oscillograph galvanometer, the pointer of the usual D'Arsonval mechanism* is replaced by a light beam reflected from a small mirror which is cemented to the stretched ribbon as indicated in Fig. 21-1.

When a direct current flows through the ribbon, both conductors

---

* See page 39.

twist in either a clockwise or counterclockwise direction, depending on the direction of the current, and cause the mirror to turn about a vertical axis. The effect of the turning effort and the restraining torque of the stretched phosphor-bronze ribbon is to cause a deflection of the mirror and light beam which is very nearly proportional to the instantaneous current in the galvanometer ribbon. When used with alternating current, the instantaneous deflection will be proportional to the instantaneous current in the ribbon, provided that the natural period of oscillation of the galvanometer is small compared with the period of the alternating current. Regardless of the fact that the ribbon is light in weight and tightly stretched, the natural period of oscillation of most galvanometers is generally not less than 0.0002 second, although some have been built with natural periods as low as 0.0001 second. Since the galvanometers are immersed in a viscous oil to damp free oscillations and to reduce the tendency to overshoot when recording steep wave fronts, the damped natural periods of oscillation are greater than the values given above. It is therefore apparent that the use of this type of oscillograph is limited to frequencies of a few thousand cycles per second.

Photographic Recording of the Light-Beam Trace. The instantaneous deflections of the galvanometer are made usable by directing a fine beam of light on the galvanometer mirror and photographing or viewing the trace produced by the light beam reflected from the galvanometer mirror. When a photographic record is made, a film is moved at right angles to the reflected light beam. With the film moving and no current in the galvanometer, a time axis is produced. With the film stationary and current in the galvanometer, the light beam makes a trace on the film perpendicular to the time axis. The result of the two actions occurring simultaneously is a light trace on the film in rectangular coordinates showing the variation of the instantaneous current in the galvanometer as a function of time.

Visual Observation of the Light-Beam Trace. Wave forms for visual observation are produced by reflecting the galvanometer mirror light beam onto a viewing screen by means of an oscillating mirror or a polygon of mirrors synchronized with the current variation in the galvanometer. This is shown schematically in Fig. 21-2. With the oscillating mirror operating and no current in the galvanometer, a trace of light moves across the viewing screen. When the beam reaches the right side of the screen a shutter cuts off the beam of the light, and the oscillating mirror returns to its initial position. The shutter then opens and lets the light beam through, and another trace moves across the screen. This is rapid enough to give the appearance of a stationary time axis.   When the oscillating mirror is operating and the galvanometer carries current, the oscillating mirror causes the light trace to move from left to right on the viewing screen while the galvanometer produces deflections of the light beam at right angles to the time axis.   The result is a light trace showing the variation in the instantaneous current in the galvanometer as a function of time. When a polygon of mirrors is used in place of an oscillating mirror, no shutter is required.   When the light beam reaches the right side of the viewing screen, the reflected light beam coming from the galvanometer mirror falls on the next side of the polygon of mirrors and another light trace is produced on the viewing screen.

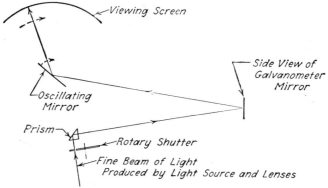

Fig. 21-2.   Schematic diagram of the optical system of an oscillating-mirror type of electromagnetic oscillograph.

Methods of Connecting an Oscillograph Galvanometer in a Circuit. The current that the small galvanometer ribbon can safely carry is a few hundred milliamperes for standard galvanometers and is less than a hundred milliamperes for the more sensitive types.   Oscillograph galvanometers therefore must be connected in a circuit in much the same manner as the usual D'Arsonval mechanisms are connected when measuring currents and voltages.*   In Fig. 21-3(a) an oscillograph galvanometer is shown connected for use in indicating current wave forms, and in Fig. 21-3(b) are shown the connections for indicating voltage wave forms.   The variable rheostats provide a means of controlling the amplitude of the current or voltage wave forms on the screen or photographic film.

Instantaneous-Power and Average-Power Galvanometers.   Oscillograph galvanometers are also available for showing wave forms of

---

* See pages 50–54.

instantaneous power, in other words, wave forms of the product of the instantaneous voltage and current. The main difference between the galvanometer previously discussed and the instantaneous-power galvanometer is that the permanent magnet of the galvanometer shown in Fig. 21-1 is replaced in the instantaneous-power galvanometer by a current coil wound on a laminated pole structure. This current

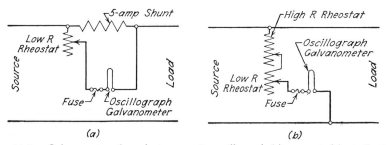

Fig. 21-3. Galvanometer of an electromagnetic oscillograph (a) connected for indicating current waveforms and (b) connected for indicating voltage waveforms.

coil is usually designed to carry 5 amperes and can be connected directly in the 5-ampere secondary of a current transformer. The phosphor-bronze ribbon of the usual galvanometer in conjunction with a series rheostat serves as the potential circuit of the instantaneous-power galvanometer. This type of galvanometer is connected in a circuit in the same manner as an indicating wattmeter. Highly damped power galvanometers can be used to show wave forms of average power.

3. Cathode-Ray Oscillograph. *The Cathode-Ray Tube.* The essential part of the cathode-ray oscillograph is the cathode-ray tube, which

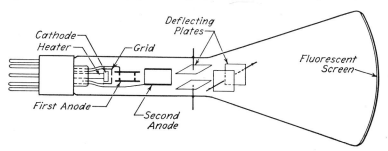

Fig. 21-4. Schematic diagram of a cathode-ray tube.

is shown schematically in Fig. 21-4. The cathode-ray tube consists of three major parts: an electron gun, two sets of deflecting plates, and a fluorescent screen. The heater, cathode, grid, first anode, and second anode comprise the electron gun.

The Electron Beam. Free electrons are emitted by the heated cathode. These electrons pass through a hole in the grid, the negative potential of the grid controlling the number of electrons passing through. The electrons are then accelerated by a positive potential on the first anode, or focusing anode. A small hole in the end of the anode cylinder permits only an electron stream, or beam, of small cross-section to pass through. This beam of electrons is further accelerated by a positive potential on the second anode, or accelerating anode. Here another small hole helps to confine the electrons in a fine beam.

The electron gun thus produces a high-velocity beam of electrons which strike the fluorescent screen at the end of the tube. When the electrons strike a spot on the screen, some of their energy is imparted to the active fluorescent material, causing it to fluoresce brilliantly. The brightness or intensity of the spot depends upon the number of electrons striking the screen per unit time and is usually controlled by the potential on the grid. The focus or sharpness of the spot on the screen is controlled by the potentials on the first and second anodes.

Deflection of the Electron Beam by an Electric Field. The high-velocity beam of electrons can be deflected by either an electric field or a magnetic field. For electric deflection, two sets of parallel plates are arranged perpendicular to one another as shown in Fig. 21-4. In practice the tube is mounted so that one pair of plates produces an electric field in a horizontal or X-axis direction when a potential difference is applied to the plates. A horizontal electric field deflects the electron beam in a horizontal direction toward the positive plate, since the electrons are negative charges. The other pair of plates is used to produce deflections in a vertical or Y-axis direction.

If an a-c voltage is applied to one pair of plates, the spot on the screen moves back and forth over a straight-line path. Because of the phosphorescent property of the screen material and persistence of vision, an observer sees this as a straight line. If an a-c voltage is applied to each set of plates, the spot on the screen traces a path which in the general case does not close on itself, and appears as a moving pattern. However, if the ratio of the frequencies of the two voltages is a rational number, the path closes, and a stationary pattern appears on the screen. This type of pattern is called a *Lissajous* figure. Lissajous figures can be used to determine the frequency and phase relation of an unknown voltage with respect to a known voltage, by applying the known voltage to one pair of deflecting plates and the unknown voltage to the other pair.

Sweep. When the cathode-ray tube is used to show the wave form of a voltage as a function of time, it is necessary that the X-axis deflection vary linearly with time. This means that the spot must move or sweep horizontally across the screen at a uniform velocity, return quickly to the starting position, and then repeat the sweep across the screen. The sweep must be periodic in order that it shall be possible for phosphoresence and persistence of vision to produce the appearance of a stationary wave form on the screen. If the time taken for the sweep across the screen is equal to the time of one cycle of the voltage applied to the vertical or Y-axis plates, the wave form on the screen will consist of one cycle. If the sweep frequency is f_{sweep} and the frequency of the voltage on the Y-axis plates is f_y, the ratio f_y/f_{sweep} gives the number of cycles shown on the screen. This ratio must be an integer to produce a single stationary wave form on the screen.

The horizontal sweep of uniform velocity is produced by applying to the X-axis plates a periodic voltage which increases at a uniform rate from zero to a given maximum value and then drops abruptly to zero. This type of sweep voltage is called a saw-tooth voltage, and in the oscillograph is supplied by a special variable-frequency oscillator.* In some oscillographs a high negative voltage is applied to the grid during the very short time the sweep voltage is dropping to zero. This cuts off the beam and prevents a trace being made on the screen as the beam returns to the starting point. Most oscillographs have a synchronization control in which a controllable portion of the voltage under observation is used to initiate each cycle of the sweep voltage. This eliminates any drifting of the wave form on the screen which might otherwise result from small variations in the sweep frequency.

Deflection of the Electron Beam by a Magnetic Field. When the electron beam is to be deflected magnetically, two pairs of coils are mounted so that they can produce magnetic fields perpendicular to one another and to the electron beam. The electron beam will be deflected by the magnetic field, since a charge moving in a magnetic field experiences a force at right angles to its direction of motion and to that of the field. Magnetic deflection is not ordinarily used in oscillographic work, since appreciable power is required in the deflecting coils, and the driving voltage required to produce a given current in a deflecting coil varies with frequency. The latter disadvantage, however, can be overcome by use of special circuit arrangements.

Screen Materials. The type of material used in making the screen of the cathode-ray tube is very important in determining its usefulness

---

* Ryder, J. D., *Electronic Fundamentals and Applications*, pp. 602–607, 722. New York: Prentice-Hall, Inc., 1950.

for a particular application. Zinc orthosilicate is commonly used where the oscillographic work consists of visual observation and photographic recording of repetitive phenomena. This material produces a relatively brilliant green trace of medium persistence. Zinc sulfide gives a blue trace having a persistence which is short enough for the great majority of oscillographic recording applications. Calcium tungstate results in a blue trace of very short persistence. The major oscillographic application requiring this shorter persistance is in photography on continuous-motion film where there are frequency components above approximately 200 kc. Some materials, such as zinc magnesium fluoride, produce very long-persistence screens which permit viewing a single trace of a transient for several seconds before it fades out. There are also several dual purpose screens which have both short and long persistence screen characteristics. Zinc sulfide cascaded on zinc and calcium sulfide produces a blue fluorescence of short persistence and a yellow phosphorescence of long persistence. In continuous-motion recording where the long persistence phosphorescence would cause blurring, the yellow component can be eliminated by use of a standard blue filter. The blue "flash" component can be removed from the yellow component by means of a yellow filter. This is recommended when it is necessary to observe the screen visually for long periods. The various fluorescent screen materials deteriorate rapidly under steady bombardment by the electron stream, and consequently the spot should not be allowed to remain stationary on the screen.

Complete Oscillograph. The complete cathode-ray oscillograph consists of the cathode-ray tube and the necessary apparatus to make the operation of the oscillograph simple and flexible. The oscillograph usually consists of the following components in conjunction with the cathode-ray tube:

1. Power supply to furnish d-c voltages
2. Oscillator to produce the variable-frequency saw-tooth sweep voltage
3. Wide-band amplifiers* for the X-axis and Y-axis deflecting plates for use with low voltages
4. Spot focusing control
5. Spot intensity control
6. Synchronization control
7. Axis-shifting controls

---

* MIT Staff, *Applied Electronics*, pp. 519–525. New York: John Wiley & Sons, Inc., 1943.

Connection of the Oscillograph in a Circuit.   When the cathode-ray oscillograph is used to show voltage wave forms, the voltage to be observed, or a portion of it, is generally applied directly to the input terminals of the *Y*-axis amplifier.   When the voltage has a d-c component and it is necessary to observe the true zero axis, the voltage to be observed must be applied directly to the *Y*-axis deflecting plates, since the amplifier blocks out the d-c component.   When the oscillograph is used to show current wave forms, a low resistance shunt is inserted in the line, and the voltage drop across the shunt is applied to the input terminals of the *Y*-axis amplifier or plates.

Advantages and Disadvantages.   The advantages of the cathode-ray oscillograph include its wide frequency range, high input impedance, low power requirements, flexibility of control, ruggedness, and relative low cost.   The major disadvantages are the loss of the true zero axis when the amplifiers are used and the inability of the commonly used type to show two or more wave forms simultaneously without use of auxiliary electronic switches.   However, some oscillographs are available which have dual-beam cathode-ray tubes for showing two wave forms simultaneously.

Laboratory Problem No. 21-1

THE OSCILLOGRAPH

Laboratory

1. Examine the oscillograph designated by the instructor and become familiar with the various controls.

2. Assuming that the oscillograph is to be used to show wave forms of voltages and current having maximum amplitudes of 200 volts and 2 amperes, respectively, calibrate the oscillograph for voltage and current measurements.

3. In the following tests use the resistor, inductance coil, condenser, and non-sinusoidal, periodic voltage source designated by the instructor.   Maintain the effective value of the voltage constant at the value specified by the instructor.

(a) Connect the resistor to the non-sinusoidal voltage source. Using the oscillograph, observe and record the wave form of the voltage and current of the resistor.

(b) Repeat (a) using the inductance coil.

(c) Repeat (a) using the condenser.

Report

A. Explain the method used to calibrate the oscillograph for voltage and current measurements.

B. Draw the wave forms of the voltage and current for the following:

    (a) Resistor
    (b) Inductance coil
    (c) Condenser

C. For each case in **B**, explain the position and shape of the current wave form with respect to the voltage wave form.*

---

* For help in explaining the shape of the current wave form with respect to the shape of the voltage wave form, see Section 1, Chapter 22.

CHAPTER 22
NON-SINUSOIDAL PERIODIC WAVES

1. Representation of Non-Sinusoidal Periodic Waves by Fourier Series. Many problems in electrical engineering involve non-sinusoidal wave forms which repeat in form at regular intervals. These periodic waves or functions may be represented by an infinite trigonometric series, known as the Fourier series, provided:

1. The function is everywhere single valued.
2. The function is everywhere finite.
3. The function has a finite number of discontinuties in one period.
4. The function has a finite number of maxima and minima in one period.

All periodic functions found in practical engineering work satisfy the above limitations and therefore can be represented by a Fourier series.

Probably the most common form of the Fourier series is

$$y = A_0 + A_1 \cos x + A_2 \cos 2x + \cdots + A_n \cos nx + \cdots$$
$$+ B_1 \sin x + B_2 \sin 2x + \cdots + B_n \sin nx + \cdots. \quad (22\text{-}1)$$

It will be noted that the Fourier series consists of a constant term and sine and cosine terms of integral multiple frequencies. In electrical engineering the constant term A_0 is the d-c component. The sine and cosine terms having the longest period or lowest frequency, that is, $A_1 \cos x$ and $B_1 \sin x$, are called fundamental terms or first harmonics. The period of the fundamental is the same as for the periodic wave. The terms $A_n \cos nx$ and $B_n \sin nx$ are called nth harmonics and have a frequency n times as great as that of the fundamental terms.

The constant term and harmonic terms of the Fourier series

$$y = 1.5 + 4 \sin x - 1 \cos 2x - 0.5 \sin 3x$$

are plotted in Fig. 22-1(a). The sum of these component waves is shown in Fig 22-1(b). The resultant wave is seen to be a non-sinusoidal periodic wave having the same period as the $(4 \sin x)$ term which is the lowest frequency component.

Equation (22-1) can be written more compactly as

$$y = A_0 + \sum_{n=1}^{\infty} (A_n \cos nx + B_n \sin nx). \qquad (22\text{-}2)$$

Another equivalent form of the Fourier series is

$$y = A_0 + \sum_{n=1}^{\infty} C_n \sin (nx + \alpha_n), \qquad (22\text{-}3)$$

where $$C_n = \sqrt{A_n{}^2 + B_n{}^2}$$

and $$\alpha_n = \tan^{-1}\frac{A_n}{B_n}.$$

Equation (22-3) can be obtained by combining the sine and cosine terms of like frequencies in equation (22-1) or equation (22-2).

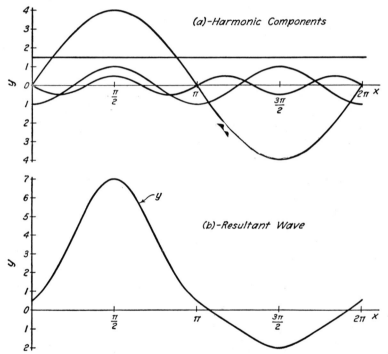

Fig. 22-1.   Graphs showing (a) several harmonic components and (b) the sum or resultant of these components.

The fact that the Fourier series is an infinite series is not so much of a disadvantage as might be expected.   In practical cases the higher harmonics are generally small enough so that they can be neglected without introducing much error.   Thus the Fourier series usually converges rapidly, and only a comparatively few terms need be considered.

2. Determination of the Coefficients of the Fourier Series.

The A and B coefficients in equation (22-1) are known as the Fourier coefficients. The magnitude and sign of these coefficients must be determined before the Fourier series can be written to represent a particular periodic wave form. Equations will not be developed for use in calculating these coefficients.

To obtain an expression for determining A_0, multiply both sides of equation (22-1) by dx and integrate from 0 to 2π. It will be found that all terms are zero except the one containing A_0,* the result being

$$\int_0^{2\pi} y\, dx = 2\pi A_0 \quad \text{or} \quad A_0 = \frac{1}{2\pi} \int_0^{2\pi} y\, dx.$$

To obtain an equation for A_n, multiply both sides of equation (22-1) by $\cos nx\, dx$ and integrate from 0 to 2π. This will result in

$$\int_0^{2\pi} y \cos nx\, dx = \pi A_n \quad \text{or} \quad A_n = \frac{1}{\pi} \int_0^{2\pi} y \cos nx\, dx.$$

To obtain an equation for B_n, multiply both sides of equation (22-1) by $\sin nx\, dx$ and integrate from 0 to 2π. This will give

$$\int_0^{2\pi} y \sin nx\, dx = \pi B_n \quad \text{or} \quad B_n = \frac{1}{\pi} \int_0^{2\pi} y \sin nx\, dx.$$

The preceding equations for the Fourier coefficients can be summarized as follows:

$$A_0 = \frac{1}{2\pi} \int_0^{2\pi} y\, dx \qquad\qquad\qquad (22\text{-}4a)$$

$$= \frac{\text{Area under one cycle of original } y \text{ curve}}{\text{Base}} \qquad (22\text{-}4b)$$

$$= \text{Average value of one cycle of original } y \text{ curve.} \qquad (22\text{-}4c)$$

---

* The following table of integrals will be helpful in developing the equations for the Fourier coefficients (a and b are integers).

$$\int_0^{2\pi} \cos ax\, dx = 0; \qquad \int_0^{2\pi} \sin ax\, dx = 0.$$

$$\int_0^{2\pi} \cos ax \cos bx\, dx = 0, \quad a \neq b$$

$$= \pi, \quad a = b.$$

$$\int_0^{2\pi} \sin ax \cos bx\, dx = 0, \quad a \neq b \quad \text{or} \quad a = b.$$

$$\int_0^{2\pi} \sin ax \sin bx\, dx = 0, \quad a \neq b$$

$$= \pi, \quad a = b.$$

$$A_n = \frac{1}{\pi} \int_0^{2\pi} y \cos nx \, dx \qquad\qquad\qquad (22\text{-}5a)$$

$$= 2 \times \frac{\text{Area under one cycle of derived curve } y \cos nx}{\text{Base}} \qquad (22\text{-}5b)$$

$$= 2 \times \text{Average value of one cycle of derived curve } y \cos nx. \quad (22\text{-}5c)$$

$$B_n = \frac{1}{\pi} \int_0^{2\pi} y \sin nx \, dx \qquad\qquad\qquad (22\text{-}6a)$$

$$= 2 \times \frac{\text{Area under one cycle of derived curve } y \sin nx}{\text{Base}} \qquad (22\text{-}6b)$$

$$= 2 \times \text{Average value of one cycle of derived curve } y \sin nx. \quad (22\text{-}6c)$$

In equations (22-5b) and (22-5c) the term derived curve $y \cos nx$ is used. The meaning of this term should be apparent, since the ordinate for any angle x of the derived curve is found by multiplying the ordinate of the original y curve at the angle x by $\cos nx$. Thus the curve $y \cos nx$ is derived from the y curve. The term derived curve $y \sin nx$ found in equations (22-6b) and (22-6c) has a similar meaning.

Equations (22-4a), (22-5a), and (22-6a) for determining the Fourier coefficients are useful when the y curve can be expressed mathematically in each of a finite number of intervals which cover one complete cycle, as for example, in the case of a triangular wave. When it is not possible to express the y curve mathematically, equations (22-4b), (22-5b), and (22-6b) or equations (22-4c), (22-5c), and (22-6c) can be used. The area under a given curve, or the average value of the curve, can be determined by any of the standard methods. One of the most convenient methods is briefly outlined below.

Divide one cycle of the given curve into a number of equal intervals along the x axis. The number of intervals should be large enough so that the curve being investigated is approximately a straight line over each interval. The value of the ordinate at the mid-point of each interval is determined from the curve. These mid-point ordinates can then be used to determine either the area under one cycle of the curve or the average value of the ordinates over one cycle of the curve. The approximate area under the curve for each interval is found by multiplying the mid-point ordinate of the interval by the base of the interval. The approximate average value of one cycle can be determined directly by averaging the midpoint ordinates for one cycle. It is not necessary to plot the derived curves $y \cos nx$ and $y \sin nx$ in order to use the above method, since the mid-point ordinates for the derived curves can be obtained directly by calculation, using the mid-point ordinates of the original y curve. When applied to the field of electrical engineering, the wave form of the original y curve is obtained by means of an oscillograph.

Considerable work may be saved in determining the Fourier coefficients if the y curve has certain symmetrical properties. Depending on the type of symmetry, some of the coefficients are zero and therefore no attempt need be made to calculate these coefficients. For an analysis of the different types of symmetry and the effect on the magnitude of the Fourier coefficients, the reader should consult the literature on this subject.*

3. Effective Value of a Non-Sinusoidal Periodic Wave. Let V_0 represent the d-c component and V_{m_n} be the maximum value of the nth harmonic component of a non-sinusoidal periodic voltage wave. The equation for the instantaneous voltage as a function of time can be written according to equation (22-3) as

$$v = V_0 + V_{m_1} \sin(\omega t + \alpha_1) + V_{m_2} \sin(2\omega t + \alpha_2) \\ + V_{m_3} \sin(3\omega t + \alpha_3) + \cdots. \quad (22\text{-}7)$$

The effective value of this voltage can be determined by applying the definition of an effective value given in equation (5-10). Thus

$$V = \sqrt{(\mathrm{av}\, v^2)} = \sqrt{\frac{1}{2\pi} \int_0^{2\pi} v^2 \, d\omega t}.$$

Upon subsituting the value of v given in equation (22-7) in the above equation, the effective value can be shown to be†

$$V = \sqrt{V_0{}^2 + \frac{V_{m_1}{}^2}{2} + \frac{V_{m_2}{}^2}{2} + \frac{V_{m_3}{}^2}{2} + \cdots} \quad (22\text{-}8)$$

or $\qquad V = \sqrt{V_0{}^2 + V_1{}^2 + V_2{}^2 + V_3{}^2 + \cdots}. \quad (22\text{-}9)$

where V_1 is the effective value of the fundamental component of the voltage wave, V_2 is the effective value of second harmonic component, and the other harmonic components are similarly defined.

Suppose that the instantaneous current in a circuit, which has an impressed voltage given by equation (22-7), is represented by

$$i = I_0 + I_{m_1} \sin(\omega t + \alpha_1 + \theta_1) + I_{m_2} \sin(2\omega t + \alpha_2 + \theta_2) \\ + I_{m_3} \sin(3\omega t + \alpha_3 + \theta_3) + \cdots. \quad (22\text{-}10)$$

---

* For an excellent discussion see Knight, A. R., and Fett, G. H., *Introduction to Circuit Analysis*, pp. 410–415. New York: Harper & Brothers, 1943.

† The following integrals will be useful in deriving equation (22-8) (a and b are integers).

$$\int_0^{2\pi} \sin(ax + \alpha_a) \, dx = 0.$$

$$\int_0^{2\pi} \sin^2(ax + \alpha_a) \, dx = \pi.$$

$$\int_0^{2\pi} \sin(ax + \alpha_a) \sin(bx + \alpha_b) \, dx = 0, \quad a \neq b.$$

where θ_n is the phase angle of the nth harmonic current component with respect to the nth harmonic voltage component, and all other symbols are defined in the same manner as similar symbols used in the preceding voltage equations. Following the same procedure as for voltage, the effective value of the current is found to be

$$I = \sqrt{I_0{}^2 + \frac{I_{m1}{}^2}{2} + \frac{I_{m2}{}^2}{2} + \frac{I_{m3}{}^2}{2} + \cdots} \qquad (22\text{-}11)$$

or $\qquad I = \sqrt{I_0{}^2 + I_1{}^2 + I_2{}^2 + I_3{}^2 + \cdots}. \qquad (22\text{-}12)$

Examination of equations (22-8) (22-9), (22-11), and (22-12) shows that the effective value of a periodic wave made up of a constant component and harmonic components of integral multiple frequencies is not affected by the phase positions of the harmonic components, but depends only on the effective values of the components. It should be recognized that this is very different from the case of determining the effective value of the sum of sinusoidal waves of the same frequency. Here the phase angles between the sinusoids must be taken into account, that is, the vector sum must be determined.

4. Power in a Circuit with Non-Sinusoidal Periodic Waves of Voltage and Current. Let the instantaneous voltage impressed on a circuit be given by equation (22-7) and the instantaneous current by equation (22-10). The instantaneous power delivered to the circuit is

$$p = vi \qquad (22\text{-}13)$$

and the average power is

$$P = \frac{1}{2\pi} \int_0^{2\pi} p \, d\omega t = \frac{1}{2\pi} \int_0^{2\pi} vi \, d\omega t.$$

When the values of v and i from their respective equations are substituted in the above equation for P, the result is*

$$P = V_0 I_0 + \frac{V_{m1} I_{m1}}{2} \cos \theta_1 + \frac{V_{m2} I_{m2}}{2} \cos \theta_2 + \frac{V_{m3} I_{m3}}{2} \cos \theta_3 + \cdots$$

$$(22\text{-}14)$$

$$= V_0 I_0 + V_1 I_1 \cos \theta_1 + V_2 I_2 \cos \theta_2 + V_3 I_3 \cos \theta_3 + \cdots \quad (22\text{-}15)$$

each symbol having the meaning given in the preceding section.

---

* The integrals involved in the proof of equation (22-14) are as follows (a and b are integers).

$$\int_0^{2\pi} \sin (ax + \alpha_a + \theta_a) \, dx = 0.$$

$$\int_0^{2\pi} \sin (ax + \alpha_a + \theta_a) \sin (bx + \alpha_b) \, dx = 0, \quad a \neq b$$

$$= \pi \cos \theta_a, \quad a = b.$$

In the process of substituting the value of v given by equation (22-7) and of i given by equation (22-10) in equation (22-13), it will be noted that a given harmonic voltage component produces power instantaneously with each harmonic current component. Equations (22-14) and (22-15) show, however, that on the average, power is not supplied to a circuit by a given voltage component except with the harmonic current component which has the same frequency as the voltage.* With respect to all other harmonic current components, as much energy is returned to the source each cycle as is supplied to the circuit; in other words, the average power is zero. Thus each individual harmonic produces its part of the average power independently of the other harmonics. The above statements concerning instantaneous power and average power are important and should be kept in mind.

Laboratory Problem No. 22-1

NON-SINUSOIDAL PERIODIC WAVE SYNTHESIS

Prior to Laboratory Period

Before the laboratory period, determine the Fourier series for each of the four wave forms shown in Fig. 22-2. These wave forms have

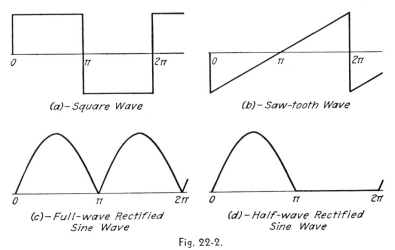

(a) – Square Wave

(b) – Saw-tooth Wave

(c) – Full-wave Rectified Sine Wave

(d) – Half-wave Rectified Sine Wave

Fig. 22-2.

been selected because they are frequently encountered in electrical engineering work.

---

* The d-c component can be thought of as a zero-frequency harmonic.

Laboratory

In this problem use a cathode-ray or electromagnetic oscillograph and a harmonic generator set of either the oscillator or rotating machine type.

1. Make the necessary connections and adjustments of the oscillograph so that a convenient size wave form of the output voltage of the fundamental frequency generator can be viewed on the oscillograph screen. Establish a reference zero. Do not make any further adjustments of the oscillograph, since it is to be used as the calibrating device in determining the relative amplitude and relative phase of each harmonic voltage with respect to the fundamental voltage.

2. Connect the output voltage of each required harmonic generator in turn to the oscillograph and adjust the relative amplitude and relative phase of each harmonic voltage with respect to the fundamental voltage so that the mathematical conditions for a square wave are satisfied.

3. Without disturbing the controls of the oscillograph or harmonic generator set, connect the fundamental and harmonic generators in series and observe the composite wave form on the oscillograph screen. Carefully sketch the composite wave form.

4. Repeat **2** and **3** for the saw-tooth wave.

5. Repeat **2** for the full-wave rectified sine wave. After completing **2** and with no voltage applied to the oscillograph, shift the horizontal trace on the screen a distance above the horizontal reference axis which corresponds to the constant term in the Fourier series for the wave under consideration. Now repeat **3**.

6. Repeat 5 for the half-wave rectified sine wave.

Report

A. Write the Fourier series for a square wave.

B. Draw the composite wave form which was synthesized in **3**. Under the wave form, write the Fourier series which contains only those terms used in synthesizing the wave form.

C. Repeat **A** and **B** for the saw-tooth wave.

D. Repeat **A** and **B** for the full-wave rectified sine wave.

E. Repeat **A** and **B** for the half-wave rectified sine wave.

Laboratory Problem No. 22-2

ANALYSIS OF A NON-SINUSOIDAL PERIODIC WAVE—I

Laboratory

The wave form of the exciting current of an iron-core transformer will be studied in this problem.

1. Impress 120 per cent of rated voltage at rated frequency on one winding of an iron-core transformer which has all other windings on open circuit. Measure the impressed voltage and the exciting current. *Be certain that the ammeter shunting switch is closed when the transformer is connected to the power source.**

2. By means of an oscillograph, obtain the wave form of the exciting current for the conditions of **1** or obtain data from which the wave form can be plotted.

Report

A. Divide one cycle of the exciting current wave form into 20° intervals along the abscissa. Record the value of the ordinate at the mid-point of each interval.

B. Using the mid-point ordinate values determined in **A,** find the Fourier coefficients A_1, B_1, A_3, and B_3.

C. Using the mid-point ordinate values determined in **A** and equation (5-9), calculate the effective value of the exciting current.

D. Using the Fourier coefficients determined in **B,** calculate the effective value of the exciting current.

E. How do the effective values of the exciting current calculated in **C** and **D** compare with the measured value? Explain any significant differences.

Laboratory Problem No. 22-3

ANALYSIS OF A NON-SINUSOIDAL PERIODIC WAVE—II

Laboratory

In this problem a wattmeter will be used in conjunction with a variable-frequency source as a type of harmonic analyzer to determine

---

* This is a necessary precaution since the initial inrush current may be many times the steady-state exciting current of the transformer.

the harmonic content of the exciting current of an iron-core transformer. The circuit for this type of analyzer is shown in Fig. 22-3. As indicated, the current to be analyzed is sent through the current coil of the wattmeter, and the variable-frequency source is connected to the potential circuit.

If the current in the current coil is given by equation (22-10) but the voltage impressed on the potential circuit consists only of the nth term of equation (22-7), then according to equation (22-14) the power reading of the wattmeter will be $\frac{1}{2}V_{m_n}I_{m_n}\cos\theta_n$. By adjusting the

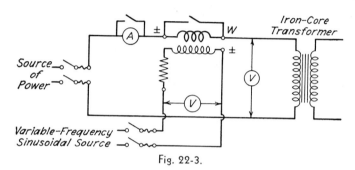

Fig. 22-3.

phase of the variable-frequency source to give the maximum reading $\frac{1}{2}V_{m_n}I_{m_n}$ of the wattmeter, I_{m_n} can be easily calculated if V_{m_n} is known. It should be noted that this method gives the amplitude of the harmonic but not its relative phase.

1. Set up the circuit shown in Fig. 22-3, using the equipment designated by the instructor. The frequency of the source of power should be equal to the rated frequency of the transformer. *Be certain that the ammeter and wattmeter shunting switches are closed when the transformer is connected to the source of power.**

Adjust the voltage across the transformer winding to give 120 per cent of rated transformer voltage. Measure the impressed voltage and the exciting current.

2. Using the voltage specified by the instructor for the variable-frequency source, obtain data from which the amplitude of each harmonic component of the exciting current can be calculated.

3. By means of an oscillograph, observe the wave form of the exciting current. Carefully sketch the wave form.

---

* This is a necessary precaution, since the initial inrush current may be many times the steady-state exciting current of the transformer.

Report

A. Calculate the amplitude of each harmonic component of the transformer exciting current.

B. Calculate the effective value of the exciting current. How does this compare with the measured value? Explain any significant difference.

C. Carefully sketch the wave form of the transformer exciting current.

D. The symmetry of the wave sketched in C is of such a nature that only odd harmonics are present. Explain why this is evident.

CHAPTER 23
FILTERS

IN THE discussion that follows, the term *filter* refers to a passive four-terminal reactance network designed to be inserted between a sending network, or source, and a receiving network, or load, for the purpose of rejecting source currents of frequencies contained within one or more bounded bands of frequencies but allowing currents of all frequencies outside of these bands to reach the load with only small reduction, or attenuation. Rejected bands of frequencies will be called stop bands, and the unattenuated bands will be called pass bands. A system containing a filter is shown in Fig. 23-1.

1. Classification of Filters. Filters are classified according to the location of the pass band in the frequency spectrum. There are four general classes: *low-pass*, *high-pass*, *band-pass* and *band-suppression*. In the *low-pass* filter the pass band is from zero frequency to

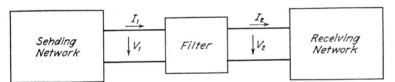

Fig. 23-1.   Filter inserted between source and load.

the cutoff frequency f_C, the stop band being from f_C to infinite frequency. In the case of the *high-pass* filter the bands are just the reverse of those of the *low-pass type*, the stop band being from zero frequency to f_C and the pass band from f_C to infinite frequency.

As the name implies, the pass band of a *band-pass* filter is between the cutoff frequencies f_{C_1} and f_{C_2}. In this type there are two stop bands: one from zero frequency to f_{C_1} and one from f_{C_2} to infinite frequency. The *band-suppression* has a stop band between frequencies f_{C_1} and f_{C_2} and pass bands from zero frequency to f_{C_1} and from f_{C_2} to infinite frequency. It should be noted that in the symbolism used here f_{C_2} is a frequency greater, or higher, than f_{C_1}.

The characteristics of the various filter types are illustrated qualitatively in Fig. 23-2. In this figure attenuation is a measure of the ratio of the filter input current to its output current.

303

2. Criterion For Pass Band. Among the simpler forms of circuits that a filter can take are the symmetrical T and π networks shown, respectively, between terminals 1–1' and 2–2' in (a) and (b) of Fig. 23-3. In these networks Z_1 is the total series impedance and Z_2 is the total shunt impedance.

The characteristic impedance of a symmetrical four-terminal network is that terminating (load) impedance which when connected to

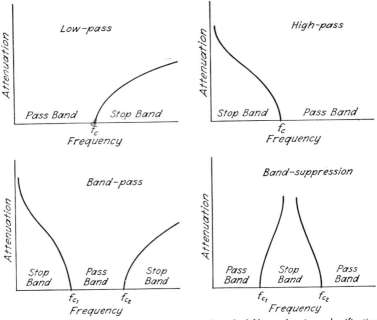

Fig. 23-2. Curves of attenuation vs frequency for ideal filters of various classifications.

the output terminals of the network causes the driving-point impedance at the network input terminals to be equal to the terminating impedance, as is indicated in Fig. 23-3. It will be noted that the characteristic impedance of the T network is symbolized by Z_{0T} and of the π network by $Z_{0\pi}$.

Referring to (a) Fig. 23-3, the input driving-point impedance and the characteristic impedance of the T network is

$$\bar{Z}_{\text{in}} = \bar{Z}_{0T} = \frac{\bar{Z}_1}{2} + \frac{\bar{Z}_2\left(\dfrac{\bar{Z}_1}{2} + \bar{Z}_{0T}\right)}{\dfrac{\bar{Z}_1}{2} + \bar{Z}_2 + \bar{Z}_{0T}}.$$

This will reduce to

$$\bar{Z}_{in} = \bar{Z}_{0T} = \sqrt{\bar{Z}_1\bar{Z}_2 + \frac{\bar{Z}_1{}^2}{4}}. \tag{23-1}$$

Now referring to (b) of the figure, the input driving-point imped-ance and the characteristic impedance of the π network is

$$\bar{Z}_{in} = \bar{Z}_{0\pi} = 2\bar{Z}_2 \left(\frac{\bar{Z}_1 + \dfrac{2\bar{Z}_2\bar{Z}_{0\pi}}{2\bar{Z}_2 + \bar{Z}_{0\pi}}}{\bar{Z}_1 + 2\bar{Z}_2 + \dfrac{2\bar{Z}_2\bar{Z}_{0\pi}}{2\bar{Z}_2 + \bar{Z}_{0\pi}}} \right).$$

This will reduce to

$$\bar{Z}_{in} = \bar{Z}_{0\pi} = \frac{\bar{Z}_1\bar{Z}_2}{\sqrt{\bar{Z}_1\bar{Z}_2 + \dfrac{\bar{Z}_1{}^2}{4}}} = \frac{\bar{Z}_1\bar{Z}_2}{\bar{Z}_{0T}}. \tag{23-2}$$

In equations (23-1) and (23-2) only the positive sign before the radical gives a physically realizable impedance.

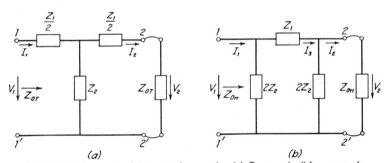

(a) (b)

Fig. 23-3. Symmetrical 4-terminal networks: (a) T network, (b) π network.

The ratio of the input voltage $\bar{V}_1$ to the output voltage $\bar{V}_2$ for each of the networks with characteristic impedance termination can now be determined. For the T network,

$$\bar{V}_2 = \bar{V}_1 - \frac{\bar{I}_1\bar{Z}_1}{2} - \frac{\bar{I}_2\bar{Z}_1}{2}. \tag{23-3}$$

With $\bar{Z}_{0T}$ at the output terminals, the impedance at the input ter-minals is $\bar{Z}_{0T}$, so

$$\bar{I}_1 = \frac{\bar{V}_1}{\bar{Z}_{0T}} \quad \text{and} \quad \bar{I}_2 = \frac{\bar{V}_2}{\bar{Z}_{0T}}. \tag{23-4}$$

Substituting equation (23-4) in equation (23-3) yields

$$\bar{V}_2 = \bar{V}_1 - \frac{\bar{V}_1 \bar{Z}_1}{2\bar{Z}_{0T}} - \frac{\bar{V}_2 \bar{Z}_1}{2\bar{Z}_{0T}}$$

and

$$\frac{\bar{V}_1}{\bar{V}_2} = \frac{2\bar{Z}_{0T} + \bar{Z}_1}{2\bar{Z}_{0T} - \bar{Z}_1}. \qquad (23\text{-}5)$$

For the π network,

$$\bar{I}_2 = \bar{I}_3 - \frac{\bar{V}_2}{2\bar{Z}_2} \qquad (23\text{-}6)$$

and

$$\bar{I}_3 = \bar{I}_1 - \frac{\bar{V}_1}{2\bar{Z}_2}. \qquad (23\text{-}7)$$

Eliminating $\bar{I}_3$ from equations (23-6) and (23-7),

$$\bar{I}_2 + \frac{\bar{V}_2}{2\bar{Z}_2} = \bar{I}_1 - \frac{\bar{V}_1}{2\bar{Z}_2} \qquad (23\text{-}8)$$

With the network terminated in $\bar{Z}_{0\pi}$, the impedance at the imput terminals is $\bar{Z}_{0\pi}$, so

$$\bar{I}_1 = \frac{\bar{V}_1}{\bar{Z}_{0\pi}} \quad \text{and} \quad \bar{I}_2 = \frac{\bar{V}_2}{\bar{Z}_{0\pi}}. \qquad (23\text{-}9)$$

Substituting equation (23-9) in equation (23-8) yields

$$\frac{\bar{V}_2}{\bar{Z}_{0\pi}} + \frac{\bar{V}_2}{2\bar{Z}_2} = \frac{\bar{V}_1}{\bar{Z}_{0\pi}} - \frac{\bar{V}_1}{2\bar{Z}_2}$$

so

$$\frac{\bar{V}_1}{\bar{V}_2} = \frac{2\bar{Z}_2 + \bar{Z}_{0\pi}}{2\bar{Z}_2 - \bar{Z}_{0\pi}}. \qquad (23\text{-}10)$$

From equation (23-2) $\bar{Z}_{0\pi} = \dfrac{\bar{Z}_1 \bar{Z}_2}{\bar{Z}_{0T}}$, so equation (23-10) becomes

$$\frac{\bar{V}_1}{\bar{V}_2} = \frac{2\bar{Z}_2 + \dfrac{\bar{Z}_1 \bar{Z}_2}{\bar{Z}_{0T}}}{2\bar{Z}_2 - \dfrac{\bar{Z}_1 \bar{Z}_2}{\bar{Z}_{0T}}}$$

$$= \frac{2\bar{Z}_{0T} + \bar{Z}_1}{2\bar{Z}_{0T} - \bar{Z}_1} \qquad (23\text{-}11)$$

It should be noted that equations (23-5) and (23-11) are the same. The significance of this fact is important, for it shows that if a symmetrical T network and a symmetrical π network have the same values of $\bar{Z}_1$ and $\bar{Z}_2$, as indicated in Fig. 23-4, the ratio of input voltage to output voltage is the same for both networks if each is terminated in its own characteristic impedance.

From equations (23-4), (23-9), and (23-11),

$$\frac{\bar{I}_1}{\bar{I}_2} = \frac{\bar{V}_1}{\bar{V}_2} = \frac{2\bar{Z}_{0T} + \bar{Z}_1}{2\bar{Z}_{0T} - \bar{Z}_1}. \qquad (23\text{-}12)$$

It will be noted that if $\bar{Z}_{0T}$ is a pure resistance and $\bar{Z}_1$ is a pure reactance, the numerator and denominator of equation (23-12) will be

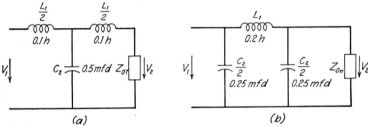

Fig. 23-4. Low-pass filters having same values of Z_1 and Z_2: (a) T configuration, (b) π configuration.

conjugates. Under this condition the absolute value I_1/I_2 of the current ratio is unity. This condition, then, establishes the criterion for the pass band.

It has been shown that

$$\bar{Z}_{0T} = \sqrt{\bar{Z}_1\bar{Z}_2 + \frac{\bar{Z}_1^2}{4}}.$$

If $\bar{Z}_1/2$ is a pure reactance, $\bar{Z}_1^2/4$ will be a negative real quantity. This being the case, $\bar{Z}_1\bar{Z}_2$ must be a real positive quantity in order that $\bar{Z}_{0T}$ shall be a pure resistance. This will be the case when $\bar{Z}_2$ is a pure reactance of opposite kind to $\bar{Z}_1$. In addition to this requirement, Z_1Z_2 must be greater than $Z_1^2/4$.

It has now been established that a four-terminal symmetrical network will have a pass band in the frequency range where

1. $\bar{Z}_1$ and $\bar{Z}_2$ are pure reactances of opposite kind and
2. Z_1Z_2 is greater than $Z_1^2/4$.

3. Constant-k Prototypes. The two-terminal impedances $\bar{Z}_1$ and $\bar{Z}_2$ may each result from single reactance elements or from a combination of several interconnected elements. When the product $\bar{Z}_1\bar{Z}_2$ is a constant real positive quantity and independent of frequency, the filter in which these elements are used is said to be a constant-k type. If, in addition, $\bar{Z}_1$ and $\bar{Z}_2$ each consists of the least possible number of elements, the filter is called the prototype.

4. Low-Pass Prototype. Constant-k, low-pass prototypes of both T and π configuration are illustrated in (a) and (b), respectively, of Fig. 23-5.

For these networks,

$$\bar{Z}_1 = j\omega L_1 = jX_1, \qquad \bar{Z}_2 = \frac{1}{j\omega C_2} = -jX_2.$$

Obviously $\bar{Z}_1$ and $\bar{Z}_2$ are reactances of opposite kind. Also

$$\bar{Z}_1\bar{Z}_2 = \frac{L_1}{C_2} \quad \text{and} \quad \frac{\bar{Z}_1{}^2}{4} = -\frac{\omega^2 L_1{}^2}{4}.$$

Within the frequency band from zero frequency to some value f_C,

$$\frac{L_1}{C_2} > \frac{\omega^2 L_1{}^2}{4}$$

and the criteria for a pass band are fulfilled.

At the frequency f_C

$$\frac{L_1}{C_2} = \frac{\omega_C{}^2 L_1{}^2}{4} \tag{23-13}$$

and for frequencies greater than f_C,

$$\frac{L_1}{C_2} < \frac{\omega^2 L_1{}^2}{4}.$$

The band of frequencies from f_C on up constitutes the stop band.

The value of f_C in terms of L_1 and C_2 is determined from equation (23-13).

$$f_C = \frac{1}{\pi \sqrt{L_1 C_2}}. \tag{23-14}$$

This particular value is the *cutoff* frequency of the filter.

The manner in which the characteristic impedance $\bar{Z}_{0T}$ of the T network and also that of the π network $\bar{Z}_{0\pi}$ change with frequency can be determined from the equations for these quantities, namely:

$$\bar{Z}_{0T} = \sqrt{\frac{L_1}{C_2} - \frac{\omega^2 L_1{}^2}{4}}.$$

$$\bar{Z}_{0\pi} = \frac{\bar{Z}_1\bar{Z}_2}{\bar{Z}_{0T}} = \frac{L_1}{C_2\sqrt{\dfrac{L_1}{C_2} - \dfrac{\omega^2 L_1{}^2}{4}}}.$$

It will be noted that in the stop band where $L_1/C_2 < \omega^2 L_1{}^2/4$ both of these characteristic impedances are pure reactances. The manner in which $\bar{Z}_{0T}$ and $\bar{Z}_{0\pi}$ change with frequency is also shown in Fig. 23-5. The solid line indicates pure resistance impedance and the dashed line indicates pure reactance impedance.

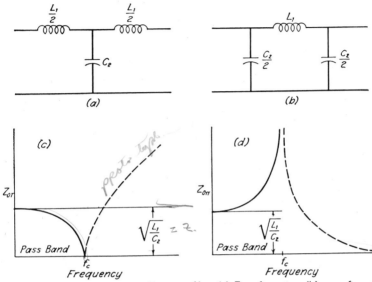

Fig. 23-5.   Constant-k prototypes of low-pass filter: (a) T configuration, (b) π configuration. Characteristic impedance vs frequency for (c) T prototype, (d) π prototype.

5. High-Pass Prototype.   In Fig. 23-6 are shown the T and π high-pass prototypes.   In these networks

$$\bar{Z}_1 = \frac{1}{j\omega C_1}, \qquad \bar{Z}_2 = j\omega L_2.$$

In these filter networks

$$\bar{Z}_1\bar{Z}_2 = \frac{L_2}{C_1},$$

and the pass band includes the frequencies for which

$$Z_1Z_2 > \frac{Z_1^2}{4} \quad \text{or} \quad \frac{L_2}{C_1} > \frac{1}{4\omega^2C_1^2}.$$

The cutoff frequency is determined by

$$\frac{L_2}{C_1} = \frac{1}{4\omega_c^2C_1^2}$$

and is

$$f_c = \frac{1}{4\pi \sqrt{L_2C_1}}. \qquad (23\text{-}15)$$

The following two equations define the characteristic impedances.

$$\bar{Z}_{0T} = \sqrt{\frac{L_2}{C_1} - \frac{1}{4\omega^2 C_1{}^2}}, \qquad \bar{Z}_{0\pi} = \frac{L_2}{C_1 \sqrt{\frac{L_2}{C_1} - \frac{1}{4\omega^2 C_1{}^2}}}.$$

These are shown plotted against frequency in Fig. 23-6.

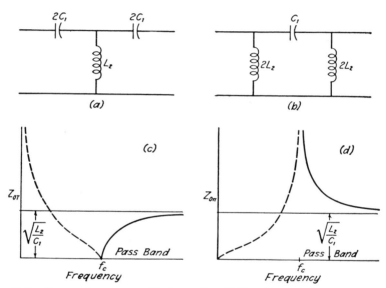

Fig. 23-6. Constant-*k* prototypes of high-pass filter: (a) T configuration, (b) π configuration. Characteristic impedance vs frequency for (c) T prototype, (d) π prototype.

6. Band-Pass Prototype. In the band-pass filter, Z_1 and Z_2 each result from combining two reactance elements as shown in Fig. 23-7. In this prototype

$$L_1 C_1 = L_2 C_2, \qquad (23\text{-}16)$$

so

$$\bar{Z}_1 \bar{Z}_2 = \left(j\omega L_1 + \frac{1}{j\omega C_1}\right)\left(\frac{1}{j\omega C_2 + \frac{1}{j\omega L_2}}\right)$$

$$= \left(\frac{1 - \omega^2 L_1 C_1}{j\omega C_1}\right)\left(\frac{j\omega L_2}{1 - \omega^2 L_2 C_2}\right).$$

Substitution of equation (23-16) in the above leads to

$$\bar{Z}_1 \bar{Z}_2 = \frac{L_2}{C_1} = \frac{L_1}{C_2}.$$

The two cutoff frequencies are determined from

$$Z_1 Z_2 = \frac{Z_1{}^2}{4}, \qquad \frac{L_2}{C_1} = \left(\frac{\omega_c{}^2 L_1 C_1 - 1}{2 \omega_c C_1} \right)^2,$$

$$f_c = \frac{1}{2\pi \sqrt{L_1 C_2}} \left(\sqrt{\frac{L_1}{L_2} + 1} \pm 1 \right).$$

The smaller of the two values is the lower cutoff frequency f_{c_1}

$$f_{c_1} = \frac{1}{2\pi \sqrt{L_1 C_2}} \left(\sqrt{\frac{L_1}{L_2} + 1} - 1 \right). \tag{23-17}$$

The other is the upper cutoff frequency f_{c_2}:

$$f_{c_2} = \frac{1}{2\pi \sqrt{L_1 C_2}} \left(\sqrt{\frac{L_1}{L_2} + 1} + 1 \right). \tag{23-18}$$

The geometric mean of the two cutoff frequencies is

$$\sqrt{f_{c_1} f_{c_2}} = \frac{1}{2\pi \sqrt{L_2 C_2}}$$

This is the antiresonant frequency of the shunt branches of the networks, and since $L_1 C_1 = L_2 C_2$, it is also the resonant frequency of the series branches; hence

$$f_r = \sqrt{f_{c_1} f_{c_2}} = \frac{1}{2\pi \sqrt{L_1 C_1}}.$$

Substituting for $\bar{Z}_1$ and $\bar{Z}_2$ in equation (23-1),

$$\bar{Z}_{0T} = \sqrt{\frac{L_2}{C_1} - \frac{(\omega^2 L_1 C_1 - 1)^2}{4 \omega^2 C_1{}^2}} \tag{23-19}$$

and

$$\bar{Z}_{0\pi} = \frac{L_2}{C_1 \sqrt{\dfrac{L_2}{C_1} - \dfrac{(\omega^2 L_1 C_1 - 1)^2}{4 \omega^2 C_1{}^2}}}. \tag{23-20}$$

For the resonant frequency, the second term under each of the radicals disappears, since for this frequency

$$\omega^2 = \frac{1}{L_1 C_1}, \qquad \omega^2 L_1 C_1 - 1 = 0,$$

and

$$\bar{Z}_{0T} = \bar{Z}_{0\pi} = \sqrt{\frac{L_2}{C_1}} = \sqrt{\frac{L_1}{C_2}}.$$

Successive substitutions of ω_{c_1} and ω_{c_2} for ω in equation (23-19) give

$$\bar{Z}_{0T} = 0$$

for each of the two cutoff frequencies.

Similar substitutions in equation (23-20) give

$$Z_{0\pi} = \infty.$$

For the frequencies in the range $f_{C_1} < f < f_{C_2}$ the second term under the radical in equations (23-19) and (23-20) will be less than the first term, and $\bar{Z}_{0T}$ and $\bar{Z}_{0\pi}$ will be real positive quantities, or pure resistance impedances. For the frequencies in the ranges $0 < f < f_{C_1}$ and $f > f_{C_2}$ the second term under the radical will be greater than the first term, and $\bar{Z}_{0T}$ and $\bar{Z}_{0\pi}$ will be pure reactance impedances. Curves

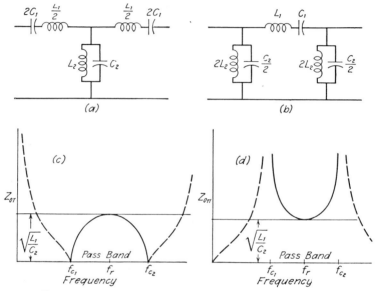

Fig. 23-7. Constant-k prototypes of band-pass filter: (a) T configuration, (b) π configuration. Characteristic impedance vs frequency for (c) T prototype, (d) π prototype.

which are characteristic of the variation of $\bar{Z}_{0T}$ and $\bar{Z}_{0\pi}$ with frequency change are shown in Fig. 23-7.

7. Band-Suppression Prototype. Figure 23-8 shows the circuits of the band-suppression prototype. As in the band-pass prototype,

$$L_1 C_1 = L_2 C_2.$$

By following the same procedure as that used in the treatment of the band-pass filter it can be shown that

$$\bar{Z}_1 \bar{Z}_2 = \frac{L_1}{C_2} = \frac{L_2}{C_1},$$

that $\qquad f_{C_1} = \dfrac{1}{8\pi \sqrt{L_2 C_1}} \left(\sqrt{\dfrac{L_1 + 16L_2}{L_1}} - 1 \right),$ $\qquad$ (23-21) and $\qquad f_{c_2} = \dfrac{1}{8\pi \sqrt{L_2 C_1}} \left(\sqrt{\dfrac{L_1 + 16L_2}{L_1}} + 1 \right),$ $\qquad$ (23-22)

and that $\qquad f_r = \sqrt{f_{c_1} f_{c_2}}.$

Furthermore it can be shown that

$$\bar{Z}_{0T} = 0 \quad \text{and} \quad \bar{Z}_{0\pi} = \infty$$

for $f = f_{c_1}$ and for $f = f_{c_2}$. For the range of frequencies $0 < f < f_{c_1}$ and $f > f_{c_2}$, both $\bar{Z}_{0T}$ and $\bar{Z}_{0\pi}$ will be found to be pure resistance impedances, and in the range $f_{c_1} < f < f_{c_2}$ they will be found to be

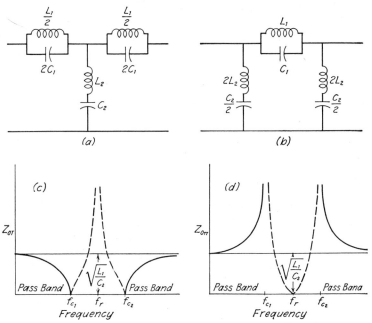

Fig. 23-8. Constant-k prototypes of band-suppression filter: (a) T configuration, (b) π configuration. Characteristic impedance vs frequency (c) T prototype, (b) π prototype

pure reactance impedances. Curves of $\bar{Z}_{0T}$ and $\bar{Z}_{0\pi}$ vs frequency are shown in Fig. 23-8.

8. Design Equations For the Prototypes. As has been pointed out in the foregoing, $\bar{Z}_1 \bar{Z}_2$ is a constant, being L_1/C_2 or L_2/C_1 for all the types which have been considered. From an inspection of the curves of Z_{0T} and $Z_{0\pi}$ vs frequency, it will be noted that the characteristic impedances approach $\sqrt{\bar{Z}_1 \bar{Z}_2}$ asymptotically. Because of this it is usual practice to make

$$\bar{Z}_1 \bar{Z}_2 = R^2,$$ $\qquad$ (23-23)

where R is the impedance of the load to be connected to the output terminals of the filter.

From the equations already established, the equations which determine the inductances and capacitances of the various filter elements can be derived. The known quantities will be the values of R and the cutoff frequencies.

Low-pass Prototype. For the low-pass type,

$$R^2 = \frac{L_1}{C_2} \quad \text{and} \quad f_c = \frac{1}{\pi \sqrt{L_1 C_2}}.$$

From these two equations,

$$L_1 = \frac{R}{\pi f_c} \quad \text{and} \quad C_2 = \frac{1}{\pi f_c R}, \tag{23-24}$$

or
$$C_2 = \frac{L_1}{R^2}. \tag{23-25}$$

High-Pass Prototype. In the case of the high-pass type,

$$R^2 = \frac{L_2}{C_1}, \qquad f_c = \frac{1}{4\pi \sqrt{L_2 C_1}}.$$

Solving for L_2 and C_1,

$$L_2 = \frac{R}{4\pi f_c}, \qquad C_1 = \frac{1}{4\pi f_c R}, \tag{23-26}$$

or
$$C_1 = \frac{L_2}{R^2}. \tag{23-27}$$

Band-Pass Prototype. The known relationships for the band-pass filter are

$$R^2 = \frac{L_1}{C_2} = \frac{L_2}{C_1}, \qquad L_1 C_1 = L_2 C_2,$$

$$f_{c_1} = \frac{1}{2\pi \sqrt{L_1 C_2}} \left(\sqrt{\frac{L_1}{L_2} + 1} - 1 \right),$$

and
$$f_{c_2} = \frac{1}{2\pi \sqrt{L_1 C_2}} \left(\sqrt{\frac{L_1}{L_2} + 1} + 1 \right).$$

The four quantities to be determined are L_1, C_1, L_2, and C_2. These can be found by simultaneous solution of the preceding four equations. This solution gives

$$L_1 = \frac{R}{\pi (f_{c_2} - f_{c_1})}. \tag{23-28}$$

$$C_1 = \frac{f_{c_2} - f_{c_1}}{4\pi f_{c_1} f_{c_2} R}. \tag{23-29}$$

$$L_2 = \frac{R(f_{c_2} - f_{c_1})}{4\pi f_{c_1} f_{c_2}} = R^2 C_1. \qquad (23\text{-}30)$$

$$C_2 = \frac{1}{\pi R(f_{c_2} - f_{c_1})} = \frac{L_1}{R^2}. \qquad (23\text{-}31)$$

Band-Suppression Prototype. For the band-suppression prototype

$$R^2 = \frac{L_1}{C_2} = \frac{L_2}{C_1}, \qquad L_1 C_1 = L_2 C_2,$$

$$f_{c_1} = \frac{1}{8\pi \sqrt{L_2 C_1}} \left(\sqrt{\frac{L_1 + 16 L_2}{L_1}} - 1 \right),$$

$$f_{c_2} = \frac{1}{8\pi \sqrt{L_2 C_1}} \left(\sqrt{\frac{L_1 + 16 L_2}{L_1}} + 1 \right).$$

From these four equations

$$L_1 = \frac{R(f_{c_2} - f_{c_1})}{\pi f_{c_1} f_{c_2}}. \qquad (23\text{-}32)$$

$$C_1 = \frac{1}{4\pi (f_{c_2} - f_{c_1}) R}. \qquad (23\text{-}33)$$

$$L_2 = \frac{R}{4\pi (f_{c_2} - f_{c_1})} = C_1 R^2. \qquad (23\text{-}34)$$

$$C_2 = \frac{(f_{c_2} - f_{c_1})}{\pi f_{c_1} f_{c_2} R} = \frac{L_1}{R^2}. \qquad (23\text{-}35)$$

9. *m*-Derived T Filters. A curve of attenuation vs frequency for a prototype low-pass filter is shown in Fig. 23-9. The solid curve is that for the ideal network, one in which the elements are pure react-

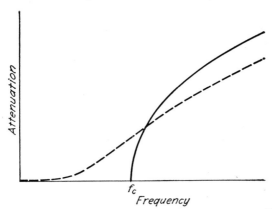

Fig. 23-9. Curves of attenuation vs frequency for low-pass prototype filter: solid line is for an ideal filter terminated in Z_{0T} at all frequencies; dashed line is for a filter having dissipative elements and which is terminated in a pure resistance of value $\sqrt{L_1/C_2}$.

ances and which is terminated in its characteristic impedance at all frequencies. The dashed curve is for the same type of network but in which the elements have some resistance, and which is terminated in a constant pure resistance, $R = \sqrt{L_1/C_2}$, instead of in $\bar{Z}_{0\text{T}}$. It is seen that in the latter case the cutoff is not sharp; that is, attenuation does not begin abruptly and does not increase sharply. Hence in the practical case, the prototype alone does not do a very good job of filtering. However, modifications of the prototype can be made which will produce a new filter network that will have a much sharper cutoff.

Consider the network in (b) of Fig. 23-10. At some frequency f_r the branch containing $\bar{Z}'_2$ will be resonant. For all frequencies less than f_r this branch has a capacitive reactance, and $\bar{Z}_1$ and $\bar{Z}_2$ are reactances of opposite kind. For frequencies greater than f_r, the branch containing $\bar{Z}'_2$ has an inductive reactance, and $\bar{Z}'_1$ and $\bar{Z}'_2$ are

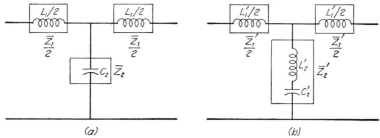

Fig. 23-10. Low-pass filters: (a) prototype, (b) modified type.

reactances of the same kind. Because of this, the network is a low-pass filter. This network has an advantage over the prototype in that the attenuation is infinite at f_r, since $\bar{Z}'_2$ is a short circuit at this frequency. For this reason, f_r is called the frequency of infinite attenuation and is symbolized by f_∞.

For frequencies greater than f_∞, or f_r, impedance Z'_2 increases with frequency, causing the attenuation to decrease. The manner in which the attenuation changes with frequency is shown by the solid curve in Fig. 23-11. The dashed curve in this figure is that of attenuation for the low-pass prototype. From these curves it is apparent that the prototype does not attenuate so rapidly as the other, but does have the advantage that the attenuation increases with frequency. Were the two networks to be cascaded, as shown in Fig. 23-12, the resulting attenuation characteristic would possess the advantages of both without the disadvantage of either. This is indicated by the dot-dash curve.

For operation in cascade the two networks should have identical characteristic impedances at every frequency. The two networks can

be generalized, as shown in (a) and (b) of Fig. 23-13.   It is seen in
Fig. 23-12 that $\bar{Z}'_1$ is of the same kind as $\bar{Z}_1$, so

$$\bar{Z}'_1 = m\bar{Z}_1,$$

where m is a real positive number.   Impedance $\bar{Z}'_2$ is made of two elements, one like $\bar{Z}_1$, and one like $\bar{Z}_2$, so we may write

$$\bar{Z}'_2 = a\bar{Z}_1 + b\bar{Z}_2.$$

Here again it is necessary that a and b be real positive numbers.

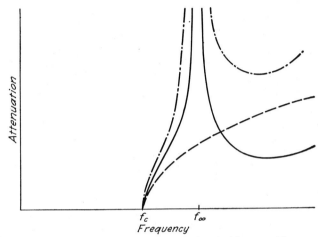

Fig. 23-11.   Curves of attenuation vs frequency for ideal low-pass filters terminated in
characteristic impedance at all frequencies.   Dashed line is for prototype, solid line is for
modified type, and dot-dash line is for cascaded prototype and modified type.

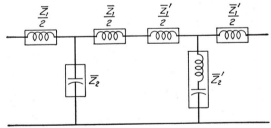

Fig. 23-12.   Cascade connection of prototype and modified type low-pass filter networks.

Since the characteristic impedances of the networks are to be identical,

$$\sqrt{\bar{Z}_1\bar{Z}_2 + \frac{\bar{Z}_1{}^2}{4}} = \sqrt{\bar{Z}'_1\bar{Z}'_2 + \frac{(\bar{Z}'_1)^2}{4}}$$

$$= \sqrt{m\bar{Z}_1(a\bar{Z}_1 + b\bar{Z}_2) + \frac{m^2\bar{Z}_1{}^2}{4}}. \quad (23\text{-}36)$$

The solution of this equation gives

$$a = \frac{1 - m^2}{4m}.$$

(23-37)

$$b = \frac{1}{m}.$$

(23-38)

Substitution for a and b in (b) Fig. 23-12 yields the network shown in (c). When these relationships are applied to (b) of Fig. 23-10, the network shown in Fig. 23-14 is obtained. It should be clear now that

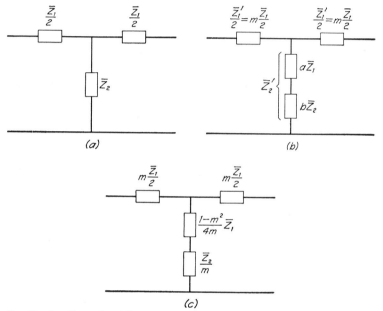

(a)   (b)

(c)

Fig. 23-13. Generalized T networks. (a) simple T network, (b) modified T network having elements related to those in the simple T network, (c) the modified T network showing necessary relationships of its elements to those in the simple T network in order that both networks shall have the same characteristic impedance.

m must be a positive real number, and also must not be greater than unity. Were it negative, $b\bar{Z}_2$ would not be the same kind of reactance as $\bar{Z}_2$. Were it greater than unity, $(1 - m^2)\bar{Z}_1/4m$ would not be the same kind of reactance as $\bar{Z}_1$.

Because of the use of the constant m, this type of network is known as the m-derived type; and being derived from the prototype T network, is referred to as the m-derived T section.

Equations (23-37) and (23-38) were derived from the absolutely generalized network relationship, equation (23-36); so (a) and (c) of Fig. 23-13 are general, and m-derived filters of any class can be deter-

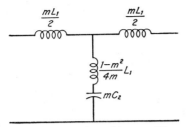

Fig. 23-14. *m*-derived low-pass filter.

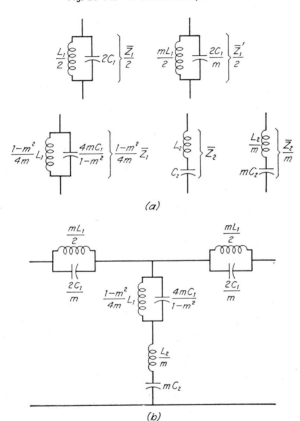

(a)

(b)

Fig. 23-15. Band-suppression filter: (a) elements of prototype and of *m*-derived type, (b) *m*-derived filter.

mined from this generalization. As an example, consider the band-suppression filter. In Fig. 23-8(a), $\bar{Z}_1/2$ consists of $L_1/2$ and $2C_1$ connected in parallel; and $\bar{Z}_2$ consists of L_2 and C_2 in series. The impedances $m\bar{Z}_1/2$, $(1 - m^2)\bar{Z}_1/4m$, and $\bar{Z}_2/m$ are shown in Fig. 23-15(a), and the completed *m*-derived filter in 23-15(b).

10. Determination of the Value of m. The constant m determines the resonant frequency or frequencies of the shunt arm $\bar{Z}'_2$. In the case of the high-pass prototype,

$$\bar{Z}_1 = \frac{1}{j\omega C_1}, \qquad \bar{Z}_2 = j\omega L_2.$$

The shunt arm of the m-derived T network has an impedance

$$\bar{Z}'_2 = \frac{1 - m^2}{4m} \bar{Z}_1 + \frac{\bar{Z}_2}{m} \qquad (23\text{-}39)$$

$$= \frac{1 - m^2}{j4m\omega C_1} + j \frac{\omega L_2}{m}. \qquad (23\text{-}40)$$

Let ω_∞ be the radian velocity for the desired resonant frequency f_∞. For this frequency,

$$\bar{Z}'_2 = 0 \quad \text{and} \quad \frac{\omega_\infty L_2}{m} = \frac{1 - m^2}{4m\omega_\infty C_1},$$

or

$$m = \sqrt{1 - 16\pi f_\infty^2 L_2 C_1}.$$

But

$$16\pi L_2 C_1 = \frac{1}{f_c^2},$$

so

$$m = \sqrt{1 - \left(\frac{f_\infty}{f_c}\right)^2} \qquad (23\text{-}41)$$

The values of m for the other classes of filters are derived in a similar manner. These values are as follows:

Low-pass

$$m = \sqrt{1 - \left(\frac{f_c}{f_\infty}\right)^2}. \qquad (23\text{-}42)$$

Band-pass

$$m = \sqrt{1 - \left[\frac{f_\infty(f_{c_2} - f_{c_1})}{f_\infty^2 - f_{c_1}f_{c_2}}\right]^2}. \qquad (23\text{-}43)$$

Band-suppression

$$m = \sqrt{1 - \left[\frac{f_\infty^2 - f_{c_1}f_{c_2}}{f_\infty(f_{c_2} - f_{c_1})}\right]^2}. \qquad (23\text{-}44)$$

It will be noted that in all cases m is a function of f_∞, the frequency of infinite attenuation, and of the cutoff frequency f_C or frequencies f_{c_1} and f_{c_2}. In connection with the band-pass and band-suppression types it should be noted that in each case the shunt branch of the m-derived T network contains four reactance elements. Consequently there are two resonant frequencies and one antiresonant frequency. The resonant frequencies usually are designated by f_{∞_1} and f_{∞_2}. Either f_{∞_1} or f_{∞_2} can be used in equations (23-43) and (23-44). Once one has been specified the other is automatically fixed. In Fig. 23-16 are shown typical attenuation curves for ideal m-derived filters.

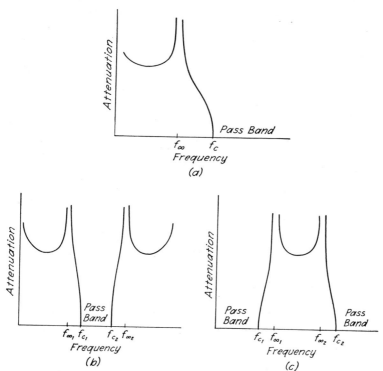

Fig. 23-16. Curves of attenuation vs frequency for m-derived filters: (a) high-pass, (b) band-pass, and (c) band-suppression.

11. π Network Constructed from the m-Derived T Network. A network formed from an m-derived T network is shown in (b) of Fig. 23-17. As will be explained in the following, a half of such a π network is an impedance transformation network and is very useful in matching a constant load resistance to the filter characteristic impedance.

From equation (23-2) the characteristic impedance of the network in (b) is

$$\bar{Z}'_{0\pi_m} = \frac{\bar{Z}'_1 \bar{Z}'_2}{\sqrt{\bar{Z}'_1 \bar{Z}'_2 + \left(\dfrac{\bar{Z}'_1}{2}\right)^2}} \tag{23-45}$$

which becomes
$$\bar{Z}'_{0\pi_m} = \frac{\bar{Z}_1 \bar{Z}_2 + \left(\dfrac{1 - m^2}{4}\right) \bar{Z}_1{}^2}{\sqrt{\bar{Z}_1 \bar{Z}_2 + \left(\dfrac{\bar{Z}_1}{2}\right)^2}} \tag{23-46}$$

after substituting for $\bar{Z}'_1$ and $\bar{Z}'_2$.

Let the π network in (b) be cut through the middle and be terminated in $\bar{Z}'_{0\pi_m}$ as shown in (c). The impedance into terminals 22' is

$$\bar{Z}'_{22'} = \frac{\bar{Z}'_1}{2} + \frac{2\bar{Z}'_2\bar{Z}'_{0\pi_m}}{2\bar{Z}'_2 + \bar{Z}'_{0\pi_m}} = \sqrt{\bar{Z}_1\bar{Z}_2 + \left(\frac{\bar{Z}_1}{2}\right)^2} = \bar{Z}_{0T}$$

upon substituting for $\bar{Z}'_{0\pi_m}$ from equation (23-46). This is the characteristic impedance of the prototype T network, and also of the m-derived T network. Either one of these—or both in cascade—can

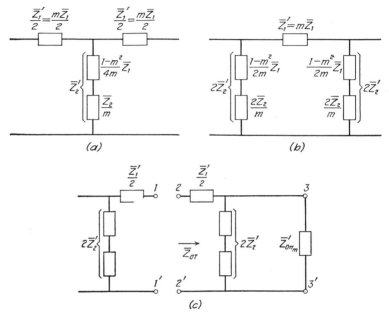

Fig. 23-17. Generalized m-derived filter networks: (a) m-derived T, (b) π network constructed from m-derived T, (c) half-π sections.

be connected between terminals 1–1' and 2–2', and it would be terminated properly in its characteristic impedance as is shown in Fig. 23-18. In this type of connection it is said that the T network is terminated in a half-π section.

One advantage of this kind of termination is indicated in Fig. 23-19. In (a) of the figure, $\bar{Z}_{0T}$ and $\bar{Z}'_{0\pi_m}$ are plotted vs frequency (in the pass band only) for the low-pass type.

It will be noted that throughout most of the pass band, $\bar{Z}'_{0\pi_m}$ remains substantially constant when $m = 0.6$. Furthermore, it is a pure resistance in this band. This means that a constant resistance of value $R = \sqrt{L_1/C_2}$ or $\sqrt{L_2/C_1}$ may be substituted for $\bar{Z}'_{0\pi_m}$ in

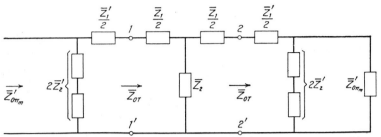

Fig. 23-18. Generalized prototype T filter network with half-π sections constructed from the
m-derived T.

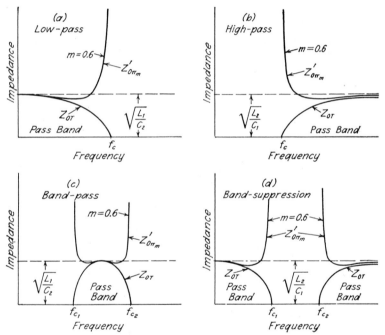

Fig. 23-19. Curves of characteristic impedance vs frequency of π filter networks constructed
from m-derived T networks.

Fig. 23-18 without deviating too widely from the requirement that the
termination be the characteristic impedance.

For other classes of filters the impedance characteristics are shown
in (b), (c), and (d) of Fig. 23-19. In all these it will be noted that
within the pass band $\bar{Z}'_{0\pi_m}$ remains substantially constant.

The terminating half-π sections should each be called a half section
of the π network constructed from the m-derived T rather than the
commonly used term "a half m-derived π section."

12. m-Derived π Filters. In (a) of Fig. 23-20 is shown the proto-type low-pass filter of π configuration. The network in (b) is also a low-pass filter of similar configuration. In the latter Z''_1 will be anti-resonant at some frequency f_{ar}; a condition that will prevent voltage from appearing at the output terminals when driven at the input ter-minals by a voltage of this frequency. This is equivalent to infinite attenuation, since the ratio of input voltage to output voltage will be infinite. For this reason f_∞ is used instead of f_{ar}.

When terminated in their respective characteristic impedances the attenuation vs frequency curves of the two networks will be like those shown in Fig. 23-11. When designed to have like characteristic

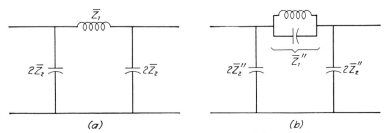

(a)   (b)

Fig. 23-20. Low pass filters: (a) prototype, (b) modified type.

impedances they can be cascaded and will have an attenuation vs frequency characteristic similar to that shown by the dot-dash line in Fig. 23-11.

The networks shown in Fig. 23-20 can be generalized, and relation-ships between their respective elements can be established such that the two networks will have like characteristic impedances. The generalized networks are shown in (a) and (b) of Fig. 23-21.

If these two networks are to have like characteristic impedances, then from equation (23-2),

$$\bar{Z}_{0\pi} = \frac{\sqrt{\bar{Z}_1 \bar{Z}_2}}{\sqrt{1 + \dfrac{\bar{Z}_1}{4\bar{Z}_2}}} = \frac{\sqrt{\bar{Z}''_1 \bar{Z}''_2}}{\sqrt{1 + \dfrac{\bar{Z}''_1}{4\bar{Z}''_2}}} \qquad (23\text{-}47)$$

where
$$\bar{Z}''_1 = \frac{qn\bar{Z}_1 \bar{Z}_2}{q\bar{Z}_1 + n\bar{Z}_2} \quad \text{and} \quad \bar{Z}''_2 = \frac{\bar{Z}_2}{m}.$$

Substitution in equation (23-47) yields

$$\frac{1}{\sqrt{\bar{Z}_1 + 4\bar{Z}_2}} = \sqrt{\frac{qn}{m[(4q + qmn)\bar{Z}_1 + 4n\bar{Z}_2]}} \qquad (23\text{-}48)$$

or
$$\bar{Z}_1 + 4\bar{Z}_2 = \frac{m}{n}(4 + mn)\bar{Z}_1 + \frac{4m\bar{Z}_2}{q}. \tag{23-49}$$

This equation is satisfied when

$$\frac{m}{n}(4 + mn) = 1 \tag{23-50}$$

and
$$\frac{m}{q} = 1. \tag{23-51}$$

From equation (23-50),

$$n = \frac{4m}{1 - m^2},$$

and from equation (23-51),

$$q = m.$$

The network (c) of Fig. 23-21 is now obtained by substituting for n and q in the network shown in (b). It is called the m-derived π network.

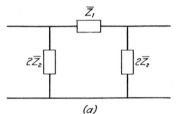

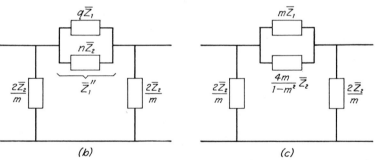

Fig. 23-21. Generalized π networks: (a) simple π network, (b) modified π network which has elements related to those in the simple π network, (c) the modified π network showing necessary relationships of its elements to those in the simple π network in order that both networks shall have the same characteristic impedance.

The m-derived π networks with their respective prototypes are shown in Fig. 23-22.

The equations for evaluating the constant m are the same as for the m-derived T sections. These are equations (23-41), (23-42), (23-43), and (23-44).

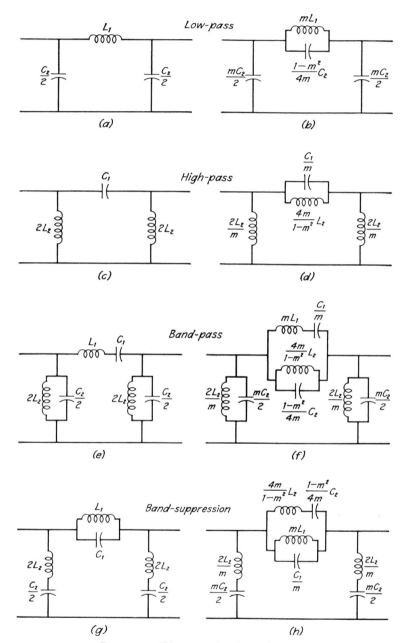

Fig. 23-22. Filter networks of π configuration.

A prototype π network and its corresponding m-derived π network having like characteristic impedances and cutoff frequencies can be cascaded. The cascade connection for the band-pass filter is shown in Fig. 23-23. It is obtained by cascading the prototype and m-derived networks shown in (e) and (f) of Fig. 23-22.

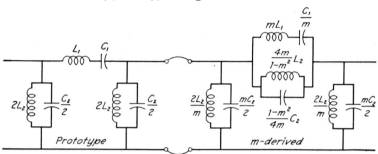

Fig. 23-23. Band-pass prototype of π configuration cascaded with its m-derived π type.

13. T Network Constructed From the m-Derived π Network. A T network constructed from an m-derived π network is shown in generalized form in (a) of Fig. 23-24. Here the shunt branch has been split into two parallel branches. In (b) of the figure is shown the corresponding network of the high-pass type.

The characteristic impedance of the network in (a) is

$$\bar{Z}'_{0T_m} = \sqrt{\bar{Z}''_1 \bar{Z}''_2 + \left(\frac{\bar{Z}''_1}{2}\right)^2}.$$

Upon substituting for $\bar{Z}''_1$ and $\bar{Z}''_2$

$$\bar{Z}'_{0T_m} = \frac{2\sqrt{\bar{Z}_1 \bar{Z}_2}}{(1-m^2)\bar{Z}_1 + 4\bar{Z}_2}\sqrt{\bar{Z}_2(\bar{Z}_1 + 4\bar{Z}_2)}. \qquad (23\text{-}52)$$

Let the network in (a) be terminated in its characteristic impedance $\bar{Z}'_{0T_m}$ and then split through the middle as shown in (c). The impedance at terminals 22' is

$$\bar{Z}_{22'} = \frac{2\bar{Z}''_2\left(\bar{Z}'_{0T_m} + \dfrac{\bar{Z}''_1}{2}\right)}{2\bar{Z}''_2 + \dfrac{\bar{Z}''_1}{2} + \bar{Z}'_{0T_m}}$$

$$= \frac{\bar{Z}_1 \bar{Z}_2}{\sqrt{\bar{Z}_1 \bar{Z}_2 + \dfrac{\bar{Z}_1^2}{4}}} = \bar{Z}_{0\pi} \qquad (23\text{-}53)$$

after substituting for $\bar{Z}''_1$, $\bar{Z}''_2$ and $\bar{Z}'_{0T_m}$.

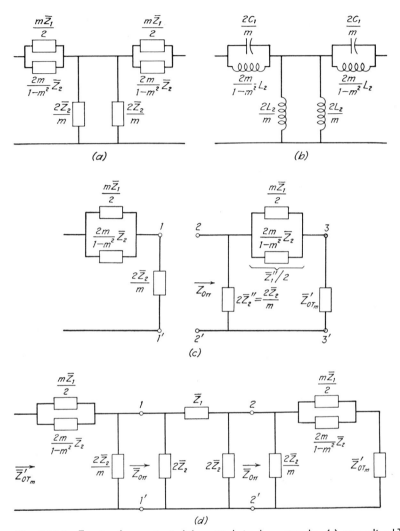

Fig. 23-24. T networks constructed from m-derived π networks: (a) generalized T network, (b) high-pass filter, (c) half sections of T network, (d) generalized π network terminated in a half section of a T network which was constructed from m-derived π network.

A prototype π network or an m-derived π network—or both in cascade—can be connected between terminals 1–1' and 2–2', and it would be terminated properly in its characteristic impedance. This is indicated in (d) of the figure. In this type of connection it is said that the π network is terminated in a half-T network. The advantage of the use of the half-T sections is indicated in Fig. 23-25. Here $\bar{Z}_{0\pi}$ and $\bar{Z}'_{0T_m}$ are shown plotted vs frequency (in the pass band only) for each filter classification. It will be noted that the use of the half-T network constructed from the m-derived π network with $m = 0.6$ makes it possible to obtain a good impedance match between the filter and the load resistance, since $\bar{Z}'_{0T_m}$ remains more nearly constant throughout the pass band than does $\bar{Z}_{0\pi}$.

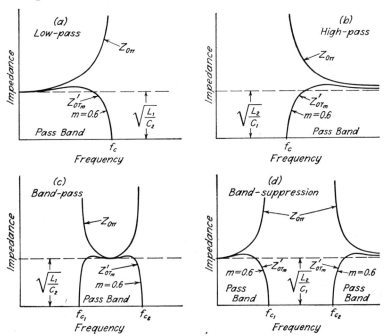

Fig. 23-25.   Curves of characteristic impedance vs. frequency of T filter networks constructed from m-derived π networks.

14. Determination of Characteristic Impedance. Characteristic impedance can be calculated from the measured short-circuit impedance $\bar{Z}_{SC}$ and the measured open-circuit impedance $\bar{Z}_{OC}$, and can be shown to be

$$\bar{Z}_0 = \sqrt{\bar{Z}_{OC}\bar{Z}_{SC}}. \qquad (23\text{-}54)$$

Equation (23-54) is applicable when the network is symmetrical, such as shown in Fig. 23-3 and Figs. 23-5 through 23-8. Since the network is symmetrical, it matters not at which end the measurements are made.

In the case of dissymmetrical networks, as shown in Figs. 23-17(c) and 23-24(c), the point of measurement is not arbitrary. In connection with the former $\bar{Z}_{OT}$ is determined from measurements made at terminals 2–2' with 3–3' open—no impedance connected to these terminals—and then short-circuited. The value of $\bar{Z}'_{0\pi_m}$ is determined by making the impedance measurements at terminals 3–3', first with terminals 2–2' open-circuited and then short-circuited. Similarly $\bar{Z}_{0\pi}$ and Z'_{0T_m} can be obtained for the circuit of Fig. 23-24(c).

15. Attenuation Units. Attenuation is a measure of the ratio of the current or voltage at the input terminals of a filter to the current or voltage, respectively, at the output terminals. When this ratio is greater than one, the attenuation is positive. The decibel is commonly used as the unit of attenuation and is defined by

$$\text{db} = 20 \log_{10} \frac{I_1}{I_2}.$$

This gives the current attenuation in decibels. The voltage attenuation is given by

$$\text{db} = 20 \log_{10} \frac{V_1}{V_2}.$$

When the filter is terminated in its characteristic impedance the current attenuation and voltage attenuation are equal. The neper may also be used as a measure of attenuation. In this case current attenuation is

$$\text{nepers} = \log_\epsilon \frac{I_1}{I_2},$$

and voltage attenuation is

$$\text{nepers} = \log_\epsilon \frac{V_1}{V_2}.$$

16. Insertion Loss of a Filter. Insertion loss of a filter is a measure of the effectiveness of the filter. It is a measure of the relation between the power transmitted from a source to a load impedance without the filter in the circuit and the power transmitted from the same source to the same load impedance after insertion of the filter.

The unit of the insertion loss is usually the decibel which is defined as follows:

$$\text{db} = 10 \log_{10} \frac{P_1}{P_2}. \tag{23-55}$$

In the case of insertion loss P_1 is the power in the load impedance before insertion of the filter, and P_2 is the power after insertion.

Usually the load impedance will be a pure resistance R of fixed value. Therefore, to determine the power it is necessary only to measure current in the load resistance or the voltage across it. This is illustrated in Fig. 23-26. The power P_1 is $I_1^2 R$ or V_1^2/R, and the

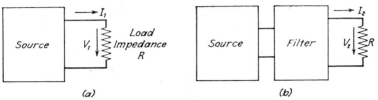

Fig. 23-26. Generalized circuits for determination of insertion loss.

power P_2 is $I_2{}^2 R$ or $V_2{}^2/R$,

so
$$\frac{P_1}{P_2} = \left(\frac{I_1}{I_2}\right)^2 = \left(\frac{V_1}{V_2}\right)^2$$

and
$$\text{db} = 10 \log_{10}\left(\frac{I_1}{I_2}\right)^2 = 10 \log_{10}\left(\frac{V_1}{V_2}\right)^2, \qquad (23\text{-}56)$$

or
$$\text{db} = 20 \log_{10}\frac{V_1}{V_2}. \qquad (23\text{-}57)$$

If a true measure of insertion loss is to be obtained, the internal, or generated, voltage of the source must not be changed between measurements.

Laboratory Problem No. 23-1

CHARACTERISTIC IMPEDANCE OF FILTER NETWORKS

Design a low-pass composite filter to have a cutoff frequency f_C cycles and to operate into a load impedance of R ohms. The values of f_C and R will be specified by the instructor.*

The filter is to include a prototype T section and an m-derived T section for which f_∞ is 5 per cent greater than f_C. The filter is to be provided with proper terminating half sections in order to obtain good impedance matching.

Laboratory

1. Set up the prototype section of the filter. Measure the open-circuit and short-circuit impedances of this network. Do this for frequencies in the range from 200 cycles per second up to and including a frequency about 20 per cent greater than f_C. Calculate the values of the characteristic impedances.

2. Set up the m-derived T section. Make measurements and calculations as in **1.** In the vicinity of f_C measurements should be

---

* Laboratory problems Nos. 23-1 and 23-2 are applicable to other classifications of filters. The changes needed are those concerning f_C, f_∞, and the percentages of these in specifying frequency ranges within which measurements are to be made.

taken at intervals which are short enough to provide data which will adequately define the curve of characteristic impedance vs frequency in the vicinity of the cutoff frequency.

3. Construct a π section using values from the m-derived T section for which m is 0.6. Make measurements and calculations as in **2.** Extend the range of measurements to about 30 per cent above f_c.

Report

A. On one set of axes plot characteristic impedance (magnitude) vs frequency from data obtained in **1, 2,** and **3.** From a point $\sqrt{L_1/C_2}$ ohms on the impedance axis draw a horizontal line parallel to the frequency axis.

B. If the characteristic impedance curves are all extended to zero frequency, will they intersect the impedance axis at the theoretically correct value of impedance? Explain.

C. Is the relationship between the curves plotted from data taken in **1** and **2** consistent with theory? Explain.

D. In the pass band what should have been the angles of the characteristic impedances if the elements of the filter sections had been lossless? Do the results obtained tend to bear this out? Explain.

E. Same as **D** except relating to the frequency range outside the pass band.

Laboratory Problem No. 23-2

MEASUREMENT OF INSERTION LOSS

Laboratory

1. Obtain data from which the decibel insertion loss of the prototype section can be calculated. Do this for the frequency range from 10 per cent of f_c to 200 per cent of f_c.*

In Fig. 23-27 are shown circuits which may be used to obtain data for calculating the insertion loss.

2. Obtain data from which the decibel insertion loss of the m-derived T section can be calculated. Use the same frequency range as in **1,** but take data at much shorter frequency intervals in the vicinity of f_c and f_∞.

---

* The filter sections to be used in this problem are those referrred to in Problem 23-1.

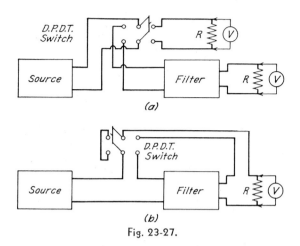

Fig. 23-27.

3. Construct a π section using values from the m-derived T section for which m is 0.6.   Take data as in **2.**

4. Set up the composite filter that has been designed.   Obtain data from which the decibel insertion loss of the filter can be calculated. Take data as in **2.**

Report

A. On one set of axes, draw curves of insertion loss vs frequency for each section of the filter and for the composite filter.

B. Discuss the results obtained in this experiment.

CHAPTER 24

COUPLED CIRCUITS

1. Definition. In practice, single-mesh circuits are not usually encountered. In both the power and communication fields the electrical systems consist generally of interconnected circuits, or meshes. In such networks, energy is introduced in one or more of the circuits or meshes and is transferred to others. When two such circuits or meshes are so related, or arranged, that energy introduced in one is transferred to another, the circuits or meshes are said to be coupled.

2. The General Coupled Circuit. Circuits may be *directly coupled* by means of mutual impedances such as resistances, inductances, and

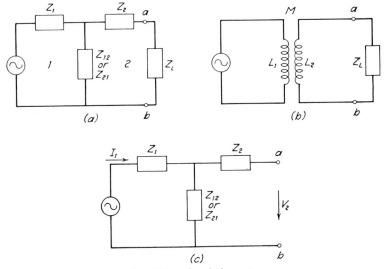

Fig. 24-1. Coupled circuits.

capacitances or combinations of such impedances. This type of coupling is illustrated in (a) of Fig. 24-1. Here meshes 1 and 2 are coupled by the mutual impedance $\bar{Z}_{12} = \bar{Z}_{21}$ which, as stated above, may be a resistance, inductance, capacitance, or a combination of these.

Circuits or meshes may also be coupled by mutual inductance. In this case energy is transferred from one mesh to another by means of a changing magnetic field which is common to both meshes. ▪ This type of coupling might better be called *magnetic coupling*, although the term *mutual inductance* is also commonly used. Coupling of this type is illustrated in (b) of Fig. 24-1. Here M is the mutual inductance.

Circuits coupled by magnetic coupling are extensively used in both the power and communication fields for stepping voltages either up or down. When used for this purpose they are called transformers. Transformers are also used for transferring power from one circuit to another without stepping up or down voltage when a physical connection between the two circuits must be avoided. In such an application the transformers are called isolation transformers.

In communication circuits the transformer is widely used for the purpose of making impedance transformations, stepping up or stepping down the ohmic value of an impedance.

Mutual impedance can be defined in terms of current and voltage by

$$\bar{Z}_{21} = \frac{\bar{V}_2}{\bar{I}_1}.$$

The voltage $\bar{V}_2$ is that induced in mesh 2 by a current $\bar{I}_1$ in mesh 1. The voltage $\bar{V}_2$ is the voltage that would appear at terminals ab when the impedance Z_L is removed, or the mesh 2 is opened as shown in (c) of the figure. The magnitude of this voltage would be that measured by an infinite-impedance voltmeter which replaces Z_L.

In a more general case consisting of many meshes,

$$\bar{Z}_{nm} = \frac{\bar{V}_n}{\bar{I}_m}.$$

Here $\bar{V}_n$ is voltage induced in the nth mesh by current $\bar{I}_m$ in the mth mesh when all meshes are open except the mth and nth, the latter being closed through an infinite-impedance voltmeter used to measure V_n.

3. The Magnetically Coupled Circuit. In the magnetically coupled circuit energy is transferred from one circuit to a second circuit by the magnetic field which is common to the two circuits. This type of coupled circuit is used so extensively that it will be investigated in some detail.

Consider the coupled circuit shown in Fig. 24-2. The voltage drops v_{L_1}, $v_{M_{12}}$, v_{L_2}, and $v_{M_{21}}$ have the same meanings as discussed in Chapter 17. With the sense of the windings and the positive directions for the currents and voltage drops as shown, the following relations exist.

$$v_{L_1} = L_1 \frac{di_1}{dt}, \quad v_{M_{12}} = M \frac{di_2}{dt}, \quad v_{L_2} = L_2 \frac{di_2}{dt}, \quad v_{M_{21}} = M \frac{di_1}{dt}.$$

Applying Kirchhoff's voltage law to the two circuits in Fig. 24-2, the following voltage drop equations are obtained.*

$$v_1 = i_1 R_1 + L_1 \frac{di_1}{dt} + M \frac{di_2}{dt}. \tag{24-1}$$

$$0 = i_2 R_2 + L_2 \frac{di_2}{dt} + M \frac{di_1}{dt} + i_2 R_L + L_L \frac{di_2}{dt} + \frac{1}{C_L} \int i_2 \, dt. \tag{24-2}$$

When the applied voltage varies sinusoidally with time, equations (24-1) and (24-2) may be written in terms of effective values as follows:

$$\bar{V}_1 = \bar{I}_1 R_1 + j\omega L_1 \bar{I}_1 + j\omega M \bar{I}_2, \tag{24-3}$$
$$0 = \bar{I}_2 R_2 + j\omega L_2 \bar{I}_2 + j\omega M \bar{I}_1 + \bar{I}_2 \bar{Z}_L, \tag{24-4}$$

where $\bar{Z}_L$ is the impedance of the load on the coupled circuit. The preceding equations are useful in analysis of the magnetically coupled circuit.

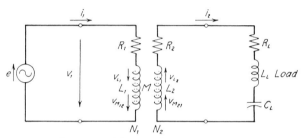

Fig. 24-2. Magnetically coupled circuit.

4. Driving-Point Impedance and Transfer Impedance of a Magnetically Coupled Circuit. Driving-point impedance is defined as the ratio of the voltage applied in a given loop or mesh to the current flowing in that mesh with all other generators in the network replaced with their internal impedances. Thus the driving point impedance $\bar{Z}_D$ for the coupled circuit of Fig. 24-2 is

$$\bar{Z}_D = \frac{\bar{E}}{\bar{I}_1} = \frac{\bar{V}_1}{\bar{I}_1}$$

If equation (24-4) is solved for $\bar{I}_2$ and this value is substituted for $\bar{I}_2$ in equation (24-3), the preceding equation becomes

$$\begin{aligned}
\bar{Z}_D = \frac{\bar{V}_1}{\bar{I}_1} &= R_1 + j\omega L_1 + \frac{\omega^2 M^2}{(R_2 + j\omega L_2) + (R_L \pm jX_L)} \\
&= R_1 + j\omega L_1 + \frac{\omega^2 M^2}{(R_2 + R_L)^2 + (\omega L_2 \pm X_L)^2} \\
&\qquad\qquad [(R_2 + R_L) - j(\omega L_2 \pm X_L)]. \tag{24-5}
\end{aligned}$$

---

* The signs of the $M \, di/dt$ terms in equations (24-1) and (24-2) could have been determined by using the rule given in the footnote on page 212.

In these equations X_L is the reactance of the load, the positive sign before X_L being used when the load is inductive, and the minus sign when it is capacitive.

When circuit 2 is moved far enough away from circuit 1 so that there is no magnetic coupling between the circuits, the driving-point or input impedance to circuit 1 is the self-impedance of circuit 1, that is, $R_1 + j\omega L_1$. When there is coupling between the circuits, the driving-point impedance is given by equation (24-5). Thus it is seen that because of the coupling between circuits 1 and 2, the impedance looking into circuit 1 has changed by the amount

$$\frac{\omega^2 M^2}{(R_2 + R_L)^2 + (\omega L_2 \pm X_L)^2} [(R_2 + R_L) - j(\omega L_2 \pm X_L)]$$

This effect will be discussed in more detail in the following section.

The transfer impedance between meshes m and n of a network is defined as the ratio of the voltage applied in mesh m to the current in mesh n with all other generators in the network replaced by their internal impedances. Referring to Fig. 24-2, the transfer impedance $\bar{Z}_{T_{12}}$ for circuits 1 and 2 is

$$\bar{Z}_{T_{12}} = \frac{\bar{E}}{\bar{I}_2} = \frac{\bar{V}_1}{\bar{I}_2}.$$

The above equation can be evaluated in terms of the circuit constants by solving equation (24-4) for $\bar{I}_1$ and then substituting this value in equation (24-3). When this is done,

$$\bar{Z}_{T_{12}} = \frac{\bar{V}_1}{\bar{I}_2} = j\omega M + j\frac{[(R_2 + R_L) + j(\omega L_2 \pm X_L)](R_1 + j\omega L_1)}{\omega M}, \quad (24\text{-}6)$$

where $\pm X_L$ has the same meaning as used previously.

Consider now the conditions which exist when the source in Fig. 24-2 is taken out of circuit 1 and inserted in circuit 2, circuit 1 remaining closed. In a manner similar to that used above it can be shown that the transfer impedance $\bar{Z}_{T_{21}}$ between circuits 2 and 1 is the same as $\bar{Z}_{T_{12}}$. It should be noted, however, that the driving-point impedances are not the same.

At this point the question might be raised as to the effect of choosing the positive direction of i_2 opposite to that shown in Fig. 24-2, making the mmfs due to the positive currents buck instead of aid on the common magnetic path. Using this positive direction for i_2 and proceeding as before, it will be found that the driving-point impedance $\bar{Z}_D$ will be the same as given in equation (24-5), but the transfer impedance $\bar{Z}_{T_{12}}$ will be equal to minus one times the right-hand side of equation (24-6). A little thought will show that is as it should be.

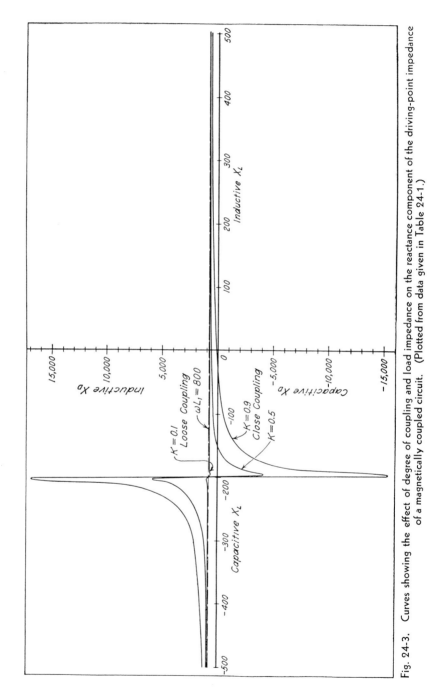

Fig. 24-3. Curves showing the effect of degree of coupling and load impedance on the reactance component of the driving-point impedance of a magnetically coupled circuit. (Plotted from data given in Table 24-1.)

5. Effect of Load Impedance on the Driving-Point Impedance of a Magnetically Coupled Circuit. The term

$$\frac{\omega^2 M^2}{(R_2 + R_L)^2 + (\omega L_2 \pm X_L)^2} [(R_2 + R_L) - j(\omega L_2 \pm X_L)]$$

of the driving-point impedance equation is often called the impedance of circuit 2 reflected into circuit 1, or more simply, the reflected impedance of circuit 2. It is important to note that it is the *entire* impedance of circuit 2 which is reflected into circuit 1 and not only the load impedance. Failure to keep this fact in mind has resulted in considerable confusion regarding the effect of a load impedance on the driving-point impedance of a magnetically coupled circuit. It must also be remembered that the reflected impedance of circuit 2 must be added to $R_1 + j\omega L_1$ to obtain the driving-point impedance.

Typical curves showing the variation of the reactance component of the driving-point impedance of a coupled circuit with changes in the magnitude and kind of load reactance are given in Fig. 24-3. In studying the shape of these curves, it will be convenient to use a driving-point reactance equation which has a slightly changed form from that taken directly from equation (24-5). Writing from equation (24-5),

$$\pm jX_D = j\left[\omega L_1 - \frac{\omega^2 M^2}{(R_2 + R_L)^2 + (\omega L_2 \pm X_L)^2} (\omega L_2 \pm X_L) \right].$$

This can be altered to

$$\pm jX_D = j\left[\omega L_1 - \omega L_1 \frac{K^2 \omega L_2}{(R_2 + R_L)^2 + (\omega L_2 \pm X_L)^2} (\omega L_2 \pm X_L) \right]$$

$$(24\text{-}7)$$

where K is the coefficient of coupling and has a value $K = M/\sqrt{L_1 L_2}$ as given by equation (17-30).

An examination of equation (24-7) shows that when the load reactance X_L is inductive, the driving-point reactance X_D can be only inductive. This is true regardless of the magnitude of the load reactance or the coefficient of coupling. For very large values of inductive X_L, the reactance of circuit 2 reflected into circuit 1 is so small that X_D approaches ωL_1 in value. These statements are illustrated graphically in Fig. 24-3.

Until stated otherwise, consider that the coefficient of coupling is nearly unity. A study of equation (24-7) shows that if the load reactance is capacitive and is gradually increased from a very small value, X_D will be inductive until the capacitive X_L becomes large enough to make the reflected reactance of circuit 2 equal to ωL_1, thus making $X_D = 0$. This value of capacitive X_L can be found by setting

$$\frac{K^2 \omega L_2}{(R_2 + R_L)^2 + (\omega L_2 - X_L)^2} (\omega L_2 - X_L) = 1$$

and solving for X_L. This procedure gives

$$X_{L_{(X_D=0)}} = \frac{\omega L_2 (2 - K^2) \pm \sqrt{K^4 \omega^2 L_2^2 - 4(R_2 + R_L)^2}}{2}, \quad (24\text{-}8)$$

where the root involving the minus sign is the one under consideration. This value of X_L for a given curve in Fig. 24-3 is the smaller of the two values of capacitive reactance which make $X_D = 0$.

Further examination of equation (24-7) shows that if the capacitive load reactance is slightly greater than the above value which made $X_D = 0$, the driving-point reactance becomes capacitive. If the capacitive X_L continues to increase in value, the capacitive X_D will go through a maximum value. The value of the capacitive X_L which results in the maximum value of X_D can be determined by differentiating equation (24-7) with respect to X_L (using only the minus sign before X_L), equating the derivative to zero, and solving for X_L. When this is done it will be found that

$$X_{L_{(X_{D_{\max}})}} = \omega L_2 \pm (R_2 + R_L), \quad (24\text{-}9)$$

the minus sign being applicable for the condition under discussion. The value of $X_{D_{\max}}$ can be found by substituting the capacitive load reactance given by equation (24-9) in equation (24-7). This gives

$$\pm j X_{D_{\max}} = j \left[\omega L_1 \pm \omega L_1 \frac{K^2 \omega L_2}{2(R_2 + R_L)} \right], \quad (24\text{-}10)$$

where the minus sign is the one being considered at present.

If the capacitive X_L is increased from the value which makes the capacitive X_D a maximum, X_D decreases and remains capacitive until it becomes zero again, when the capacitive X_L is equal to the value determined by using the positive sign before the radical in equation (24-8). Any further increase in the value of the capacitive X_L results in X_D becoming inductive. The inductive X_D will increase with increase in the capacitive X_L and become a maximum when X_L is equal to the value obtained by using the plus sign in equation (24-9). The magnitude of this inductive $X_{D_{\max}}$ is given by equation (24-10) when the plus sign is used. It should be noted that the capacitive load reactances which produce the maximum values of the driving-point reactance are independent of the coefficient of coupling, whereas the magnitudes of $X_{D_{\max}}$ depend on the coefficient of coupling. These facts are also shown by the curves of Fig. 24-3.

As shown in Fig. 24-3, continuous increase in the capacitive X_L above the value $[\omega L_2 + (R_2 + R_L)]$ results in decreasing values of inductive X_D, the magnitude of X_D approaching ωL_1 in the limit. This can be seen from equation (24-7), since the term

$$\frac{K^2 \omega L_2}{(R_2 + R_L)^2 + (\omega L_2 - X_L)^2}$$

decreases faster than the term $(\omega L_2 - X_L)$ increases for values of capacitive X_L greater than $[\omega L_2 + (R_2 + R_L)]$.

With very loose coupling, K very small, the magnitude of the reactance of circuit 2 which is reflected into circuit 1 is very small. The driving-point reactance X_D is therefore inductive for all values of load reactance X_L, whether inductive or capacitive. This is illustrated by the curve for loose coupling in Fig. 24-3. The largest value that K can have and X_D be inductive for all values of inductive or capacitive X_L can be determined by setting

$$\left[\omega L_1 - \omega L_1 \frac{K^2 \omega L_2}{2(R_2 + R_L)} \right]$$

from equation (24-10) equal to zero and solving for K. This will give

$$K = \sqrt{\frac{2(R_2 + R_L)}{\omega L_2}}. \tag{24-11}$$

In Fig. 24-3 it will be observed that all the curves intersect at a common point. At this point the driving-point reactance for all curves is inductive and is equal to ωL_1, regardless of the coefficient of coupling. Under this condition circuit 2 is resonant and the reactance of circuit 2 reflected into circuit 1 is zero. The capacitive load reactance which produces resonance in circuit 2 can be seen from equation (24-7) to be

$$X_{L_R} = \omega L_2. \tag{24-12}$$

The effect of load impedance on the driving-point impedance of a magnetically coupled circuit is further shown in Table 24-1, where calculated values of the driving-point impedance are tabulated for various load impedances and coefficients of coupling. It will be instructive to study the variation in the resistance component of the driving-point impedance as well as the reactance component.

TABLE 24-1

VARIATION OF DRIVING-POINT IMPEDANCE WITH LOAD IMPEDANCE AND COEF-
FICIENT OF COUPLING FOR THE COUPLED CIRCUIT OF FIG. 24-2 (when $R_1 =$
16 ohms, $R_2 = 4$ ohms, $\omega L_1 = 800$ ohms, and $\omega L_2 = 200$ ohms)

Load Impedance $\bar{Z}_L$	Driving-Point Impedance $\bar{Z}_D$		
	$K = 0.9$	$K = 0.5$	$K = 0.1$
$0 + j500$	$17.1 + j615.1$	$16.3 + j742.9$	$16.0 + j797.7$
$0 + j100$	$21.8 + j368$	$17.8 + j666.7$	$16.1 + j794.7$
$0 + j50$	$24.3 + j284$	$18.6 + j640.1$	$16.1 + j793.6$
$0 + j10$	$27.7 + j183$	$19.6 + j609.5$	$16.1 + j792.4$
$0 + j0$	$29.0 + j152$	$20.0 + j600$	$16.2 + j792$
$0 - j10$	$30.4 + j118$	$20.4 + j589.5$	$16.2 + j791.6$
$0 - j50$	$39.0 - j63.4$	$23.1 + j533.5$	$16.3 + j789.3$
$0 - j100$	$67.8 - j493.9$	$32.0 + j400.6$	$16.6 + j784$
$0 - j150$	$222 - j1776$	$79.6 + j5.1$	$18.5 + j768.2$
$0 - j190$	$4484 - j10,360$	$1396 - j2650$	$71.2 + j622.1$
$0 - j194$	$9984 - j14,150$	$3092 - j3815$	$139.1 + j615.4$
$0 - j196$	$16,216 - j15,400$	$5016 - j4200$	$216 + j600$
$0 - j200$	$32,416 + j800$	$10,016 + j800$	$416 + j800$
$0 - j204$	$16,216 + j17,000$	$5016 + j5800$	$216 + j1000$
$0 - j206$	$9984 + j15,750$	$3092 + j5420$	$139.1 + j984.6$
$0 - j210$	$4484 + j11,980$	$1396 + j4250$	$71.2 + j938$
$0 - j250$	$222 + j3375$	$79.6 + j1595$	$18.5 + j831.8$
$0 - j300$	$67.8 + j2096$	$32.0 + j1200$	$16.6 + j816$
$0 - j500$	$21.8 + j1232$	$17.8 + j933.2$	$16.1 + j805.3$

6. Equivalent Circuits of a Magnetically Coupled Circuit. For convenience in circuit analysis it is many times desirable to replace a magnetically coupled circuit by an equivalent circuit which has only direct coupling. Two such equivalent circuits will now be developed.

Equivalent Circuit 1. Refer to equations (24-3) and (24-4). If $\bar{I}_1 j\omega M$ and $-\bar{I}_1 j\omega M$ are added to the right-hand side of equation (24-3) and $\bar{I}_2 j\omega M$ and $-\bar{I}_2 j\omega M$ are added to the right-hand side of equation (24-4), the value of each equation remains unchanged. When this is done

$$\bar{V}_1 = \bar{I}_1[R_1 + j\omega(L_1 - M)] + \bar{I}_1 j\omega M + \bar{I}_2 j\omega M. \tag{24-13}$$
$$0 = \bar{I}_2[R_2 + j\omega(L_2 - M)] + \bar{I}_2 j\omega M + \bar{I}_1 j\omega M + \bar{I}_2 \bar{Z}_L. \tag{24-14}$$

Equations (24-13) and (24-14) are the same as the equations which are obtained by applying Kirchhoff's voltage law to the two meshes of the circuit shown in Fig. 24-4. Therefore the direct-coupled circuit of Fig. 24-4 is an equivalent circuit for the magnetically coupled circuit of Fig. 24-2. Since the $\bar{V}_1$, $\bar{I}_1$, and $\bar{I}_2$ of the equivalent circuit are the $\bar{V}_1$, $\bar{I}_1$, and $\bar{I}_2$ of the original magnetically coupled circuit, the driving-point impedance and the transfer impedance of the equivalent circuit are equal, respectively, to the driving-point impedance and transfer impedance of the original circuit. This can be verified by calculating the driving-point impedance and the transfer impedance of the equivalent circuit and comparing the results with equations (24-5) and (24-6), respectively.

If one of the self inductances L_1 or L_2 is less than the mutual inductance M, one of the $\omega(L - M)$ reactances of the equivalent circuit becomes a negative quantity. This does not, however, represent a capacitive reactance, since the magnitude of the reactance is directly proportional to frequency. Although this condition makes it difficult to visualize the physics involved, it does not present any difficulty in the mathematical solution of the equivalent circuit. Because of the

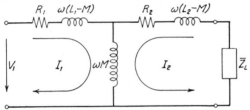

Fig. 24-4. Equivalent circuit of the magnetically coupled circuit shown in Fig. 24-2.

negative reactance, the equivalent circuit is sometimes referred to as the *fictitious inductance* equivalent circuit.

The equivalent circuit of Fig. 24-4 is very useful where the self-inductance and mutual inductance are constant as in air-core transformers and in iron-core transformers which are operated over the straight-line portion of their magnetization curves and which have negligible core losses. It should be apparent that when using the equivalent circuit, the positive directions for I_1 and I_2 may be arbitrarily chosen.

Equivalent Circuit 2. In the analysis which follows, a given actual flux will be considered to be replaced by an equivalent flux. An equivalent flux is assumed to link all the turns of the winding involved and produce the same total flux linkages as the actual flux produces with the winding. In the equations used in the analysis, all fluxes will be expressed in webers (1 weber $\equiv 10^8$ maxwells), currents in amperes, and inductances in henrys.

Refer to Fig. 24-2. Let ϕ_1 be the flux produced when a current i_1, flows in the N_1 turns of winding 1 with winding 2 open-circuited.

Therefore the self-inductance of winding 1 is $L_1 = N_1\phi_1/i_1$. Of the total flux ϕ_1 linking winding 1, a portion $k_1\phi_1$ links winding 2. The flux $k_1\phi_1$ is called the mutual flux since it links both windings, the mutual inductance being $M = N_2k_1\phi_1/i_1$. The difference between the total flux of winding 1 and the mutual flux, $\phi_1 - k_1\phi_1$, is called the leakage flux of winding 1. The leakage inductance of winding 1 is then $S_1 = N_1(1 - k_1)\phi_1/i_1$. The relationship between the various inductances can be determined as follows:

$$L_1 = \frac{N_1\phi_1}{i_1} = \frac{N_1k_1\phi_1}{i_1} + \frac{N_1(1 - k_1)\phi_1}{i_1}$$

$$= \frac{N_1}{N_2}\frac{N_2k_1\phi_1}{i_1} + \frac{N_1(1 - k_1)\phi_1}{i_1} = \frac{N_1}{N_2}M + S_1 \qquad (24\text{-}15)$$

and similarly

$$L_2 = \frac{N_2}{N_1}M + S_2, \qquad\qquad\qquad (24\text{-}16)$$

where S_2 is the leakage inductance of winding 2.

Substituting the above values of L_1 and L_2 in equations (24-3) and (24-4) yields

$$V_1 = \bar{I}_1\left[R_1 + j\omega\left(\frac{N_1}{N_2}M + S_1\right)\right] + \bar{I}_2 j\omega M.$$

$$0 = \bar{I}_2\left[R_2 + j\omega\left(\frac{N_2}{N_1}M + S_2\right)\right] + \bar{I}_1 j\omega M + \bar{I}_2 \bar{Z}_L.$$

These equations can be changed to the following forms by rearrangement of both equations and multiplying both sides of the second equation by N_1/N_2.

$$\bar{V}_1 = \bar{I}_1[R_1 + j\omega S_1] + \bar{I}_1 j\omega\frac{N_1}{N_2}M + \frac{N_2}{N_1}\bar{I}_2 j\omega\frac{N_1}{N_2}M. \quad (24\text{-}17)$$

$$0 = \frac{N_2}{N_1}\bar{I}_2\left[\left(\frac{N_1}{N_2}\right)^2 R_2 + j\omega\left(\frac{N_1}{N_2}\right)^2 S_2\right] + \frac{N_2}{N_1}\bar{I}_2 j\omega\frac{N_1}{N_2}M$$

$$+ \bar{I}_1 j\omega\frac{N_1}{N_2}M + \frac{N_2}{N_1}\bar{I}_2\left(\frac{N_1}{N_2}\right)^2 \bar{Z}_L. \quad (24\text{-}18)$$

Equations (24-17) and (24-18) are the same as the Kirchhoff voltage law equations for the circuit in Fig. 24-5. The direct-coupled circuit of Fig. 24-5 is then an equivalent circuit for the magnetically coupled circuit of Fig. 24-2.

Since the $\bar{V}_1$ and $\bar{I}_1$ of the equivalent circuit are the $\bar{V}_1$ and $\bar{I}_1$ of the original magnetically coupled circuit, the driving-point impedances of the two circuits are the same. The transfer impedances of the two circuits, however, are not equal, since the current in the second mesh of the equivalent circuit is $\frac{N_2}{N_1}\bar{I}_2$, while in the original coupled circuit it is $\bar{I}_2$. It should also be noted that the load impedance in the equivalent circuit is $(N_1/N_2)^2\bar{Z}_L$ and the voltage across the load is $\frac{N_1}{N_2}\bar{I}_2\bar{Z}_L$, while for the coupled circuit the load impedance is $\bar{Z}_L$ and voltage across it is $\bar{I}_2\bar{Z}_L$. The equivalent circuit of Fig. 24-5 can be modified to make the terminal conditions at the load the same as in the original coupled circuit. This has been done in Fig. 24-6 by the use of an ideal transformer having a turn ratio equal to N_1/N_2, the turn ratio of the original coupled circuit.

An ideal transformer has zero losses, perfect coupling, and self-inductances which are infinitely large but have a finite ratio. It is

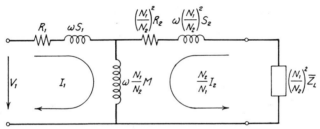

Fig. 24-5.   Equivalent circuit of the magnetically coupled circuit shown in Fig. 24-2.

shown in the next section that an impedance $\bar{Z}_L$ connected to the N_2 winding of an ideal transformer appears at the terminals of the N_1 winding as $(N_1/N_2)^2\bar{Z}_L$. For such a transformer the terminal volts per turn of both windings are the same, and the ampere turns of both windings are the same. Thus when the voltage across the N_1 winding in Fig. 24-6 is $\frac{N_1}{N_2}\bar{I}_2\bar{Z}_L$, the voltage across the N_2 winding is $\bar{I}_2\bar{Z}_L$; and when the current in the N_1 winding is $\frac{N_2}{N_1}\bar{I}_2$ the current in the N_2 winding is $\bar{I}_2$. Therefore the terminal conditions for the load impedance in Fig. 24-6 are the same as for the original circuit. All the resistances, reactances, voltages, and currents in Figs. 24-5 and 24-6 which are multiplied by a factor involving the ratio of turns are said to be referred to the N_1 winding of the original coupled circuit.

The equivalent circuits of Figs. 24-5 and 24-6 are usually called *leakage-reactance* equivalent circuits. In a slightly modified form these equivalent circuits are widely used in the field of iron-core transformers. This is because the leakage inductances S_1 and S_2 are nearly constant, even though the self-inductances and mutual inductances vary cyclically with the magnetic flux in the iron core. The leakage inductances are nearly constant, since the paths for the leakage fluxes are largely in air.

The core loss of the iron-core transformer is taken into account in the equivalent circuit by connecting a resistance in parallel with the $\omega \dfrac{N_1}{N_2} M$ branch in Fig. 24-5 or 24-6. The magnitude of this resistance is such that, for a given applied voltage and load impedance, the power loss in the resistance is equal to the core loss of the transformer. This

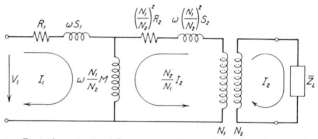

Fig. 24-6.   Equivalent circuit of the magnetically coupled circuit shown in Fig. 24-2.

resistance branch is usually called the core-loss branch, conductance branch, or G branch of the equivalent circuit.

The $\omega \dfrac{N_1}{N_2} M$ branch is the magnetizing branch, since it carries a current equal to the current which produces the mutual flux in the actual transformer.* For an iron-core transformer this branch is represented by a susceptance B. The value of B is such that, for a given applied voltage and load impedance, the effective value of the sinusoidal current which it carries is equal to the effective value of the actual magnetizing current of the iron-core transformer. The actual magnetizing current is not sinusoidal when a sinusoidal voltage is impressed on an iron-core transformer, since the magnetization curve of the core is not a straight line. The values of G and B are reasonably constant over the range of flux densities which occurs in the normal operation of an iron-core power transformer.

7. Impedance Transformation by a Magnetically Coupled Circuit. An ideal transformer is a coupled circuit in which (1) the losses are zero, (2) the coupling is perfect, and (3) the self-inductances are infinitely large but have a finite ratio. On the basis of conditions

---

* See equation (24-15).

(1) and (2), $R_1 = R_2 = 0$ and $M = \sqrt{L_1 L_2}$. Substituting these values in equation (24-5) produces the following result:

$$\bar{Z}_D = j\omega L_1 + \frac{\omega L_1 \omega L_2}{j\omega L_2 + \bar{Z}_L} = \frac{j\omega L_1 \bar{Z}_L}{j\omega L_2 + \bar{Z}_L}.$$

Applying condition (3) to the above equation,

$$\bar{Z}_D = \frac{j\omega L_1 \bar{Z}_L}{j\omega L_2} = \frac{L_1}{L_2} \bar{Z}_L.$$

Equations (17–27), (17–28), (17–29), and (17–30) show that $L_1/L_2 = (N_1/N_2)^2$ when $K = 1$. Therefore the preceding equation may be written

$$\bar{Z}_D = \left(\frac{N_1}{N_2}\right)^2 \bar{Z}_L. \tag{24-19}$$

Equation (24-19) shows that an ideal transformer can be used to transform an impedance from one magnitude to another without changing the phase angle of the impedance. With the impedance connected to the N_2 winding, the magnitude transformation is directly proportional to $(N_1/N_2)^2$.

Although the ideal transformer cannot be exactly realized in practice, it is closely approached by the iron-core transformers used for transformation of impedances at audio frequencies. These transformers usually have efficiencies of 90% or more and coefficients of coupling of 0.97 or larger. Hence conditions (1) and (2) are closely approximated. Condition (3) is met by selecting a transformer which has winding reactances ωL_1 and ωL_2 which are very large compared with Z_L. It should be noted that it is possible to select many transformers having the proper ratio N_1/N_2, but that of these transformers only those which have very large winding reactances compared with Z_L will be satisfactory. Thus the proper ratio N_1/N_2 is a necessary but not sufficient condition in the selection of a transformer for an impedance transformation.

Laboratory Problem No. 24-1

DRIVING-POINT AND TRANSFER IMPEDANCES OF A MAGNETICALLY COUPLED CIRCUIT

Laboratory

Set up a coupled circuit consisting of two inductance coils placed to give maximum coupling. Make certain that the coils remain in this position throughout the test. Designate one coil as 1 and the other as 2.

1. Obtain data from which the effective resistances, self-inductances, and mutual inductance of the coupled circuit can be determined.

2. Connect a resistor to the terminals of coil 2. Apply an a-c voltage, of the magnitude and frequency designated by the instructor, to the terminals of coil 1. Obtain data from which the vector expression for each of the following quantities can be determined:

(a) Voltage impressed on coil 1, this being taken as the reference vector.
(b) Current in coil 1.
(c) Current in coil 2.
(d) Voltage across the terminals of coil 2.

3. Repeat **2,** using an inductance coil as the load on coil 2.

4. Repeat **2,** using a condenser load which has a capacitance such that the driving-point impedance of the coupled circuit will be capacitive.

5. Repeat **2,** using a condenser load which has a capacitance such that the driving-point impedance of the coupled circuit will be inductive.

Report

A. From the data obtained in **2, 3, 4,** and **5,** determine the driving-point impedance $\bar{Z}_D$ and the transfer impedance $\bar{Z}_{T_{12}}$ of the coupled circuit for each of the loads used.

B. From the data obtained in **2, 3, 4,** and **5,** determine the load impedance $\bar{Z}_L$ for each of the loads used.

C. From the data obtained in **1,** determine the effective resistances, self-inductances, and mutual inductance of the coupled circuit.

D. Using the constants of the coupled circuit and each load as determined in **B** and **C,** calculate the driving-point impedance $\bar{Z}_D$ and the transfer impedance $\bar{Z}_{T_{12}}$ of the coupled circuit for each load by means of the following:

(1) Equations for $\bar{Z}_D$ and $\bar{Z}_{T_{12}}$.
(2) The equivalent circuit of Fig. 24-4.
(3) The equivalent circuit of Fig. 24-5.

E. Make up a table showing comparative values of $\bar{Z}_D$ and $\bar{Z}_{T_{12}}$ as determined in **A** and **D.** Discuss any significant discrepancies.

Laboratory Problem No. 24-2
IMPEDANCE TRANSFORMATION BY A MAGNETICALLY COUPLED CIRCUIT

Laboratory

Designate one winding of an iron-core transformer as N_1, or the primary, and the other as N_2, or the secondary. Record the ratio of transformation, N_1/N_2.

1. Obtain data from which the d-c resistances of the primary and of the secondary can be determined.

2. (a) Using the voltage and frequency designated by the instructor, obtain data for determining the magnitude of the primary impedance with the secondary on open circuit.

(b) Using the same voltage per turn as in (a), obtain data for determining the magnitude of the secondary impedance with the primary on open circuit.

3. Connect a variable resistor to the secondary. With the voltage impressed on the primary maintained constant at the value used in **2**(a), reduce the resistance from a value about equal to the self-impedance of the secondary, as determined in **2**(b), to as small a value as can be used without exceeding rated current of either the primary or the secondary. At each step, obtain data for determining the magnitude of the primary input impedance and the magnitude of the load impedance.

Report

A. From the data obtained in **1** and **2** calculate:

(1) The d-c resistance of the primary and the secondary.

(2) The magnitude of the primary self-impedance and of the secondary self-impedance.

B. (1) From the data obtained in **3**, plot a curve of primary input impedance vs load impedance.

(2) On the same set of coordinate axes as used in (1), plot the curve showing the relation $Z_{\text{input}} = (N_1/N_2)^2 Z_{\text{load}}$ vs load impedance.

C. On a second set of coordinate axes, replot the curves of **B** for the range where the two curves do not differ by more than 5 per cent.

D. Develop the equation for the driving-point or input impedance of a magnetically coupled circuit which is loaded by a resistor, and which has a coefficient of coupling of 1.

E. By means of the equation developed in **D** and the results of **A**, explain any discrepancies between the two curves plotted in **B**.

CHAPTER 25
NETWORK THEOREMS

THERE are a number of circuit theorems that are useful in circuit analysis and synthesis. Only those most commonly used are treated in this chapter, namely: equivalent T and π networks, superposition theorem, maximum power transfer, equivalent constant voltage generator (Thevenin's theorem), equivalent constant current generator (Norton's theorem), and reciprocity theorem.

In what follows, all impedance elements are considered to be passive, linear, and bilateral.

1. Equivalent T and π networks. In Fig. (25-1) are shown two 4-terminal networks. One is a T, or wye, network, shown in (a); the other is a π, or delta, network, shown in (b). Given the values of

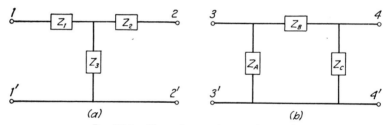

Fig. 25-1.   Three-element 4-terminal networks.

the impedances of the elements in one of these networks, the values of the impedances of the elements of the other can be evaluated so that the second network will be identically equivalent to the first at all pairs of terminals.

To determine the relationships between the impedances of the T network and those of the equivalent π network, let Z_{mn} represent the impedance at the terminals mn with all other terminals free, where m and n correspond to any pair of terminals 1, 1', 2, and 2' of the T network or 3, 3', 4, and 4' of the π network. If the two networks are to be equivalent, the following relationships must hold:

$$\bar{Z}_{11'} = \bar{Z}_{33'}. \tag{25-1}$$
$$\bar{Z}_{12} = \bar{Z}_{34}. \tag{25-2}$$
$$\bar{Z}_{22'} = \bar{Z}_{44'}. \tag{25-3}$$

350

From an inspection of the networks it can be seen that

$$\bar{Z}_{11'} = \bar{Z}_1 + \bar{Z}_3. \tag{25-4}$$

$$\bar{Z}_{12} = \bar{Z}_1 + \bar{Z}_2. \tag{25-5}$$

$$\bar{Z}_{22'} = \bar{Z}_2 + \bar{Z}_3. \tag{25-6}$$

$$\bar{Z}_{33'} = \frac{\bar{Z}_A(\bar{Z}_B + \bar{Z}_C)}{\bar{Z}_A + \bar{Z}_B + \bar{Z}_C}. \tag{25-7}$$

$$Z_{34} = \frac{\bar{Z}_B(\bar{Z}_A + \bar{Z}_C)}{\bar{Z}_A + \bar{Z}_B + \bar{Z}_C} \tag{25-8}$$

$$Z_{44'} = \frac{\bar{Z}_C(\bar{Z}_A + \bar{Z}_B)}{\bar{Z}_A + \bar{Z}_B + \bar{Z}_C}. \tag{25-9}$$

Simultaneous solution of equations (25-1), (25-2), and (25-3) after making substitutions from equations (25-4) through (25-9) gives

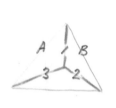

parallel cht.

$$\bar{Z}_1 = \frac{\bar{Z}_A \bar{Z}_B}{\bar{Z}_A + \bar{Z}_B + \bar{Z}_C}. \tag{25-10}$$

fudge factor

$$\bar{Z}_2 = \frac{\bar{Z}_B \bar{Z}_C}{\bar{Z}_A + \bar{Z}_B + \bar{Z}_C}. \tag{25-11}$$

$$\bar{Z}_3 = \frac{\bar{Z}_A \bar{Z}_C}{\bar{Z}_A + \bar{Z}_B + \bar{Z}_C}. \tag{25-12}$$

series cht.

$$\bar{Z}_A = \frac{\bar{Z}_1 \bar{Z}_2 + \bar{Z}_2 \bar{Z}_3 + \bar{Z}_1 \bar{Z}_3}{\bar{Z}_2}. \tag{25-13}$$

$= \bar{Z}_1 + \bar{Z}_3 + \dfrac{\bar{Z}_1 \bar{Z}_3}{\bar{Z}_2}$ *fudge factor*

$$\bar{Z}_B = \frac{\bar{Z}_1 \bar{Z}_2 + \bar{Z}_2 \bar{Z}_3 + \bar{Z}_1 \bar{Z}_3}{\bar{Z}_3}. \tag{25-14}$$

$$\bar{Z}_C = \frac{\bar{Z}_1 \bar{Z}_2 + \bar{Z}_2 \bar{Z}_3 + \bar{Z}_1 \bar{Z}_3}{\bar{Z}_1}. \tag{25-15}$$

Equivalent networks determined by application of the foregoing equations will in general be equivalent for only one frequency. This should be obvious, since the values of $\bar{Z}_1, \bar{Z}_2, \bar{Z}_3, \bar{Z}_A, \bar{Z}_B, \bar{Z}_C$, in the general case, would vary with frequency. However, in a case where the impedances of all the elements of one network vary identically with frequency—pure resistances, pure inductances, or pure capacitances—the equivalent network will maintain its equivalence at all frequencies.

2. Multimesh Network and Its Equivalent T or π Network. The elements of a multimesh network can be rearranged in such a manner that the network can be seen to consist of a number of T and π networks. By a continued process of substituting for the T or π networks their equivalent π or T networks, respectively, the multimesh network can be reduced to a single equivalent T or π four-terminal network having any chosen element of the original multimesh network as the load impedance.* This is illustrated in Fig. 25-2. In (a) is shown a multimesh network; in (b) is shown the equivalent T network. The impedance Z_L has been chosen as the load.

3. Equivalent Three-Element Network from Physical Measurements. When the input and output terminals of a 4-terminal multimesh network are accessible, physical measurements can be made from which the values of the elements of an equivalent T or π network can be calculated. In general the equivalence will exist only with respect to the input terminals and output terminals of the networks. A multimesh 4-terminal network is indicated in (a) of Fig. 25-3. In (b) and (c) of the figure are shown the equivalent T and π networks.

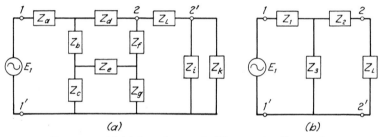

Fig. 25-2.   (a) Multimesh network, (b) equivalent T network.

Here the equivalence means that the driving-point impedances or admittances at terminals MN of all the networks are the same for an impedance of any value connected to terminals XY of each of the networks and vice versa. Similar identities will exist for the transfer impedances or admittances when restricted to the input meshes and output meshes of the equivalent networks. Impedances or admittances at terminals MX, MY, NX, and NY will not in general be the same. In view of the foregoing, one may state that the equivalence exists only with respect to the input terminals MN and output treminals XY of the equivalent networks.

Since the equivalent T and π networks contain but three elements, three independent impedance measurements made on the multimesh network are sufficient for determination of the values of the elements of the equivalent T or π. There are two measurements that can be made

---

* Everitt, W. L., *Communication Engineering*, pp. 44–46. New York: McGraw-Hill Book Company, 1937.

Reed, M. B., *Alternating-Current Circuit Theory*, pp. 351–355. New York: Harper & Brothers, 1948.

conveniently at each of the pairs of terminals MN and XY. These are measurements of the open-circuit impedance and short-circuit impedance. Hence four measurements are possible: Z_{oc_1} the impedance at MN with XY open-circuited, Z_{sc_1} the impedance at MN with XY

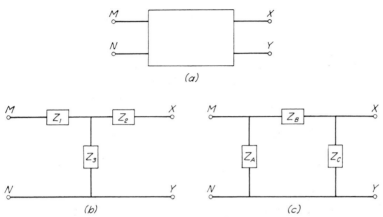

Fig. 25-3. (a) Any multimesh 4-terminal network, (b) equivalent T-network, (c) equivalent π network.

short-circuited, Z_{oc_2} the impedance at XY with MN open-circuited, and Z_{sc_2} the impedance at XY with MN short-circuited. Only three of the four possible impedances are independent, and any three may be chosen.

To determine the equivalent T the following can be used:

$$\bar{Z}_{oc_1} = \bar{Z}_1 + \bar{Z}_3, \qquad (25\text{-}16)$$

$$\bar{Z}_{sc_1} = \bar{Z}_1 + \frac{\bar{Z}_2\bar{Z}_3}{\bar{Z}_2 + \bar{Z}_3}, \qquad (25\text{-}17)$$

$$\bar{Z}_{oc_2} = \bar{Z}_2 + \bar{Z}_3, \qquad (25\text{-}18)$$

where $\bar{Z}_1$, $\bar{Z}_2$, and $\bar{Z}_3$ are the impedances of the three elements of the equivalent T network. Simultaneous solution of these equations yields

$$\bar{Z}_3 = \pm \sqrt{\bar{Z}_{oc_2}(\bar{Z}_{oc_1} - \bar{Z}_{sc_1})}. \qquad (25\text{-}19)$$

$$\bar{Z}_1 = \bar{Z}_{oc_1} - \bar{Z}_3. \qquad (25\text{-}20)$$

$$\bar{Z}_2 = \bar{Z}_{oc_2} - \bar{Z}_3. \qquad (25\text{-}21)$$

With the values of $\bar{Z}_1$, $\bar{Z}_2$, and $\bar{Z}_3$ known, the values of $\bar{Z}_A$, $\bar{Z}_B$, and $\bar{Z}_C$ of the equivalent π network can be determined by use of equations (25-13) through (25-15). These values are

$$\bar{Z}_A = \frac{\bar{Z}_{sc_1}\bar{Z}_{oc_2}}{\bar{Z}_{oc_2} \mp \sqrt{\bar{Z}_{oc_2}(\bar{Z}_{oc_1} - \bar{Z}_{sc_1})}} . \qquad (25\text{-}22)$$

$$\bar{Z}_B = \frac{\bar{Z}_{sc_1}\bar{Z}_{oc_2}}{\pm \sqrt{\bar{Z}_{oc_2}(\bar{Z}_{oc_1} - \bar{Z}_{sc_1})}} . \qquad (25\text{-}23)$$

$$\bar{Z}_C = \frac{\bar{Z}_{sc_1}\bar{Z}_{oc_2}}{\bar{Z}_{oc_1} \mp \sqrt{\bar{Z}_{oc_2}(\bar{Z}_{oc_1} - \bar{Z}_{sc_1})}} \qquad (25\text{-}24)$$

The choice of either the plus or minus sign in equations (25-19) through (25-24) will be determined by the use to which the equivalent T or π is to be put. If the equivalent network is to be physically constructed, the choice must be such as to result in physically realizable impedance elements. It should be noted that if the plus sign is chosen in equation (25-19) the minus signs must be used in equations (25-22 and 25-24) and vice versa. It is entirely possible that physically unrealizable elements will result, regardless of which sign is chosen.

4. Superposition Theorem. In a network containing more than one generator, or source, the current in any branch is the vector sum of

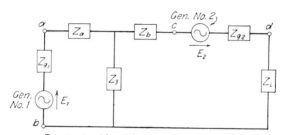

Fig. 25-4. Network containing two generators.

the separate currents which would be obtained if each generator acted alone, all other generated or source voltages being removed at the time, but the internal impedances of all the sources remaining in the circuit. This is the *superposition theorem.*

In Fig. 25-4 is shown a network in which there are two generators supplying current to the impedance Z_L. In the figure Z_{g_1} represents the internal impedance of generator No. 1 connected between terminals ab, and Z_{g_2} represents the internal impedance of generator No. 2 connected between terminals cd. Since these internal impedances stay in the circuit at all times the circuit can be simplified by replacing Z_{g_1} and Z_a by a single impedance Z_1, and also replacing Z_{g_2} and Z_b by a single impedance Z_2. The equivalent circuit then becomes that shown in (a) of Fig. 25-5.

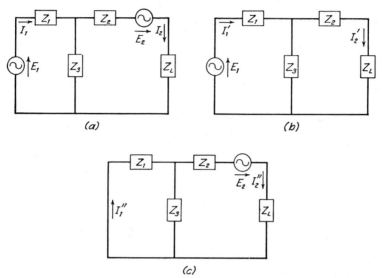

Fig. 25-5. (a) Simplified diagram of network of Fig. 25-4. (b) Circuit illustrating current contribution of E_1. (c) Circuit illustrating current contribution of E_2.

From (a) of the figure,

$$\bar{E}_1 = (\bar{Z}_1 + \bar{Z}_3)\bar{I}_1 - \bar{Z}_3\bar{I}_2$$
$$\bar{E}_2 = -\bar{Z}_3\bar{I}_1 + (\bar{Z}_2 + \bar{Z}_3 + \bar{Z}_L)\bar{I}_2.$$

Simultaneous solution of these two equations yields

$$\bar{I}_2 = \frac{\bar{E}_1\bar{Z}_3}{\begin{vmatrix} \bar{Z}_1 + \bar{Z}_3 & -\bar{Z}_3 \\ -\bar{Z}_3 & \bar{Z}_2 + \bar{Z}_3 + Z_L \end{vmatrix}} + \frac{\bar{E}_2(\bar{Z}_1 + \bar{Z}_3)}{\begin{vmatrix} \bar{Z}_1 + \bar{Z}_3 & -\bar{Z}_3 \\ -\bar{Z}_3 & \bar{Z}_2 + \bar{Z}_3 + Z_L \end{vmatrix}}.$$

(25-25)

From (b) of the figure,

$$\bar{E}_1 = (\bar{Z}_1 + \bar{Z}_3)\bar{I}'_1 - \bar{Z}_3\bar{I}'_2, \qquad 0 = -\bar{Z}_3\bar{I}'_1 + (\bar{Z}_2 + \bar{Z}_3 + \bar{Z}_L)\bar{I}'_2.$$

Solving for $\bar{I}'_2$,

$$\bar{I}'_2 = \frac{\bar{E}_1\bar{Z}_3}{\begin{vmatrix} \bar{Z}_1 + \bar{Z}_3 & -\bar{Z}_3 \\ -\bar{Z}_3 & \bar{Z}_2 + \bar{Z}_3 + \bar{Z}_L \end{vmatrix}}.$$

(25-26)

From (c) of the figure,

$$0 = (\bar{Z}_1 + \bar{Z}_3)\bar{I}''_1 - \bar{Z}_3\bar{I}''_2$$
$$\bar{E}_2 = -\bar{Z}_3\bar{I}''_1 + (\bar{Z}_2 + \bar{Z}_3 + \bar{Z}_L)\bar{I}''_2.$$

Solving for $\bar{I}''_2$,

$$\bar{I}''_2 = \frac{\bar{E}_2(\bar{Z}_1 + \bar{Z}_3)}{\begin{vmatrix} \bar{Z}_1 + \bar{Z}_3 & -\bar{Z}_3 \\ -\bar{Z}_3 & \bar{Z}_2 + \bar{Z}_3 + \bar{Z}_L \end{vmatrix}}. \tag{25-27}$$

By the superposition theorem,

$$\bar{I}_2 = \bar{I}'_2 + \bar{I}''_2. \tag{25-28}$$

It will be noted that when using the values shown in equations (25-26) and (25-27), this sum gives the same value as that shown in equation (25-25), thus proving the superposition theorem.

When the generators, or sources, do not produce currents of the same frequency, the rms value of the current in a particular branch of the network is not obtained by taking the vector sum as has been done in the foregoing. In such a case each separate current produced by each generator is calculated in the same manner as shown above. The rms value of current is now

$$I_2 = \sqrt{(I'_2)^2 + (I''_2)^2}. \tag{25-29}$$

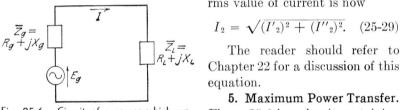

Fig. 25-6. Circuit of a source which supplies power to a load impedance Z_L.

The reader should refer to Chapter 22 for a discussion of this equation.

5. Maximum Power Transfer. Figure 25-6 is a circuit containing a generator, or source, having an internal impedance $\bar{Z}_g = R_g + jX_g$. The generator delivers power to the load impedance $\bar{Z}_L = R_L + jX_L$. The generated voltage is E_g. The power to the load is

$$P = I^2 R_L = \frac{E_g^2 R_L}{(R_g + R_L)^2 + (X_g + X_L)^2}. \tag{25-30}$$

In the general case the load impedance will be complex as is indicated. Any change in either R_L or X_L will cause a change in the current and the power in Z_L. Thus the problem of determining the condition necessary for maximum power transfer from generator to load is that of determining what each of the two components R_L and X_L must be.

Let it first be assumed that only R_L can be varied, X_L remaining constant. The condition for maximum power transfer in such a case can be determined by finding the partial derivative of the power equation (25-30) with respect to R_L and setting it equal to zero.

$$\frac{\partial}{\partial R_L}\left[\frac{E_g^2 R_L}{(R_g + R_L)^2 + (X_g + X_L)^2}\right] = 0.$$

This leads to the equation

$$R_g{}^2 - R_L{}^2 + (X_g + X_L)^2 = 0. \qquad (25\text{-}31)$$

The next step is to assume that R_L remains constant and that only X_L can be varied. The condition for maximum power transfer under this assumption is determined by now finding the partial derivative of the power equation with respect to X_L and setting it equal to zero.

$$\frac{\partial}{\partial X_L}\left[\frac{E_g{}^2 R_L}{(R_g + R_L)^2 + (X_g + X_L)^2}\right] = 0.$$

The solution of this gives

$$X_g + X_L = 0 \qquad (25\text{-}32)$$
or
$$X_L = -X_g. \qquad (25\text{-}33)$$

So for maximum transfer of power, the reactance component of the load impedance must be equal to but of opposite kind to that of the generator. Now after substituting equation (25-32) for $(X_g + X_L)^2$ in equation (25-31), the latter becomes

$$R_g{}^2 - R_L{}^2 = 0$$
or
$$R_L = R_g. \qquad (25\text{-}34)$$

From the foregoing it is seen that for maximum transfer of power the load impedance must be the conjugate of the internal impedance of the generator.

6. **Condition for Maximum Power Transfer When the Magnitude of the Load Impedance Can Be Varied but Not Its Angle.** Referring to Fig. 25-6 let it be assumed that the magnitude Z_L of the load impedance $\bar{Z}_L = Z_L/\phi$ can be varied without changing ϕ. This being the case,

$$\bar{Z}_L = R_L + jX_L$$
and
$$R_L = Z_L \cos \phi = AZ_L, \qquad (25\text{-}35)$$
$$X_L = Z_L \sin \phi = BZ_L, \qquad (25\text{-}36)$$

where $A = \cos \phi$ and $B = \sin \phi$ are constants because of the premise already made.

The generator has an impedance $\bar{Z}_g$ which is fixed.

$$\bar{Z}_g = Z_g/\theta = R_g + jX_g$$
and
$$R_g = Z_g \cos \theta = CZ_g, \qquad (25\text{-}37)$$
$$X_g = Z_g \sin \theta = DZ_g, \qquad (25\text{-}38)$$

where $C = \cos \theta$ and $D = \sin \theta$, and both are constants.

The power transferred to the load impedance as given by equation (25-30) now becomes

$$P = \frac{E_g{}^2 A Z_L}{(CZ_g + AZ_L)^2 + (DZ_g + BZ_L)^2}.$$

To determine condition for maximum P the differentiation is done with respect to Z_L, since Z_g is assumed to remain constant; and the result is set equal to zero.

$$\frac{dP}{dZ_L} =$$
$$\frac{E_g{}^2 A\{[(CZ_g + AZ_L)^2 + (DZ_g + BZ_L)^2] - 2Z_L[A(CZ_g + AZ_L) + B(DZ_g + BZ_L)]\}}{[(CZ_g + AZ_L)^2 + (DZ_g + BZ_L)^2]^2}$$
$$= 0. \quad (25\text{-}39)$$

Solution of this equation yields

$$(A^2 + B^2)Z_L{}^2 = (C^2 + D^2)Z_g{}^2,$$

but
$$A^2 + B^2 = \cos^2\phi + \sin^2\phi = 1$$

and
$$C^2 + D^2 = \cos^2\theta + \sin^2\theta = 1, \quad (25\text{-}40)$$

so
$$Z_L = Z_g.$$

This is the condition necessary in order that maximum power shall be transferred from a generator having a fixed impedance $\bar{Z}_g$ when the magnitude Z_L of the load impedance can be changed without changing its angle.

An example of an impedance which can have its magnitude changed without changing its angle is a pure resistance. In Chapter 24 it is shown that an ideal transformer can be used to change the magnitude of a impedance without changing its angle.

7. Thevenin's Theorem. A network which consists of linear, bilateral impedances and which contains one or more generators, all of which generate voltages of the same frequency, can be replaced at any pair of terminals XY by an equivalent generator which generates a voltage E_{oc} and has an internal impedance Z_{XY}. The generated voltage E_{oc} is the open-circuit voltage at the terminals XY. The impedance Z_{XY} is the impedance looking back into the network from the terminals XY when all the generators in the network have been removed and have been replaced by impedances equal to the internal impedances of the generators which they replace.

In order to illustrate this theorem, the networks shown in Figure 25-7 will be used.

It is desired to replace the network to the left of terminals XY in (a) of the figure by an equivalent generator in accordance with the foregoing theorem. In this circuit E_{g_1} and E_{g_2} are generated voltages of the same frequencies, and Z_{g_1} and Z_{g_2} are the internal impedances of the generators.

To determine E_{oc}, the generated voltage of the equivalent generator, it is necessary to remove impedance Z_L, so terminals XY are open-circuited as shown in (b) of the figure. As indicated in the figure, E_{oc} is the voltage at these terminals under this open-circuit condition.

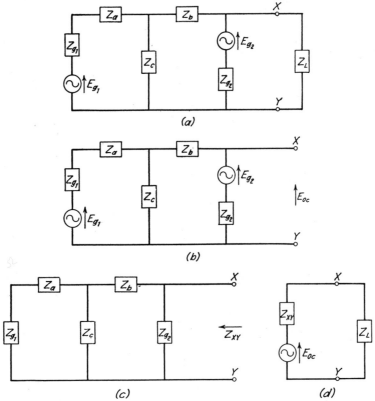

Fig. 25-7. (a) Multimesh circuit containing two generators. (b) Same as (a) but with load impedance Z_L removed. (c) Same as (b) but with generated voltage reduced to zero. (d) Circuit containing load impedance Z_L and the Thevenin's generator which is equivalent to the active network to the left of terminals XY in (a).

The impedance Z_{XY} of the equivalent generator is the impedance at terminals XY of the circuit shown in (c) of the figure. It will be noted that the generated voltages have been removed but that the internal impedances of the generators remain in the circuit.

In (d) of the figure is shown the circuit which is equivalent to that shown in (a) after that part of the circuit to the left of terminals XY has been replaced by its equivalent voltage generator.

For a complex network containing but a single generator, or source, the validity of Thevenin's theorem is readily proved. The portion of a complex network between the generator and the load impedance of such a network can be replaced by an equivalent T network as is shown in Fig. 25-2. This being the case, the theorem can be proved by use of the equivalent circuit as shown in (a) of Fig. 25-8. Here the impedance of the generator is included in Z_1.

Solving for $\bar{I}_L$ in this circuit,

$$\bar{I}_L = \frac{\bar{E}\bar{Z}_3}{\left[\bar{Z}_1 + \dfrac{\bar{Z}_3(\bar{Z}_2 + \bar{Z}_L)}{\bar{Z}_2 + \bar{Z}_3 + \bar{Z}_L}\right][\bar{Z}_2 + \bar{Z}_3 + \bar{Z}_L]}$$

$$= \frac{\bar{E}\bar{Z}_3}{\bar{Z}_1\bar{Z}_2 + \bar{Z}_1\bar{Z}_3 + \bar{Z}_1\bar{Z}_L + \bar{Z}_2\bar{Z}_3 + \bar{Z}_3\bar{Z}_L}. \qquad (25\text{-}41)$$

In (b) of the figure is shown the Thevenin's equivalent constant-voltage generator. In accordance with the theorem, $\bar{E}_{oc}$ is the voltage

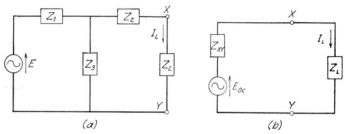

Fig. 25-8. (a) Circuit which is equivalent to Fig. 25-2a. (b) Circuit equivalent to (a) but which contains a Thevenin's equivalent generator.

at terminals XY in (a) when Z_L is disconnected; and $\bar{Z}_{XY}$ is the impedance at these same terminals when Z_L is disconnected, the voltage E is removed, and the mesh containing E is closed after the removal. The generator impedance is not removed, but continues to be included in $\bar{Z}_1$. Under these conditions,

$$\bar{E}_{oc} = \frac{\bar{E}\bar{Z}_3}{\bar{Z}_1 + \bar{Z}_3}, \qquad \bar{Z}_{XY} = \bar{Z}_2 + \frac{\bar{Z}_1\bar{Z}_3}{\bar{Z}_1 + \bar{Z}_3}.$$

Using these values in connection with (b),

$$\bar{I}_L = \frac{\bar{E}_{oc}}{\bar{Z}_L + \bar{Z}_{XY}} = \left(\frac{\bar{E}\bar{Z}_3}{\bar{Z}_1 + \bar{Z}_3}\right)\left(\frac{1}{\bar{Z}_L + \bar{Z}_2 + \dfrac{\bar{Z}_1\bar{Z}_3}{\bar{Z}_1 + \bar{Z}_3}}\right)$$

$$= \frac{\bar{E}\bar{Z}_3}{\bar{Z}_1\bar{Z}_2 + \bar{Z}_1\bar{Z}_3 + \bar{Z}_1\bar{Z}_L + \bar{Z}_2\bar{Z}_3 + \bar{Z}_3\bar{Z}_L}. \qquad (25\text{-}41a)$$

Substituting for $\bar{I}_{sc}$ the value given in equation (25-45),

$$\bar{I}_L = \frac{\bar{E}_{oc}}{\bar{Z}_{XY}} \times \frac{\bar{Z}_{XY}}{\bar{Z}_{XY} + \bar{Z}_L} = \frac{\bar{E}_{oc}}{\bar{Z}_{XY} + \bar{Z}_L}.$$

It will be noted that this is the same value as is obtained from the circuit shown in (a) of the figure. Hence, as far as the load impedance $\bar{Z}_L$ is concerned, the constant-current generator shown to the left of terminals XY in (c) is equivalent to the constant-voltage generator shown in (a).

9. Reciprocity Theorem. In (a) of Fig. 25-2 is shown a multimesh network. The current in element Z_L can be determined quite readily

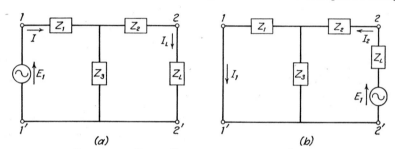

(a)   (b)

Fig. 25-11. Circuits illustrating the reciprocity theorem.

by using the equivalent circuit shown in (b) of the figure, once the elements of the equivalent circuit have been determined. Figure 25-11 is a reproduction of the latter.

In (a) of this figure,

$$\bar{I}_L = \frac{\bar{I}\bar{Z}_3}{\bar{Z}_2 + \bar{Z}_3 + \bar{Z}_L} \qquad (25\text{-}46)$$

and

$$\bar{I} = \frac{\bar{E}_1}{\bar{Z}_1 + \dfrac{\bar{Z}_3(\bar{Z}_2 + \bar{Z}_L)}{\bar{Z}_2 + \bar{Z}_3 + \bar{Z}_L}}. \qquad (25\text{-}47)$$

Substituting this value for $\bar{I}$ in equation (25-46),

$$\bar{I}_L = \frac{\bar{E}_1\bar{Z}_3}{\bar{Z}_1(\bar{Z}_2 + \bar{Z}_3 + \bar{Z}_L) + \bar{Z}_3(\bar{Z}_2 + \bar{Z}_L)}.$$

$$\frac{\bar{E}_1}{\bar{I}_L} = \frac{\bar{Z}_1(\bar{Z}_2 + \bar{Z}_3 + \bar{Z}_L) + \bar{Z}_3(\bar{Z}_2 + \bar{Z}_L)}{\bar{Z}_3} = \bar{Z}_T. \qquad (25\text{-}48)$$

Now let the voltage $\bar{E}_1$ be removed and the terminals 1-1' short-circuited as shown in (b) of the figure. In addition let a voltage $\bar{E}_1$ be introduced into the mesh containing Z_L. This is also shown in (b). In this circuit

$$\bar{I}_1 = \frac{\bar{I}_2 \bar{Z}_3}{\bar{Z}_1 + \bar{Z}_3}$$

and

$$\bar{I}_2 = \frac{\bar{E}_1}{\bar{Z}_2 + \bar{Z}_L + \dfrac{\bar{Z}_1 \bar{Z}_3}{\bar{Z}_1 + \bar{Z}_3}} . \tag{25-49}$$

Substituting this value for $\bar{I}_2$ in equation (25-49),

$$\bar{I}_1 = \frac{\bar{E}_1 \bar{Z}_3}{(\bar{Z}_1 + \bar{Z}_3)(\bar{Z}_2 + \bar{Z}_L) + \bar{Z}_1 \bar{Z}_3} = \frac{\bar{E}_1 \bar{Z}_3}{\bar{Z}_1(\bar{Z}_2 + \bar{Z}_3 + \bar{Z}_L) + \bar{Z}_3(\bar{Z}_2 + \bar{Z}_L)} .$$

$$\frac{\bar{E}_1}{\bar{I}_1} = \frac{\bar{Z}_1(\bar{Z}_2 + \bar{Z}_3 + \bar{Z}_L) + \bar{Z}_3(\bar{Z}_2 + \bar{Z}_L)}{\bar{Z}_3} = \bar{Z}_T. \tag{25-50}$$

It will be noted that the right-hand sides of equations (25-48) and (25-50) are identical. This is equivalent to stating that if a voltage $\bar{E}$ is introduced into any mesh i of a multimesh network and it produces a current $\bar{I}_k$ in an element $\bar{Z}_k$ in any other mesh k, then upon removing voltage $\bar{E}$ and closing mesh i a current equal to the former value $\bar{I}_k$ will flow in mesh i at the place formerly occupied by $\bar{E}$ when this voltage is introduced in series with element $\bar{Z}_k$ in mesh k.

The impedance $\bar{Z}_T$ is called the transfer impedance. It is so called because it is the ratio of a voltage at one point in the circuit to a current at another point. The transfer impedance $\bar{Z}_{T_{ki}}$ is the ratio of a voltage in mesh k to a current in mesh i, and $\bar{Z}_{T_{ik}}$ is the ratio a voltage in mesh i to a current in mesh k. In accordance then, $\bar{Z}_{T_{ki}} = Z_{T_{ik}}$.

Laboratory Problem No. 25-1

FOUR-TERMINAL NETWORK, ITS EQUIVALENT T AND π NETWORK, AND RECIPROCITY THEOREM

Laboratory, Part I

1. Set up the 4-terminal network shown in Fig. 25-12. Measure the impedances listed below:

$\bar{Z}_{oc_1}$ Impedance at terminals 1–2 with terminals 3–4 open

$\bar{Z}_{sc_1}$ Impedance at terminals 1–2 with terminals 3–4 short-circuited

$\bar{Z}_{oc_2}$ Impedance at terminals 3–4 with terminals 1–2 open

$\bar{Z}_{sc_2}$ Impedance at terminals 3–4 with terminals 1–2 short-circuited

Make these measurements for a frequency of 1000 cycles per second.

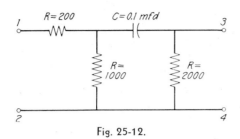

Fig. 25-12.

Report

A. Using the values shown in the figure, calculate $\bar{Z}_1$, $\bar{Z}_2$, and $\bar{Z}_3$, the values of the impedances of the equivalent T network, and also calculate the values of $\bar{Z}_A$, $\bar{Z}_B$, and $\bar{Z}_C$, the values of the impedances of the equivalent π network.

B. Using values of short-circuit and open-circuit impedances as measured in **1** above, calculate the values of $\bar{Z}_1$, $\bar{Z}_2$, $\bar{Z}_3$, $\bar{Z}_A$, $\bar{Z}_B$, and $\bar{Z}_C$ as defined in **A** above.

C. Compare the values obtained in **A** and **B**.

Draw the circuits of the equivalent T network and the equivalent π network. In these drawings insert the numerical values of the resistances and of the capacitances.

Laboratory, Part II

1. Set up the circuit shown in Fig. 25-12. Connect a load impedance $\bar{Z}_L$ to terminals 3–4. The choice of the composition of $\bar{Z}_L$ is arbitrary. Its magnitude for a frequency of 1000 cycles per second, however, should be not less than the magnitude of the combined sum of $\bar{Z}_1$ and $\bar{Z}_2$ of the equivalent T network.*

To terminals 1–2 connect a 1000-cycle generator (audio frequency oscillator). Adjust the output of the generator so that the current in or the voltage across $\bar{Z}_L$ can be measured with reasonably good accuracy.

Measure the voltage at terminals 1–2.

Measure the current in $\bar{Z}_L$, or the voltage across it.

By use of a cathode-ray oscilloscope determine the phase shift between the voltage at terminals 1–2 and the current in $\bar{Z}_L$.†

---

* This is not a necessary condition but a desirable one in order that values obtained from measurements that follow shall be more convenient to work with.

† It is desirable to determine this phase shift in order that the angle of the transfer impedance can be determined. The magnitude of the transfer impedance can be determined without knowing the phase-shift angle.

2. Set up the T network which is equivalent to the 4-terminal network used in 1.

Repeat the measurements made in **1** using the same $\bar{Z}_L$, the same frequency, and the same value of voltage applied to terminals 1–2.

3. Set up the equivalent π network and repeat **2.**

Report

A. State the values of the current in $\bar{Z}_L$ as determined in **1, 2,** and **3** above. By what percentages of the value obtained in **1** do the values found in **2** and **3** differ from that obtained in **1?** Should all the values be the same? Explain.

B. Calculate the transfer impedance $\bar{Z}_T$. Obtain a separate value from data taken in each of the tests **1, 2,** and **3** above.

If the phase-shift angles were not measured, calculate the magnitude Z_T of the transfer impedances.

Do the results obtained substantiate the reciprocity theorem?

Laboratory Problem No. 25-2
SUPERPOSITION THEOREM

Laboratory

The sources used in this problem must produce voltages of the same frequency, and the phase angle between these voltages must remain

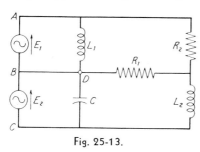

Fig. 25-13.

constant. In addition, the problem is facilitated if the two sources have one common terminal and have internal impedances which are negligibly small. A 110–220-volt power source or two phases of a three-phase power source are possibilities which meet the foregoing requirements. Another possibility is to use a transformer with a tapped secondary between a single source and the network. One tap on the secondary is then used as a common terminal.

1. Set up the circuit shown in Fig. 25-13. Impedance and voltage values to be used will be supplied by the instructor.

Measure the currents in R_1 and in L_2. The impedance of the instrument used must be very small as compared with those of R_1 and ωL_2, so that it can be neglected.

Make such additional measurements as may be necessary to determine the phase of the measured current with respect to the voltage E_1 as reference.

2. Remove voltage E_2 and connect terminals BC.   Make measurements as in **1**.

3. Open the connection between B and C and reinsert E_2.

Remove voltage E_1 and connect terminals AB.   Make measurements as in **1**.

Report

A. Using the complex values of the currents in R_1 and L_2 as found from measurements made in **2** and **3** above, calculate the current in these two elements when both E_1 and E_2 are in the circuit.   Use the superposition theorem.

B. From the values of the impedances and voltages E_1 and E_2 in the circuit, calculate the current in R_1 and that in L_2 by use of the superposition theorem.

How do the contributions of E_1 and E_2 to the currents in R_1 and in L_2 compare with the measured values as determined in **2** and **3** above?

How do the currents in R_1 and L_2 compare with the values determined in **1**?

Laboratory Problem No. 25-3

MAXIMUM POWER TRANSFER, THEVENIN'S AND NORTON'S EQUIVALENT GENERATORS

Laboratory

An audio frequency oscillator serves very well as a network containing a generator, or source.   The oscillator must be one that has a constant output impedance.   The output impedances of oscillators using feedback may not be constant.

The values specified in the directions that follow are suitable for use when the oscillator output impedance is 600 ohms plus or minus 100 ohms.

1. Carefully adjust the oscillator frequency to 1000 cycles per second and adjust its open-circuit voltage to 10 volts.   A very high-impedance voltmeter should be used for making the voltage measurement.   An electronic voltmeter will do very well for this purpose. Once the voltage has been set, it must not be changed at any time during the progress of the experiment.

To the output terminals of the oscillator connect a calibrated variable resistor, such as a decade resistance box, that can be varied

from 1200 ohms to 200 ohms. Before connecting the variable resistance to the oscillator, set it to have a value of 1200 ohms.

Using the high-impedance voltmeter, obtain data from which the
power delivered by the oscillator can be plotted against load resistance
when the latter is reduced in increments to a minimum value of 200
ohms.

2. Measure the open-circuit voltage of the oscillator. It should be
the value to which it was adjusted at the beginning of **1** above. If it is
not, the reason should be discovered, and **1** should be repeated.

If the open-circuit voltage is the proper value, short circuit the
output terminals of the oscillator through a current-measuring device
which has an impedance that is not more than 5 ohms. Measure the
short-circuit current.

Report

A. Using the data obtained in **1,** calculate the power delivered by
the oscillator for each value of R used. Draw a curve of power vs the
load resistance. By applying the " maximum power transfer theorem,"
determine the magnitude Z_g of the output impedance of the oscillator
from one point on this curve. What is the value of Z_g obtained in this
manner? Explain how this was found.

B. Draw a circuit diagram of the Thevenin's equivalent generator
of the oscillator. In the diagram insert the value of the generated
voltage and the value of the magnitude of the internal impedance of
this equivalent generator.

C. Draw a circuit diagram of the Norton's equivalent generator of
the oscillator. In the diagram insert the value of the generated
constant current and the value of the magnitude of the bridged
impedance.

D. The R_g and X_g components of Z_g, as found in **A,** can be calculated by using the Thevenin's equivalent generator determined in **B**
and the coordinates of two selected points on the power vs resistance
load. Suitable points are those for load resistances of 500 ohms and
800 ohms. The sign of X_g cannot be determined. Calculate the
values of R_g and X_g.

E. Use the Norton's equivalent generator as found in **C** and calculate the power that would be delivered to a 400-ohm resistor connected
to the output terminals of this generator. In the calculation use
$\bar{Z}_g = R_g \pm jX_g$, where R_g and X_g have the values found in **D.**

INDEX

MSOE Library
MAIN TK147 .S57 1955
Skroder, Car Circuit analysis by labora

39205000295485

DISCARDED BY
MILWAUKEE SCHOOL
OF ENGINEERING
LIBRARY

Date Due			
NO 1 8'70			
OC 1 3'71			

o 38-297